The Ultimate
SOCCER
QUIZ BOOK

ISBN 0 75252 276 0

Printed and bound in Great Britain
Questions set by The Puzzle House

The Ultimate
SOCCER
QUIZ BOOK

P
· PARRAGON ·

Contents

Introduction	6	FA & SFA Cup	58	**MEDIUM**	108
		Pot Luck 26	59	Pot Luck 1	109
EASY	8	Grounds	60	Keepers	110
Pot Luck 1	9	Pot Luck 27	61	Pot Luck 2	111
The 1950s	10	World Cup	62	The 1950s	112
Pot Luck 2	11	Pot Luck 28	63	Pot Luck 3	113
Strikers	12	Drunk & Disorderley	64	Transfer Trail	114
Pot Luck 3	13	Pot Luck 29	65	Pot Luck 4	115
Transfer Trail	14	Euro Cup Winners' Cup	66	Three Lions	116
Pot Luck 4	15	Pot Luck 30	67	Pot Luck 5	117
Three Lions	16	The 1990s	68	Alan Shearer	118
Pot Luck 5	17	Pot Luck 31	69	Pot Luck 6	119
The 1960s	18	Defenders	70	Scottish Sides	120
Pot Luck 6	19	Pot Luck 32	71	Pot Luck 7	121
Merseysiders	20	The International Scene	72	FA & SFA Cup Finals	122
Pot Luck 7	21	Pot Luck 33	73	Pot Luck 8	123
Cup Finals	22	Derby Games	74	Famous Families	124
Pot Luck 8	23	Pot Luck 34	75	Pot Luck 9	125
Famous Families	24	The Midlands	76	Euro Championship	126
Pot Luck 9	25	Pot Luck 35	77	Pot Luck 10	127
Euro 96	26	League Cup	78	Strikers	128
Pot Luck 10	27	Pot Luck 36	79	Pot Luck 11	129
Keepers	28	Managers	80	Nicknames	130
Pot Luck 11	29	Pot Luck 37	81	Pot Luck 12	131
Nicknames	30	The 1960s	82	The 1960s	132
Pot Luck 12	31	Pot Luck 38	83	Pot Luck 13	133
The 1970s	32	Red Card	84	Midlands & The North	134
Pot Luck 13	33	Pot Luck 39	85	Pot Luck 14	135
London Clubs	34	30 Somethings	86	European Cup	136
Pot Luck 14	35	Pot Luck 40	87	Pot Luck 15	137
European Cup	36	Club Colours	88	Gary Lineker	138
Pot Luck 15	37	Pot Luck 41	89	Pot Luck 16	139
Spot Kicks	38	Keepers	90	Quote, Unquote	140
Pot Luck 16	39	Pot Luck 42	91	Pot Luck 17	141
Quote Unquote	40	UEFA Cup	92	The French Connection	142
Pot Luck 17	41	Pot Luck 43	93	Pot Luck 18	143
Soccer Legends	42	Scottish Sides	94	Scottish Internationals	144
Pot Luck 18	43	Pot Luck 44	95	Pot Luck 19	145
Scottish Internationals	44	The 1970s	96	Going Up	146
Pot Luck 19	45	Pot Luck 45	97	Pot Luck 20	147
Going Up	46	Golden Goals	98	Going Down	148
Pot Luck 20	47	Pot Luck 46	99	Pot Luck 21	149
Going Down	48	North-East Clubs	100	Manchester Utd	150
Pot Luck 21	49	Pot Luck 47	101	Pot Luck 22	151
Manchester Utd	50	Wales, NI & Eire	102	The 1970s	152
Pot Luck 22	51	Pot Luck 48	103	Pot Luck 23	153
The 1980s	52	The 1980s	104	Midfield Men	154
Pot Luck 23	53	Pot Luck 49	105	Pot Luck 24	155
Midfield Men	54	Super Strikers	106	Viva España	156
Pot Luck 24	55	Pot Luck 50	107	Pot Luck 25	157
TV Pundits	56			FA & SFA Cup	158
Pot Luck 25	57			Pot Luck 26	159

Gazza	**160 HARD**	208 Pot Luck 27 261
Pot Luck 27	161 Pot Luck 1	209 World Cup 262
World Cup	162 Midfield Men	210 Pot Luck 28 263
Pot Luck 28	163 Pot Luck 2	211 Famous Firsts 264
All Round Sportsmen	164 The 1950s	212 Pot Luck 29 265
Pot Luck 29	165 Pot Luck 3	213 Cup Winners' Cup 266
Euro Cup Winners' Cup	166 Transfer Trail	214 Pot Luck 30 267
Pot Luck 30	167 Pot Luck 4	215 The 1980s 268
The 1980s	168 Three Lions	216 Pot Luck 31 269
Pot Luck 31	169 Pot Luck 5	217 Defenders 270
Defenders	170 Soccer Legends	218 Pot Luck 32 271
Pot Luck 32	171 Pot Luck 6	219 Internationals 272
International Scene	172 Liverpool & Everton	220 Pot Luck 33 273
Pot Luck 33	173 Pot Luck 7	221 Derby Games 274
Kenny Dalglish	174 FA Cup Finals	222 Pot Luck 34 275
Pot Luck 34	175 Pot Luck 8	223 Arsenal & Spurs 276
Merseysiders	176 Famous Families	224 Pot Luck 35 277
Pot Luck 35	177 Pot Luck 9	225 League Cup 278
League Cup	178 Euro Champ'ship	226 Pot Luck 36 279
Pot Luck 36	179 Pot Luck 10	227 Managers 280
Managers	180 Early Days	228 Pot Luck 37 281
Pot Luck 37	181 Pot Luck 11	229 Double Winners 282
Double Dutch	182 Nicknames	230 Pot Luck 38 283
Pot Luck 38	183 Pot Luck 12	231 Early Bath 284
Red Card	184 The 1960s	232 Pot Luck 39 285
Pot Luck 39	185 Pot Luck 13	233 England Managers 286
Kevin Keegan	186 Midlands & NW	234 Pot Luck 40 287
Pot Luck 40	187 Pot Luck 14	235 Champions 288
On Song	188 European Cup	236 Pot Luck 41 289
Pot Luck 41	189 Pot Luck 15	237 Hat-tricks 290
Germany	190 On The Spot	238 Pot Luck 42 291
Pot Luck 42	191 Pot Luck 16	239 UEFA Cup 292
UEFA Cup	192 Quote, Unquote	240 Pot Luck 43 293
Pot Luck 43	193 Pot Luck 17	241 Rangers & Celtic 294
London Clubs	194 Wonder Wingers	242 Pot Luck 44 295
Pot Luck 44	195 Pot Luck 18	243 The 1990s 296
The 1990s	196 Scotland	244 Pot Luck 45 297
Pot Luck 45	197 Pot Luck 19	245 Golden Goals 298
Golden Goals	198 Going Up	246 Pot Luck 46 299
Pot Luck 46	199 Pot Luck 20	247 Englishmen Abroad 300
Hat-tricks	200 Going Down	248 Pot Luck 47 301
Pot Luck 47	201 Pot Luck 21	249 Internationals 302
Internationals	202 Manchester Utd	250 Pot Luck 48 303
Pot Luck 48	203 Pot Luck 22	251 Int'l Managers 304
Golden Oldies	204 The 1970s	252
Pot Luck 49	205 Pot Luck 23	253
Italy	206 Keepers	254
Pot Luck 50	207 Pot Luck 24	255
	Extra Time	256
	Pot Luck 25	257
	FA Cup	258
	Pot Luck 26	259
	Full Time	260

INTRODUCTION

If you think you know about football, think again. This question-filled book has been specially designed to test the knowledge of even the ultimate footy expert. Sure, you can answer many of the Easy questions, but the Medium ones are making you think, and the difficult ones are resulting in long pauses before guessed answers. Take heart, though, by knowing that if you get through all of the questions in this book, and remember the answers to half of them as well, you'll be a real soccer expert. No, not like Trevor Francis. So if you use this book for setting quizzes for your friends and family, or for absorbing trivia for your next competitive quiz, you will be a *top* footy trivialist by the end.

The Ultimate Soccer Quiz Book is divided into Easy, Medium and Hard questions, which are all subdivided by specialist and Pot Luck rounds. If you are setting your own quizzes, the former can be chosen either to help or hinder your players. Giving Easy questions to some is bound to reveal some interesting answers, but it is possibly more challenging to tailor your questions so that the experts receive the brain-wracking Hard questions and the novices the stupefyingly simple Easy questions. Nothing hurts a fanatic more than being beaten on their specialist subject and the division of questions gives you the chance to employ a handicap system. Other handicap systems will also become apparent if you continue as quiz master. Read on... and learn.

In the interest of further clarification there follows a brief run down of each section:

Easy

In this primary round the main objective is to keep breathing and keep a pen in your hand. These questions are so easy that even the most docile idiot could gurgle their way through them in the time it takes to switch on the TV and turn the volume up for "Match of the Day". If you know what shape a football is, you shouldn't have too much difficulty.

Medium

On your toes people, things are getting tricky. By now even the hardened supporters aren't looking as smug. These questions make for a decent challenge, but you are bound to get the odd soccer nut who will fancy his chances, for whom you should continue on to section three.

Hard

Ask a full 20 of these questions and even Jimmy Hill would keep his mouth shut. Brows will be furrowed, glances exchanged and beer stared into.

All that is left to say is good luck with your testing and if you can't keep your spirits up at least try to keep them down.

The Easy Questions

If you don't know the difference between John Barnes and John Motson, then you will no doubt struggle through the next few questions. For the rest of us though these are the EASY questions, so called because if the quizzee falters on these they are either three sheets to the wind or far too young to have anything to do with this book.

These questions are perfect when used in the first round of an open entry quiz as they lull everyone into a false sense of security, although you must beware that contestants don't shout answers out which creates a problematic precedent for the later, harder questions. Another way of placing these questions is to dot them throughout your quiz, thus making sure that on every team everyone should know the answer to at least one question despite their age.

If you are running a league quiz then some of your team members may heap derision on such obvious questions but don't worry, even the cleverest quiz team member can come a cropper.

Quiz 1 Pot Luck 1

Answers – see page 11

1 Whose home, until May 1997, was the Baseball Ground?

2 Which city has a Wednesday and a United?

3 Rioch, Graham and Mee have all managed which club?

4 What second name is shared by Newcastle and Hartlepool?

5 Which country does diminutive striker John Spencer play for?

6 Which team are known as The Potters?

7 Which country do Ferencvaros come from?

8 With which football club did Ian Wright make his League debut?

9 Which club did Gordon Strachan join on leaving Manchester Utd?

10 What are the main colours on QPR's home shirts?

11 Which Tony was Port Vale's top League scorer in 1995-96?

12 What is Aston Villa's nickname?

13 Which overseas player was voted Footballer of the Year in 1996?

14 Bobby Robson became boss of which Spanish giants in 1996?

15 Which team does Danny Baker support?

16 Which Scotsman managed Galatasaray in 1995?

17 Which George of AC Milan was European Footballer of the Year in 1996?

18 Which country does Mikkel Beck play for?

19 What forename is shared by defenders Dodd and McAteer?

20 Which Robbie was PFA Young Player Year in 1995?

Quiz 2 The 1950s

Answers – see page 12

LEVEL 1

1 Which English team was involved in the Munich air disaster?

2 Which country did John Charles play for?

3 Which country did John Charles move to after leaving Leeds?

4 Bill Nicholson took over as manager of which London club?

5 Which mid-European country inflicted England's first ever Wembley defeat?

6 Stan Cullis was boss of which club side throughout the 50s?

7 In which country was Manchester City keeper Bert Trautmann born?

8 What was the nickname of Busby's young Manchester Utd team?

9 Which Walter was in charge of the England team?

10 Which club did Johnny Haynes play for?

11 Matt Busby and Andy Beattie were in charge of which international side?

12 Who did Stanley Matthews play for in the 1953 FA Cup "Matthews Final"?

13 What position did Alf Ramsey play for England?

14 Which country did Danny Blanchflower play for?

15 Who won a then-record 100th England cap in 1959?

16 Which northern team were league champions in 1952, '56 and '57?

17 Which 17-year-old played in the 1958 World Cup Final for Brazil?

18 Which country did keeper Harry Gregg play for?

19 Which Len was known as the "Clown Prince"?

20 Which club did Nat Lofthouse play for?

Answers

Strikers (see Quiz 4)
1 Blackburn Rovers. 2 Scotland. 3 Arsenal. 4 Blackburn Rovers. 5 West Ham Utd. 6 Stan Collymore. 7 Manchester Utd. 8 West Germany. 9 Dixie. 10 Aston Villa. 11 Duncan Ferguson. 12 Newcastle Utd. 13 Steve Bull. 14 England. 15 Crystal Palace. 16 Rangers. 17 Saunders. 18 Scotland. 19 Arsenal. 20 Durie.

Quiz 3   Pot Luck 2

Answers – see page 9

LEVEL 1

1 What is the last word in Hamilton's team name?

2 What colour are Arsenal's home shorts?

3 Which country has John Aldridge played for?

4 Who plays at home at Old Trafford?

5 Which Tom was Oxford's top league scorer in 1995–96?

6 What forename is shared by Scales and Barnes who played together at Liverpool?

7 Which Billy of Celtic was Scottish Footballer of the Year in 1965?

8 With which club did Nigel Winterburn make his league debut?

9 Which club did Charlie Nicholas leave to join Arsenal?

10 Doug Ellis has been chairman of which club?

11 What is Barnet's nickname?

12 Which country has Mark Bowen played for?

13 Garry Parker and Steve Claridge scored 1996 play-off goals for which team?

14 Which manager took Manchester Utd to the 1996 Premiership title?

15 Which Alan was PFA Player of the Year in 1995?

16 Which country does Edgar Davids play for?

17 Which 40-year old player manager was on show for Middlesbrough?

18 Who was Blackburn's 90s cash benefactor?

19 Sharp was on the shirts of which Premiership winners?

20 Who replaced Jack Charlton as manager of the Republic of Ireland?

Answers

Pot Luck 1 (see Quiz 1)
1 Derby County. 2 Sheffield. 3 Arsenal. 4 United. 5 Scotland.
6 Stoke City. 7 Hungary. 8 Crystal Palace. 9 Leeds Utd.
10 Blue and white. 11 Naylor. 12 The Villains. 13 Eric
Cantona. 14 Barcelona. 15 Millwall. 16 Graeme Souness.
17 Weah. 18 Denmark. 19 Jason. 20 Fowler.

11

1 Where did Alan Shearer move to on leaving Southampton?

2 Which country does John McGinlay play for?

3 Which was Dennis Bergkamp's first club in England?

4 Which club have played Sutton, Gallacher and Wilcox in the same side?

5 Tony Cottee was a favourite with which London club?

6 Who got in a tabloid tangle in 1996 about not living near enough to his club Liverpool?

7 Mark Hughes joined Chelsea from which club?

8 Which country did Gerd Müller play for?

9 What was the nickname of William Ralph Dean?

10 Milosevic and Yorke played together for which team?

11 Which Everton striker spent time in jail in 1995?

12 Malcolm Macdonald and Jackie Milburn have been famous strikers for which club?

13 Which former England striker is known as "Bully"?

14 Which country did Mick Channon play for?

15 Wright and Bright formed a strike force for which London side?

16 Which Scottish team did Mark Hateley play for?

17 Which Dean played in Turkey before joining Nottingham Forest?

18 Which country did Joe Jordan play for?

19 Which club had Kennedy and Radford as a deadly double act?

20 Which Scottish player Gordon is known as "Juke-Box"?

1 Who plays at home at Portman Road?

2 What colour are Brazil's home shorts?

3 Little, Atkinson and Taylor have all managed which club?

4 What second name is shared by Oldham and Charlton?

5 Which country does Graeme Le Saux play for?

6 Which colour goes with claret in Bradford's home shirts?

7 Which country do Sampdoria come from?

8 With which club did Gary Flitcroft make his League debut?

9 Which club did Julian Dicks join on leaving Liverpool?

10 What colour are the stripes on Sheffield Utd's home shirts?

11 Which Daniel was QPR's top League scorer in 1995-96?

12 Which club has the nicknames Tykes, Reds and Colliers?

13 Which German player won the Footballer of the Year award in 1995?

14 Which team does John Major support?

15 Tony Parkes has been caretaker manager of which club?

16 Which country has Carlos Valderrama played for?

17 Who became known as "El Tel" when he went abroad as a manager?

18 Which club did Gianfranco Zola leave to join Chelsea?

19 Which David was an ever present goalkeeper for Arsenal in 1995–96?

20 Which Kevin of Ipswich was PFA Young Player of the Year in 1974?

Answers

Pot Luck 4 (see Quiz 7)
1 Midlothian. 2 England. 3 Blue and white. 4 St James' Park.
5 Lee. 6 Manchester City. 7 Everton. 8 Leeds Utd.
9 Manchester Utd. 10 McClair. 11 The Blues. 12 N. Ireland.
13 Southampton. 14 John Aldridge. 15 Cantona. 16 Tim.
17 Wycombe Wanderers. 18 Wolves. 19 Wimbledon.
20 Kenny Dalglish.

1 Which Brazilian star found his wife could not settle in Middlesbrough?

2 Which London club signed Slaven Bilic?

3 Which club did John Hartson leave to join Arsenal?

4 The first half-a-million pound deal involving a British club involved which player going from Liverpool to Hamburg ?

5 Who became England's most expensive keeper when he moved to Blackburn in 1993?

6 Which club did Darren Peacock join on leaving QPR?

7 Which club has Mark Hughes joined on two separate occasions?

8 Which international fullback Denis got a free from Leeds before a move to Old Trafford?

9 Which Frenchman prompted "Frog On The Tyne" headlines on his move to Newcastle?

10 Which club did Gareth Southgate leave to join Aston Villa?

11 Which Dutchman joined Arsenal for £7+ million in 1995?

12 Which fullback Warren cost Newcastle £4 million?

13 Which club did Nigel Clough join on first leaving Nottingham Forest?

14 Who moved from Argentina to Barcelona then to Napoli?

15 Which club did Duncan Ferguson leave to join Everton?

16 Which manager brought Fabrizio Ravanelli to England?

17 Who became the world's first £15 million player?

18 Which club did Niall Quinn join on leaving Manchester City ?

19 Which Spanish club signed Ronaldo for over £13 million?

20 England's first £1 million transfer involved which Trevor?

Answers – see page 13

1 What is the third word in the full name of Hearts?

2 Which country has Mick Mills played for?

3 What colour are the stripes on Brighton's home shirts?

4 Which ground do Newcastle Utd play at?

5 Which Jason was Forest's joint top league scorer in 1995–96?

6 Francis Lee has been chairman of which club?

7 Which was Daniel Amokachi's first English club?

8 With which club did John Lukic make his league debut?

9 Which club did Paul McGrath leave to join Aston Villa?

10 Which Brian of Celtic was Scottish Footballer of the Year in 1987?

11 What is Birmingham's nickname?

12 Which country has Jimmy Quinn played for?

13 Dave Merrington was manager of which Premiership team for 1995–96?

14 Which veteran striker is known as "Aldo"?

15 Which Eric was PFA Player of the Year in 1994?

16 What name is shared by 1990s team-mates Flowers and Sherwood?

17 Martin O'Neill took which club into the football league?

18 The Hayward family put 90s money into which Midlands club?

19 Holdsworth and Ekoku have played together for which team?

20 Who was Blackburn boss for the 1994–95 Premiership triumph?

Quiz 8 Three Lions

Answers – see page 14

1 Which club was Steve Stone with when he made his international debut?

2 Which player opened England's account in Euro 96?

3 Who is England's all-time record goalscorer?

4 Which 20-year old winger scored a wonder goal for England in Brazil in 1984?

5 Which forward Peter had an England career stretching from 1986 to 1996?

6 Terry Butcher and Paul Mariner were colleagues at which club?

7 Who was England's first choice goalkeeper in the 1990 World Cup in Italy?

8 What is the first name of 80s striker Blissett?

9 Who was known as "The Wizard of the Dribble"?

10 Who burst into tears after the World Cup semi-final defeat in 1990?

11 Which captain married one of the Beverley Sisters?

12 What forename was shared by Francis and Brooking?

13 Which club did Ronnie Clayton play for?

14 Which club was Bobby Moore with when he became England captain?

15 Which Liverpool fullback Rob made his international debut while still 20?

16 Which David made his debut against Moldova?

17 Which Kenny made 86 appearances at fullback?

18 Which striker hit five goals in one game in the 70s?

19 Which club was Steve Coppell with during his international career?

20 What forename links Bull and McManaman?

Answers

Transfer Trail (see Quiz 6)
1 Emerson. 2 West Ham Utd. 3 Luton Town. 4 Kevin Keegan.
5 Tim Flowers. 6 Newcastle Utd. 7 Manchester Utd. 8 Irwin.
9 David Ginola. 10 Crystal Palace. 11 Dennis Bergkamp.
12 Barton. 13 Liverpool. 14 Diego Maradona. 15 Rangers.
16 Bryan Robson. 17 Alan Shearer. 18 Sunderland.
19 Barcelona. 20 Francis.

1 Who plays at home at Villa Park?

2 Which Bristol team plays in red shirts at home?

3 Dalglish and Harford have both managed which club?

4 What second name is shared by Cardiff and Bradford?

5 Which country has Andy Townsend played for?

6 Mike Newell and Chris Sutton have both played for which team?

7 Which country do Nantes come from?

8 With which club did Stuart Ripley make his League debut?

9 Which club did Vinnie Jones join on leaving Leeds?

10 What two colours are on Sheffield Wednesday's home shirts?

11 Which Jimmy was Reading's top League scorer in 1995–96?

12 What is Blackpool's nickname?

13 Which Joe became Wimbledon boss in January 1992?

14 Which country does Allan Nielsen play for?

15 Which Alan won the Footballer of the Year award in 1994?

16 Erik Thorstvedt played for which London club?

17 Which club were the first in England to have an artificial pitch?

18 What colour are the home shirts of Northern Ireland?

19 Which team does Delia Smith support?

20 Which Mervyn of West Ham was PFA Young Player of the Year in 1975?

Pot Luck 6 (see Quiz 11)
Answers
1 Thistle. 2 Blue. 3 Scotland. 4 Liverpool. 5 Agent. 6 Greig.
7 Francis. 8 Chester City. 9 Nottingham Forest. 10 The
Cherries. 11 Grobbelaar. 12 The Republic of Ireland.
13 Mabbutt. 14 Joe Royle. 15 McGrath. 16 Wimbledon.
17 France. 18 Ian Wright. 19 Switzerland. 20 Eric Cantona.

1 John Sissons played in an FA Cup Final for which team?

2 Which country did Eusebio play for?

3 Which country did Jimmy Greaves move to before joining Tottenham Hotspur?

4 Alf Ramsey guided which club to the Championship?

5 Who became the first active footballer to be knighted?

6 Who was boss of Liverpool throughout the 60s?

7 At which club did Jimmy Dickinson clock up his 700th League game?

8 Which team featured Auld, Gemmell and Murdoch?

9 Which team was thrashed 9-3 by England at Wembley in 1961?

10 Which team featured Kidd, Aston and Foulkes?

11 Who was Leeds' manager from 1961 onwards?

12 Which bearded former Fulham player became PFA Chairman?

13 Joe Mercer guided which club to the Championship?

14 Which country did Gary Sprake play for?

15 England's Moore, Hurst and Peters came from which club side until 1969?

16 Which Rodney scored a Wembley wonder goal for QPR?

17 In which position did Ron Springett play?

18 Which country did Mike England play for?

19 Roger Hunt was scoring goals for which club side?

20 Jock Stein was manager of which great Glasgow club side?

1   What is the last word in Partick's name?

2   What is the main colour in Cardiff's home strip?

3   Which country has Pat Nevin played for?

4   Who plays at home at Anfield?

5   What is the job of Rune Hauge?

6   Which John of Rangers was Scottish Footballer of the Year in 1966?

7   Which Gerry became Tottenham Hotspur's boss in November 1994?

8   With which club did Ian Rush make his league debut?

9   Which club did Lars Bohinen leave to join Blackburn?

10   What is Bournemouth's nickname?

11   Which keeper Bruce was charged with match-fixing in 1995?

12   Which country has Mark Lawrenson played for?

13   Which Gary has played 450 plus games in defence for Tottenham Hotspur?

14   Which manager won the 1995 FA Cup with Everton?

15   Which Paul was PFA Player of the Year in 1993?

16   Which team became known as "The Crazy Gang"?

17   Which country does Zinedine Zidane play for?

18   Who had "I Love The Lads" written on his T-shirt?

19   Artur Jorge was whose national coach during Euro 96 ?

20   Who returned after an 8-month suspension in October 1995?

Answers

Pot Luck 5 (see Quiz 9)
1 Aston Villa. 2 City. 3 Blackburn Rovers. 4 City.
5 The Republic of Ireland. 6 Blackburn Rovers. 7 France.
8 Middlesbrough. 9 Sheffield Utd. 10 Blue and white.
11 Quinn. 12 The Tangerines or Seasiders. 13 Kinnear.
14 Denmark. 15 Shearer. 16 Tottenham Hotspur. 17 QPR.
18 Green. 19 Norwich. 20 Day.

1 Which club did Kenny Dalglish leave to join Liverpool?

2 Which country did Ron Yeats come from?

3 Who was manager of Everton's 80s championship winning sides?

4 What position did Gordon West play?

5 Who went to Hamburg from Liverpool in 1977?

6 Which Dave skippered Everton's 1995 FA Cup winning team?

7 What name was shared by Thompson and Boersma?

8 Who moved abroad from Everton after personal scoring success in the 1986 World Cup for England?

9 Which country did Kevin Ratcliffe play for?

10 Which star of the 60s and 70s set a Liverpool appearance record?

11 Which Mersey team plays at Prenton Park?

12 Which Liverpool player was referred to as "The Great Dane"?

13 Who took over as Everton manager from Mike Walker?

14 Bob Paisley took over from which manager?

15 Which club did John Barnes join Liverpool from?

16 Which midfielder Steve played for both Everton and Liverpool in the 80s?

17 Which Alan Bleasdale TV drama featured players Souness and Lee?

18 Which fellow Liverpool forward was an Ian Rush lookalike?

19 Who was player-manager in Liverpool's 1986 double-winning team?

20 Who has made most league appearances for Everton?

1 Who plays at home at Carrow Road?

2 What is the main colour of Charlton's home shirts?

3 Kendall and Royle have both managed which club?

4 What second name is shared by Blackburn and Doncaster?

5 Which country did Ruud Gullit play for?

6 Which Lou became Stoke boss in 1994?

7 Alan Smith knocked in 23 goals when which side were champions?

8 Which British club did Oleg Salenko join in 1995?

9 Which club did Andy Thorn join on leaving Crystal Palace?

10 What colours are Southampton's home shirts?

11 Which Nathan was Sheffield Utd's top League scorer in 1995-96?

12 Which club have the nickname The Bantams?

13 Ian Branfoot was sacked in 1994 by which Premiership side?

14 Which country has Paulo Sousa played for?

15 Which team does Eddie Large support?

16 Which Chris won the Footballer of the Year award in 1993?

17 Which London club did Jan Stesjkal play for?

18 Which Mike has hit a European Cup hat-trick for Blackburn?

19 Which position does Rene Higuita play?

20 Which Peter of Manchester City was PFA Young Player of the Year in 1976?

1 Who scored Manchester Utd's winner in the '96 Final against Liverpool?

2 Gazza played in the 1991 Final with which London club?

3 Gordon Durie hit a hat-trick in which club's 5-1 demolition of Hearts?

4 In a 70s triumph, Jim Montgomery inspired underdogs Sunderland. Which position did he play?

5 Duxbury, Albiston and McQueen played together for which Cup winning club in the 80s?

6 Which English team did Bobby Robson lead to Cup Final success?

7 They sound like a London team, but who were the side to win the first Scottish Cup?

8 Who was in goal for Wimbledon when they beat Liverpool in 1988?

9 What part of his anatomy did Trevor Brooking use to score West Ham's winner against Arsenal?

10 Jim Leighton played in a Final for which English club?

11 Before joining Liverpool, John Barnes was a losing finalist for which club?

12 Dave Webb scored a winning goal for which club?

13 Which club won its first ever Scottish Cup in 1994?

14 Which Norman scored a Manchester Utd winner against Everton?

15 Howard Kendall became the youngest FA Cup Finalist when playing for which club?

16 Which star from Argentina hit a memorable goal for Tottenham Hotspur against Manchester City in a replay?

17 With which team was George Burley an FA Cup winner?

18 Sanchez hit a Wembley winner for which club?

19 Who was Manchester Utd boss when they won the 1990 Final?

20 Which Bobby scored a Final winner for Southampton?

Quiz 15 Pot Luck 8

Answers – see page 21

1 What is the last word in Raith's team name?

2 Which London team wear red and blue striped shirts at home ?

3 Which country has Barry Horne played for?

4 Who plays at home at the Vetch Field?

5 Which Gordon was Rangers' top league scorer in 1995–96?

6 Which national team has Savo Milosevic played for?

7 Steve Bould plays for which side?

8 With which club did Keith Gillespie make his League debut?

9 Which club did Mark Wright leave to join Liverpool?

10 Which Paul of Celtic was Scottish Footballer of the Year in 1988?

11 What is Brentford's nickname?

12 Which country has Terry Phelan played for?

13 David Pleat followed Trevor Francis as boss at which club?

14 Which country does Patrick Kluivert play for?

15 Which Gary of Manchester Utd was PFA Player of the Year in 1992?

16 What colour are Scotland's home shirts?

17 Durie and Dixon formed a striking duo at which London club?

18 Which Newcastle centre half had to pull out of England's Euro 96 squad?

19 Which club was dubbed as being "Lucky"?

20 Scales and Collymore were teammates for which losing FA Cup Finalists?

1 Which two brothers were in the England World Cup winning team?

2 At which club were father and son Clough connected?

3 What are the first names of the 90s Neville brothers?

4 With which club did they make their debuts?

5 What's the last name of strikers Justin and John?

6 Father Frank and son Andy Gray have both played for which club?

7 Who is goalkeeper Ian Walker's manager father?

8 What is the name of midfielder Scott Gemmill's father?

9 Did Bobby Charlton ever play at club level in the same side as his brother?

10 Which Manchester Utd manager sold his son Darren?

11 Which country did the Allchurch brothers play for?

12 What's the surname of Clive and Bradley both former QPR strikers?

13 Which club had Bobby Gould as boss and son Jonathan in goal?

14 What is Nicky Summerbee's father called?

15 What's the last name of dad Tony and son Mark, both tall centre forwards?

16 Which legendary striker was Bobby Charlton's uncle?

17 Which West Ham boss had a son playing for Liverpool and England?

18 Which Alan was boss at York while brother Brian was boss at Villa?

19 What's the name of David Holdsworth's striking brother?

20 Which Cruyff played for Manchester Utd?

Answers

Cup Finals (see Quiz 14)
1 Eric Cantona. 2 Tottenham Hotspur. 3 Rangers. 4 Goalkeeper. 5 Manchester Utd. 6 Ipswich Town. 7 Queens Park. 8 Dave Beasant. 9 His head. 10 Manchester Utd. 11 Watford. 12 Chelsea. 13 Dundee Utd. 14 Whiteside. 15 Preston North End. 16 Ricky Villa. 17 Ipswich Town. 18 Wimbledon. 19 Alex Ferguson. 20 Stokes.

1 Who plays at home at Goodison Park?

2 Ian Crook has played over 300 games for which club?

3 Graeme Souness and Walter Smith have both managed which club?

4 What is the last word in Birmingham's name?

5 Which country has Patrik Berger played for?

6 Which team does Jeremy Beadle support?

7 Which country do Cologne come from?

8 With which club did goalkeeper Bryan Gunn make his debut?

9 Which club did Ray Wilkins join on leaving Rangers?

10 What colour goes with white on Sunderland's home shirts?

11 Which Ian was Nottingham Forest's joint top League scorer in 1995–96?

12 What is Brighton's nickname?

13 Mark McGhee followed Graham Taylor as boss at which club?

14 League champions play FA Cup winners for which trophy?

15 Keeper Mark Crossley has played over 200 games for which club?

16 Which country do Ajax come from?

17 Which country did Graeme Sharp play for?

18 Which Gary won the Footballer of the Year award in 1992?

19 Which country does Rui Costa play for?

20 Which Andy of Villa was PFA Young Player of the Year in 1977?

Answers – see page 28

LEVEL 1

1 Who won the 1996 European Championship?

2 Which team were beaten in the Final?

3 What was the scoreline in the Final after 90 minutes?

4 Which player finished top scorer for the 96 tournament?

5 Which player was skipper of the Scottish Euro 96 squad?

6 Who was the German skipper?

7 What was the fatalistic nickname for Group C?

8 Which country was in the group with England, Holland and Scotland?

9 Who was manager of England's squad?

10 Who scored England's second goal against Scotland?

11 Which player took the last English penalty in the semi-final shoot out?

12 Did Eric Cantona play in the Euro 96 finals?

13 What was the new rule to affect games that went into extra time?

14 Who was England's first choice keeper?

15 Which Birmingham ground was a venue?

16 Did Turkey reach the Euro 96 finals?

17 What was the scoreline in England's game against Holland?

18 Who was Scotland's only goalscorer?

19 In the England v Germany semi-final which country played in their changed colours?

20 Which Premiership player manager was England's assistant coach in Euro 96?

Answers

Keepers (see Quiz 20)
1 Ogrizovic. 2 Tim Flowers. 3 Italy. 4 Tomas Ravelli.
5 Manchester Utd. 6 David James. 7 Arsenal. 8 USA.
9 David Seaman. 10 Mark Bosnich. 11 Andy. 12 Manchester
City. 13 Bruce Grobbelaar. 14 West Ham Utd. 15 The Republic
of Ireland. 16 Gordon Banks. 17 Newcastle Utd.
18 Manchester Utd. 19 Germany. 20 Sheffield Wednesday.

Quiz 19 Pot Luck 10

LEVEL 1 ⚽

1 What is the last word in Stirling's name?

2 Which London club wear red and white hooped socks?

3 With which club did Ray Wilkins make his League debut?

4 Which country has Terry Butcher played for?

5 Who plays at home at White Hart Lane?

6 Which Robert was Norwich's top league scorer in 1995–96?

7 Which Bobby of Celtic was Scottish Footballer of the Year in 1969?

8 Redknapp followed Bonds as boss at which club?

9 Which club did Eric Cantona leave to join Manchester Utd?

10 Who was the Scotland manager for Euro 96?

11 What is the nickname of Bristol City?

12 Which country has Willie Miller played for?

13 What colour are the home shirts of Holland?

14 'You'll Never Walk Alone' is the anthem of which team?

15 Which Mark was PFA Player of the Year in 1991?

16 Dave Merrington was coach for 11 years before becoming boss of which club?

17 River Plate play in which country?

18 Who was boss of Arsenal's 1990–91 championship winning side?

19 Which Billy became the first Celtic player also to manage the club?

20 Which country has Igor Stimac played for?

1 Which Steve has played 400 plus times for Coventry?

2 Who was Blackburn's regular keeper when they won the Premiership in 1994–95?

3 Which country did Dino Zoff play for?

4 Who is the world's most capped goalkeeper?

5 Jim Leighton and Les Sealey have both played for which club?

6 Which Liverpool keeper modelled clothes for Giorgio Armani?

7 John Lukic won a Championship medal with Leeds and also with which other club?

8 Casey Keller plays for which country?

9 Who was England's No 1 in Euro 96?

10 Who was in trouble for a Nazi-style salute made at Tottenham Hotspur in 1996?

11 Which first name is shared by keepers Dibble and Goram?

12 Joe Corrigan was a great servant for which club?

13 Which Liverpool keeper was dubbed "Jungle Man" by his teammates?

14 For which club has Ludek Miklosko played 300 plus games?

15 Which country does Shay Given play for?

16 Who was England's keeper when they won the World Cup Final?

17 Which Premiership club could boast keepers with Christian names of Pavel and Shaka?

18 Alex Stepney and Gary Bailey have played for which club?

19 Which country does Eike Immel come from?

20 Pressman and Woods have played for which club?

Answers

Euro 96 (see Quiz 18)

1 Germany. **2** Czech Republic. **3** 1–1. **4** Alan Shearer.
5 Gary McAllister. **6** Jürgen Klinsmann. **7** The Group of Death.
8 Switzerland. **9** Terry Venables. **10** Paul Gascoigne.
11 Gareth Southgate. **12** No. **13** The sudden death goal.
14 David Seaman. **15** Villa Park. **16** Yes. **17** 4–1 to England.
18 Ally McCoist. **19** England. **20** Bryan Robson.

1 Who plays at home at Elland Road?

2 Which team does Sean Bean support?

3 Who did Arsenal beat in two cup finals in 1993?

4 What is the last word in Bolton's name?

5 Which country has Chris Coleman played for?

6 Which Lee was the Leeds target man when they won the Championship in 1992?

7 Which country do Grasshoppers come from?

8 With which club did Dennis Wise make his League debut?

9 Which club did Ruel Fox join on leaving Norwich?

10 What colour are Swindon's home shirts?

11 Which David was Sheffield Wednesday's top League scorer in 1995–96?

12 Which team is known as The Pirates?

13 Which Gordon of Leeds Utd won the Footballer of the Year award in 1991?

14 Hoddle followed Ardiles as boss at which club?

15 Which Premiership player rejoices in the real name of Stig-Inge?

16 Steve Bruce played over 300 games for which team?

17 Which Liverpool legend Bob passed away in February 1996?

18 Who was Scotland's manager before Craig Brown?

19 At which stage were France knocked out of Euro 96?

20 Which Tony of Forest was PFA Young Player of the Year in 1978?

Pot Luck 12 (see Quiz 23)
Answers
1 Town. 2 The Republic of Ireland. 3 White. 4 Nottingham Forest. 5 Ferdinand. 6 West Bromwich Albion. 7 Italy. 8 Chelsea. 9 Manchester Utd. 10 Gough. 11 The Clarets. 12 Wales. 13 Graeme Souness. 14 Red. 15 Platt. 16 Middlesbrough. 17 England. 18 Merson. 19 USA. 20 Dixon.

1 Which club is known as The Gunners?

2 "Psycho" is the nickname of which fullback?

3 Which club are called The Trotters?

4 Which Midlands team have a name to be sheepish about?

5 Which London club are known as The Blues?

6 What is the animal link with Hull?

7 SLOW is an anagram of which club's nickname?

8 Which creatures could sting you at Brentford?

9 Which England player is known as Rodney?

10 At which club can you shout Cobblers to show your appreciation?

11 Management men Ron and Jack are usually described by what word?

12 Which Scottish team is known as The Dons?

13 And which English team is known as The Dons?

14 Who are The Blades?

15 Who is known as "Sparky"?

16 Which ground are you at if The Foxes are at home?

17 Which nickname dogs Huddersfield?

18 Who are The Toffees?

19 The Bhoys is the nickname of which team?

20 Which Liverpool player was nicknamed "Digger"?

Quiz 23 Pot Luck 12

Answers – see page 29

1 What is the last word in Luton's name?

2 Which country has Pat Bonner played for?

3 What colour are Fulham's home shirts?

4 Who plays at home at the City Ground?

5 Which Les was Newcastle's top league scorer in 1995–96?

6 Alan Buckley followed Keith Burkinshaw as boss at which club?

7 Gianfranco Zola plays for which country?

8 With which club did Graeme Le Saux make his League debut?

9 Which club did Dion Dublin leave to join Coventry?

10 Which Richard of Rangers was Scottish Footballer of the Year in 1989?

11 What is Burnley's nickname?

12 Which country has John Toshack played for?

13 Which manager took Liverpool to FA Cup Final triumph over Sunderland?

14 What colour are the home shirts of Switzerland?

15 Which David was PFA Player of the Year in 1990?

16 Which club brought Juninho to play in England?

17 Which national team decided to accept "collective responsibility" for damage done on a plane in 1996?

18 Which Paul said his manager gave him "unbelievable belief"?

19 Which country has Roy Wegerle played for?

20 Which England fullback Lee has made over 300 appearances for Arsenal?

Answers

Pot Luck 11 (see Quiz 21)
1 Leeds Utd. 2 Sheffield Utd. 3 Sheffield Weds. 4 Wanderers.
5 Wales. 6 Chapman. 7 Switzerland. 8 Wimbledon.
9 Newcastle. 10 Red. 11 Hirst. 12 Bristol Rovers.
13 Strachan. 14 Swindon Town. 15 Bjornebye. 16 Manchester Utd. 17 Paisley. 18 Andy Roxburgh. 19 Semi-finals.
20 Woodcock.

1 Charlie George helped which side to the double?

2 Which Derek was elected chairman of the PFA?

3 1971 witnessed over 60 deaths at which Scottish ground?

4 Giles, Lorimer and Clarke were stars of which club side?

5 League soccer was played on which day for the first time?

6 The 11-year reign of which England boss ended in 1974?

7 Which country won the 1970 World Cup?

8 Which Manchester Utd boss was sacked for an affair?

9 Which West Brom player was suspected of having a hole in the heart?

10 Which manager was known as "Big Mal"?

11 Which country was credited with developing total football?

12 Gordon Banks and George Eastham played together for which club?

13 Which manager led both Derby and Forest to the championship?

14 Which German club won the European Cup three years in a row?

15 Elton John was elected chairman of which club?

16 McGuinness and O'Farrell were managers at which club?

17 Which Brazilian player scored his 1,000th goal?

18 Which red and yellow items were introduced in the Football League in 1976?

19 Which London team were elected into the league?

20 Which England boss was banned for 10 years for bringing the game into disrepute?

Answers

Nicknames (see Quiz 22)
1 Arsenal. 2 Stuart Pearce. 3 Bolton. 4 Derby County(The Rams). 5 Chelsea. 6 Tigers. 7 Sheffield Wednesday (Owls). 8 Bees. 9 Tony Adams. 10 Northampton. 11 Big. 12 Aberdeen. 13 Wimbledon. 14 Sheffield Utd. 15 Mark Hughes. 16 Filbert Street. 17 Terriers. 18 Everton. 19 Celtic. 20 John Barnes.

Quiz 25   Pot Luck 13

Answers – see page 35

1   Who plays at home at Bloomfield Road?

2   Grobbelaar and Beasant were together at which club?

3   Brian Clough and Frank Clark have both managed which club?

4   What is the last word in Bradford's name?

5   Which country has Iain Dowie played for?

6   Who resigned as Newcastle manager in January 1997?

7   Which country do Fenerbahce come from?

8   With which club did Alan Stubbs make his league debut?

9   Which club did Colin Hendry join on leaving Manchester City?

10   What colour are Tottenham Hotspur's home shirts?

11   Which player was Southampton's top league scorer in 1995–96?

12   What is Bury's nickname?

13   What kind of creature found the stolen World Cup in 1966?

14   Which team does Elton John support?

15   Which John of Liverpool won the Footballer of the Year award in 1990?

16   Venables followed Pleat as boss at which club?

17   Which country has Danny Blind played for?

18   Which Cyrille of West Brom was PFA Young Player of the Year in 1979?

19   What colour are the Republic of Ireland's home shorts?

20   Which keeper Tony had spells for both Manchester Utd and City in the 90s?

Quiz 26 London Clubs

Answers – see page 36

LEVEL 1

1 Who plays at home at Griffin Park?

2 Which London club did Anders Limpar play for?

3 Who beat Fulham to win the 70s all London FA Cup Final ?

4 John Spencer left which London club to join QPR?

5 Graham Roberts played for Chelsea and which other London club?

6 Barry Hearn became chairman of which East London club?

7 At which Park do Wimbledon play their home games?

8 Which London club did Stan Bowles play for?

9 Have Charlton ever won an FA Cup Final?

10 Which club plays nearest to the River Thames?

11 Which London club did Peter Osgood play for?

12 Which Billy has made a record number of league appearances for West Ham?

13 George Graham and John Docherty have both managed which London club?

14 Which side did manager Steve Coppell take to an FA Cup Final?

15 Jimmy Hill has been chairman of which London team?

16 Who won 108 England caps playing for one club?

17 For which London side did Peter Shilton make his 1,000th League appearance?

18 Who are nicknamed the Hornets?

19 Which London club did Gary Lineker play for?

20 Which London side finished highest in the Premiership in season 1995–96?

Answers

European Cup (see Quiz 28)
1 Blackburn Rovers. 2 Rangers. 3 Juventus. 4 Celtic. 5 Rapid Vienna. 6 Juventus. 7 Nottingham Forest. 8 Matt Busby. 9 The 70s. 10 Four. 11 Real Madrid. 12 Alfredo di Stefano. 13 Celtic. 14 Benfica. 15 Bob Paisley. 16 Barcelona. 17 Juventus. 18 Fabrizio Ravanelli. 19 Ajax. 20 Peter Shilton.

1 What is the last word in Mansfield's name?

2 Which country has defender Mark Wright played for?

3 What colour are the stripes on Huddersfield's home shirts?

4 Who plays at home at Stamford Bridge?

5 Which Nick was Middlesbrough's top league scorer in 1995–96?

6 Which Nottingham Forest player was ribbed for his "pineapple" hair cut?

7 Which Sandy of Rangers was Scottish Footballer of the Year in 1975?

8 With which club did John Salako make his league debut?

9 Which club did Andrei Kanchelskis leave to join Everton?

10 What is Cambridge United's nickname?

11 Steve McMahon followed John Gorman as boss at which club?

12 Which country has Pat Rice played for?

13 Which manager was with Wycombe Wanderers when they came into the Football League?

14 Mick Channon is the leading all-time scorer for which club?

15 Which John of Liverpool was PFA Player of the Year in 1988?

16 Who has been top scorer for Arsenal for five consecutive seasons in the 90s?

17 Which Ron has been chairman of Crystal Palace?

18 Which country has Davor Suker played for?

19 Howard Wilkinson managed which side to the league title?

20 What is the colour of Germany's home shorts?

1 Alan Shearer first played in the competition with which club?

2 Which Scottish side represented its country in the 1996–97 tournament?

3 Which Italian side won the European Cup in 1996?

4 Which team were the first British side to win the trophy?

5 Which Austrian team did Manchester Utd beat in their final group game of 96–97?

6 Which Italian side topped Manchester Utd's group in the same season?

7 Trevor Francis scored a Final goal for which club?

8 Who was Manchester Utd's manager when they won the trophy in the 60s?

9 In which decade did Liverpool first win the competition?

10 Liverpool have won the trophy how many times before the 90s?

11 Which famous Spanish side won the first five Finals?

12 And which striker scored in all five of those Finals?

13 Which side became known as "The Lions of Lisbon"?

14 Which were the first team from Portugal to win the tournament?

15 Who was Liverpool's manager when they first won the trophy?

16 A Ronald Koeman Final goal gave which side the trophy?

17 Who were Liverpool playing in the 1985 Final overshadowed by crowd trouble?

18 Who scored in the '96 Final and started 1996–97 in English soccer?

19 Which Dutch team won the title three times in succession in the 70s?

20 Who was Nottingham Forest's goalkeeper when they first won the trophy?

1 Who plays at home at Upton Park?

2 What is the main colour of Watford's home shirts?

3 Jack Charlton and Kevin Keegan have both managed which club?

4 What is the last word in Brighton & Hove's name?

5 Which country has Phil Babb played for?

6 Which Glenn of Tottenham Hotspur was PFA Young Player of the Year in 1980?

7 Which country do Atletico Madrid come from?

8 With which club did Andy Hinchcliffe make his league debut?

9 Which club did Tony Dorigo join on leaving Chelsea?

10 Which John was Hearts' top League scorer in 1995-96?

11 What colour are Aston Villa's home shorts?

12 What is Cardiff's nickname?

13 Which team does David Mellor support?

14 Denis Smith followed Lawrie McMenemy as boss at which club?

15 What is the main colour of Spain's home shirts?

16 Which Steve of Liverpool won the Footballer of the Year award in 1989?

17 Which country did Gerson play for?

18 With which club did Chris Sutton make his League debut?

19 Who hit 34 league goals in Newcastle's first season in the Premier League?

20 Defenders Parker and Pallister were teammates with which club?

LEVEL 1 ⚽

1 Who missed a spot kick and put a bag on his head in a pizza place?

2 Beardsley and Shearer have been on the spot for which club?

3 Andy Brehme scored a World Cup Final winning penalty for which country?

4 Where should a goalkeeper stand for a penalty?

5 Who made the first Wembley save from an FA Cup Final spot kick?

6 Ron Flowers has been on the spot for which country?

7 Which England player missed in a shoot out in Italy in 1990 but scored in Euro 96?

8 Which Julian became a 90s penalty expert for West Ham?

9 Yorke and Townsend have been on the spot for which club?

10 Robbie Rensenbrink scored four penalties in the '78 World Cup finals for which team?

11 Which London team won the UEFA Cup Final of 1984 after a shoot out?

12 Who missed from the spot for Scotland against England in Euro 96?

13 Which country did The Republic of Ireland beat in a 1990 World Cup shoot out?

14 Who scored two spot kicks in an FA Cup Final for Manchester Utd in the 90s?

15 Wise and Hughes have been on the spot for which club?

16 Which country was awarded a penalty in the Euro 96 Final?

17 In 1994 the Final of which major tournament was decided on a penalty shoot out for the first time ever?

18 Which Tottenham Hotspur player failed to score from the spot in the 1991 FA Cup Final?

19 In a league game can a taker score from a rebound off the keeper?

20 Which Francis was a spot kick king for Manchester City in the 70s?

Answers

Quote, Unquote (see Quiz 32)
1 Alan Ball. 2 Sardines. 3 Mabbutt. 4 Paul Gascoigne. 5 Stan Collymore. 6 Nike. 7 George Graham. 8 Graham Taylor. 9 Pele. 10 Neal. 11 Beardsley. 12 George Best. 13 Paul Gascoigne. 14 Jürgen Klinsmann. 15 Tomatoes. 16 Before the Euro 96 semi-final. 17 Argentina. 18 Glenn Hoddle. 19 Gareth Southgate. 20 Paul Gascoigne.

1 What is the last word in Northampton's name?

2 Which country has Vinnie Jones played for?

3 What is the main colour of Hull's home shirts?

4 Which team has its stadium in South Africa Road, London?

5 Which player was Manchester Utd's top league scorer in 1995–96?

6 Which club traditionally selects its managers from the Boot Room?

7 Which midfielder Jason went from Ipswich to Tottenham Hotspur in the 90s?

8 With which club did John Wark make his league debut?

9 Which club did Kevin Gallacher leave to join Blackburn?

10 Which Alex of Aberdeen was Scottish Footballer of the Year in 1990?

11 Who are The Cumbrians?

12 Which country has Roy Keane played for?

13 What kind of animal was World Cup Willie?

14 Howard Kendall followed Dave Bassett as boss at which club?

15 Which Clive was PFA Player of the Year in 1987?

16 What colour are Croatia's home shirts?

17 Who was in goal when Liverpool won the 1995 Coca Cola Cup?

18 Which Terry has managed both Arsenal and Tottenham Hotspur?

19 England striker Alan Smith won a championship medal at which club?

20 Which Archie has been assistant manager to Walter Smith?

Quiz 32 Quote, Unquote

Answers – see page 38

LEVEL 1

1 Which Manchester City manager said, "We've got 1 point from 27 but it's not as bad as that"?

2 According to Eric Cantona what would be thrown off the trawler?

3 Which Gary said, "This is not a normal injury. Fashanu was playing without due care and attention"?

4 Whose departure from Lazio caused the president to remark, "He will only return to Rome as a tourist"?

5 Which Liverpool player was supposedly, "happier at Southend"?

6 Which company decided that, "1966 was a great year for English football. Eric was born"?

7 Which ex-Arsenal boss said, "I am as weak as the next man when it comes to temptation"?

8 Which manager suffered from the *Sun*'s turnip jibes?

9 Which Brazilian great talked of "the beautiful game"?

10 Which short-stay boss Phil said, "Watching Manchester City is probably the best laxative you can take"?

11 Which England international Peter said, "I often get called Quasimodo"?

12 Which modest 60s player said in the 90s, "I'd be worth around £14 to £15 million by today's prices"?

13 Who claimed in 1996 that he had "given up beer and guzzling"?

14 Which German said in 1994, "Me dive? Never!"?

15 What did Arrigo Sacchi say might be thrown at him after Euro 96?

16 When did Terry Venables say, "It's a football match, not a war"?

17 Which team did Alf Ramsey liken to "Animals"?

18 Who in 1996 took "the only job I would have left Chelsea for"?

19 Who said, "I've only taken one penalty before, for Crystal Palace"?

20 "As daft as a brush" Who was Bobby Robson talking about?

Spot Kicks (see Quiz 30)
1 Gareth Southgate. **2** Newcastle Utd. **3** West Germany. **4** On the goalline and between the posts. **5** Dave Beasant. **6** England. **7** Stuart Pearce. **8** Dicks. **9** Aston Villa. **10** Holland. **11** Tottenham Hotspur. **12** Gary McAllister. **13** Romania. **14** Eric Cantona. **15** Chelsea. **16** Czech Republic. **17** The World Cup. **18** Gary Lineker. **19** Yes. **20** Lee.

1 Who plays at home at Easter Road?

2 Which Ian of Liverpool was PFA Young Player of the Year in 1983?

3 Gerry Francis and David Pleat have both managed which club?

4 What is the second word in Cambridge's name?

5 Which country has Peter Schmeichel played for?

6 Which team did Eric Morecambe support?

7 Which country do Sturm Graz come from?

8 With which club did keeper David James make his league debut?

9 Which club did Pat Jennings join on leaving Tottenham Hotspur?

10 What pattern is on West Bromwich Albion's home shirts?

11 Which Mike was Stoke's top League scorer in 1995-96?

12 Who are The Addicks?

13 Which Terry of Liverpool won the Footballer of the Year award in 1980?

14 What is the main colour of the Romanian home strip?

15 What forename links players Parlour and Houghton?

16 Which Lou got the Celtic sack in 1994?

17 Which club was banned from the 1994–95 FA Cup then allowed back in?

18 Which country did Stefan Effenberg play for?

19 Ruel Fox and Andy Cole were teammates at which club?

20 Which energy giving drink has John Barnes advertised?

1   What position did Stanley Matthews play?

2   Which legend married a 23-year-old air hostess on his 49th birthday?

3   Which Dutch international player went on to managerial success at Barcelona in the 1990s?

4   With which London club did Jimmy Greaves begin his career?

5   Who was the first England captain of a World Cup winning team?

6   Which country did Zbigniew Boniek play?

7   Which League club did Billy Wright play for?

8   Who was "Wor Jackie"?

9   In which country was Ferenc Puskas born?

10   At which club did Denis Law finish his career?

11   Who was "Kaiser Franz"?

12   How many clubs did Tom Finney play for?

13   Who was known as "The Black Panther"?

14   Who was England's keeper in the 1966 World Cup winning side?

15   How did Edson Arantes do Nascimento become better known?

16   Which goalkeeper with Christian names Patrick Anthony played over 100 times for his country?

17   Which French midfielder of the 70s and 80s became France's top scorer?

18   In which city did Billy Meredith play his soccer?

19   Which player turned out in a record 21 World Cup finals matches for Argentina?

20   At which club did Stanley Matthews begin and end his career?

Answers

Scottish Internationals (see Quiz 36)
1 Coventry City. 2 Goalkeeper. 3 Celtic. 4 Denis Law. 5 John.
6 Celtic. 7 John Greig. 8 Jim Baxter. 9 Liverpool.
10 Johnston. 11 Aberdeen. 12 Jim Holton. 13 Alan Hansen.
14 Willie Johnston. 15 His front teeth. 16 Bob Wilson.
17 Willie. 18 Tottenham Hotspur. 19 John Collins. 20 McStay.

1 What is the second word in Norwich's name?

2 Which country has Jason McAteer played for?

3 What is the main colour in Ipswich's home shirts?

4 Which London club did Wimbledon ground-share with in the 90s?

5 Which German player was Manchester City's top scorer in 1995–96?

6 Rod Wallace and Gary Speed were teammates at which club?

7 Which Danny of Celtic was Scottish Footballer of the Year in 1977?

8 With which club did Roy Keane make his league debut?

9 Which club did Chris Armstrong leave to join Tottenham Hotspur?

10 What is Chelsea's nickname?

11 What colour are Denmark's home shirts?

12 Which country did Norman Whiteside play for?

13 Which Dean was Aston Villa's top scorer in 1994–95?

14 Which Mick played a record number of games for Ipswich?

15 Which Gary was PFA Player of the Year in 1986?

16 Who was Alex Ferguson's assistant for Manchester Utd for the 1995–96 double season?

17 Jeff Kenna and Ken Monkou were teammates at which club?

18 Howard Kendall got the boot as boss of which Division 1 club in 1995?

19 Graham Rix played over 350 games with which club?

20 Alan Stubbs was a losing Coca-Cola Cup Finalist with which club?

Pot Luck 17 (see Quiz 33)

Answers
1 Hibernian. 2 Rush. 3 Tottenham Hotspur. 4 United.
5 Denmark. 6 Luton Town. 7 Austria. 8 Watford. 9 Arsenal.
10 Stripes. 11 Sheron. 12 Charlton Athletic. 13 McDermott.
14 Yellow. 15 Ray. 16 Macari. 17 Tottenham Hotspur.
18 Germany. 19 Newcastle Utd. 20 Lucozade Sport.

Quiz 36 Scottish Internationals

LEVEL 1

Answers – see page 42

1 Where did Eoin Jess move to on leaving Aberdeen?

2 In what position did Frank Haffey play?

3 Which club was Kenny Dalglish with when he was first capped?

4 Which striker played for Manchester Utd and Torino in the 60s?

5 What forename is shared by strikers Collins and Spencer?

6 With which club did fullback Tommy Gemmell spend most of his career?

7 Which defender or midfielder clocked up a record 496 league games for Rangers?

8 Who was "Slim" Jim?

9 Which club did Billy Liddell play for in the 40s and 50s?

10 Which Glasgow born striker Mo notched 14 goals for his country?

11 Which club did Alex McLeish play for?

12 The chant, 'Six foot two, Eyes of Blue' was about which defender?

13 Which classy Liverpool defender of the 70s and 80s only landed 26 caps?

14 Which player failed a dope test and was sent home from the 1978 World Cup in Argentina?

15 What did a certain lager claim to restore for Joe Jordan?

16 Which Arsenal goalkeeper of the 70s played for Scotland?

17 What forename is shared by defenders Donachie and Miller?

18 Which London club did Alan Gilzean play for?

19 Who moved to Monaco as a free agent in the summer of 1996?

20 Which Paul of Celtic was injured and missed Euro 96?

Answers

Soccer Legends (see Quiz 34)
1 Outside right. 2 George Best. 3 Johan Cruyff. 4 Chelsea.
5 Bobby Moore. 6 Poland. 7 Wolves. 8 Jackie Milburn.
9 Hungary. 10 Manchester City. 11 Franz Beckenbauer.
12 One. 13 Lev Yashin. 14 Gordon Banks. 15 Pele.
16 Jennings. 17 Michel Platini. 18 Manchester. 19 Diego
Maradona. 20 Stoke City.

Quiz 37 Pot Luck 19

Answers – see page 47

LEVEL 1

1 Who plays at home at The Hawthorns?

2 Gavin Peacock and Dennis Wise were teammates at which club?

3 Stewart Houston and Ray Wilkins have both managed which club?

4 What is the second word in Carlisle's name?

5 Which country has Georgiou Kinkladze played for?

6 Which Mark of Manchester Utd was PFA Young Player of the Year in 1985?

7 Which country do Standard Liege come from?

8 With which club did Gary Speed make his league debut?

9 Which club did Peter Beardsley join on leaving Everton?

10 What is the main colour of West Ham's home shirts?

11 Which Craig was Sunderland's top League scorer in 1995–96?

12 What is Crewe's nickname?

13 Stan Flashman has been connected with which club?

14 Which player is a great admirer of the 19th century poet Rimbaud?

15 Which team does Jim Bowen support?

16 What is the main colour of France's home shirts?

17 Which Frans of Ipswich won the Footballer of the Year award in 1981?

18 Which club plays at the Nou Camp Stadium?

19 Which Scottish team are known as The Honest Men?

20 Which Paul was Everton's top scorer in 1994–95?

Answers

Pot Luck 20 (see Quiz 39)
1 United. 2 England. 3 White. 4 Charlton Athletic. 5 Roberts.
6 Malpas. 7 Yeboah. 8 John Spencer. 9 Celtic. 10 The Eagles.
11 Bolton Wanderers. 12 Wales. 13 Green. 14 Spink.
15 Wimbledon. 16 Platt. 17 Reid. 18 Endsleigh. 19 Palmer.
20 Manchester City.

Quiz 38 Going Up

Answers – see page 48

LEVEL 1

1 Which team did Kenny Dalglish lead into the Premiership?

2 Which team went up to the Premiership in 1994 and again in 1996?

3 Who was manager of Newcastle when they were promoted to the Premiership in 1993?

4 Which club made it to the First Division for the first time ever in 1985?

5 Ludek Miklosko has been in two promotion campaigns with which club?

6 Steve McMahon took which team to the First Division at the first attempt?

7 Which team did Frank Clark lead back to the Premiership in the 1990s?

8 Who gained promotion for Middlesbrough in his first season as a player/manager in 1995?

9 Which club were in Division 4 in 1982 ar ' Division 1 in 1986?

10 John McGinlay was with which club in promotions from the Second division to the Premiership?

11 Which Wanderers entered the League in 1993?

12 Steve Bruce was ever-present when which East Anglian side were Second Division champions?

13 Who was manager of Sunderland when they were promoted in 1996?

14 Which Chris took Bradford to Division 1 in 1996?

15 Which London team joined the League in 1991?

16 Which Stan was Nottingham Forest's top marksman in their '94 promotion?

17 Joachim and Walsh played in a play-off Final for which team?

18 Goals by Deane and Agana took which United to the top flight?

19 Batty and Strachan helped which club to promotion?

20 Who was the boss who took Swansea to their 1980s promotions?

Answers

Going Down (see Quiz 40)
1 Ipswich Town. 2 Ray Wilkins. 3 Four. 4 The Canaries.
5 Newport County. 6 Manchester City. 7 Sunderland.
8 Arsenal. 9 Saunders. 10 Nottingham Forest. 11 Swindon
Town. 12 Lawrence. 13 Oldham Athletic. 14 Sheffield Utd.
15 The 1970s. 16 Brighton. 17 No. 18 Crystal Palace.
19 The 1970s. 20 Norwich City.

46

1   What is the second word in Oxford's name?

2   Which country has Des Walker played for?

3   What is the main colour of Leeds' home shirts?

4   Who plays home games at The Valley?

5   Which Iwan was Leicester City's top scorer in 1995–96?

6   Which Maurice of Dundee Utd was Scottish Footballer of the Year in 1991?

7   Which Tony was Leeds' top scorer in 1994–95?

8   Who was Chelsea's leading League goalscorer in the 1995–96 season?

9   Which club did Brian McClair leave to join Manchester Utd?

10   What is Crystal Palace's nickname?

11   Jason McAteer and John McGinlay were teammates at which club?

12   Which country has Ian Rush played for?

13   What colour are Portugal's home shorts?

14   Which goalkeeper Nigel made over 300 appearances with Aston Villa?

15   Sam Hammam is connected with which club?

16   Which David was made England's new captain in March 1994?

17   Which Peter of Everton was PFA Player of the Year in 1985?

18   Which Gloucester based insurance company agreed to sponsor the Football League in 1993?

19   Which Carlton has played for Sheffield Wednesday and Leeds Utd?

20   Peter Swales was chairman of which club?

1 Five-goal Claus Thomsen was which relegated team's top scorer?

2 Which player/manager took QPR down in 1995–96?

3 Three teams went out of the Premiership in 1994. What did that number change to the following season?

4 The Eagles flew out of the Premiership in 1995, what other feathered friends joined them?

5 Which Welsh side went out of the League in 1988?

6 Which team went out of the Premiership on goal difference in 1996?

7 Marco Gabbiadini was top scorer as which side went down in 1991?

8 Which club has been in the top flight without relegation since 1913?

9 Which Dean was top scorer as Derby went down in 1991?

10 Stuart Pearce and Mark Crossley were in which relegated side?

11 Fjortoft went up with Middlesbrough the season that he left which team to go down?

12 Which Lennie did an annual escape act to keep Charlton in the top flight in the 80s?

13 Veteran striker Graeme Sharp was top scorer for which side leaving the Premiership?

14 A last-minute goal put which Dave Bassett team down in 1994?

15 In which decade were Manchester Utd last relegated from the top flight?

16 Which side rock bottom in the League in the 1996–97 season were in the top flight in 1983?

17 Have Celtic ever been relegated?

18 Which London team went out of the Premiership in 1993 and 1995?

19 In which decade were Carlisle last in the top division in England?

20 Which team was 7th in the Premiership at the start of January, yet were relegated at the end of the season in 1995?

Answers

Going Up (see Quiz 38)

1 Blackburn Rovers. 2 Leicester City. 3 Kevin Keegan. 4 Oxford Utd. 5 West Ham Utd. 6 Swindon Town. 7 Nottingham Forest. 8 Bryan Robson. 9 Wimbledon. 10 Bolton Wanderers. 11 Wycombe. 12 Norwich City. 13 Peter Reid. 14 Kamara. 15 Barnet. 16 Collymore. 17 Leicester City. 18 Sheffield. 19 Leeds Utd. 20 John Toshack.

Quiz 41 Pot Luck 21

Answers – see page 51

LEVEL 1

1 Who plays at home at The Dell?

2 Which flying winger was Manchester Utd's top League scorer in 1994–95?

3 Glenn Hoddle and Ruud Gullit have both managed which club?

4 What is the second word in Chester's name?

5 Which country has Keith Gillespie played for?

6 Which Tony of West Ham was PFA Young Player of the Year in 1986?

7 Which country do Slavia Sofia come from?

8 With which club did Michael Thomas make his League debut?

9 Which club did Tony Mowbray join on leaving Middlesbrough?

10 Wimbledon's home shirts are a dark shade of which colour?

11 Which Wayne was Swindon's top League scorer in 1995–96?

12 What is Darlington's nickname?

13 John Salako and Ray Houghton were teammates at which club?

14 Which country does Michael Laudrup play for?

15 Which team does Jo Brand support?

16 Which Steve of Tottenham Hotspur won the Footballer of the Year award in 1982?

17 What is the colour of Bulgaria's home shorts?

18 Which London club briefly had a "famous five" lineup of attackers in the 90s?

19 Which country does Dmitri Kharine of Chelsea come from?

20 Which Steve has scored most League goals in a career for Wolves?

Answers

Pot Luck 22 (see Quiz 43)
1 United. 2 The Republic of Ireland. 3 Blue. 4 Barnsley.
5 Fowler. 6 Johnstone. 7 Tottenham Hotspur. 8 Crystal Palace.
9 Rangers. 10 Ince. 11 Paine. 12 England. 13 Beardsley.
14 Yes. 15 Plymouth Argyle. 16 Rivera. 17 Rush.
18 Romania. 19 Rangers. 20 Karel Poborsky.

1 Which United manager signed Eric Cantona?

2 How old was Ryan Giggs when he made his first team debut?

3 Who wrote the autobiography *The Good, The Bad And The Bubbly*?

4 Which player went to Newcastle as part of the deal that bought Andy Cole to old?

5 In which country was Sir Matt Busby born?

6 Which club was Paul Ince bought from?

7 Mark Hughes has moved from Manchester Utd twice. Which clubs did he join?

8 Which team were the opponents in the Cantona Kung-Fu spectator attack in January 1995?

9 Alex Ferguson sold his son Darren to which club?

10 Who is the elder of the Neville brothers?

11 What was Denis Law's usual shirt number?

12 What infamous first went to Kevin Moran in the 1985 FA Cup Final?

13 What is the surname of 1970s brothers Brian and Jimmy?

14 Which United manager signed Bryan Robson?

15 Who was the scoring skipper in the 1996 FA Cup Final?

16 Paddy Roche was an international keeper for which country?

17 Who was dubbed "El Beatle" after a 60s European triumph?

18 Which forename links Beckham, May and Saddler?

19 Which two United players were members of England's World Cup winning team?

20 Who was the first Manchester Utd player to hit five goals in a Premier League match?

Answers

The 1980s (see Quiz 44)

1 Manchester City. 2 Points for a win. 3 Crystal Palace.
4 Robert Maxwell. 5 Swansea City. 6 Italy. 7 The Milk Cup.
8 Bob Paisley. 9 Tottenham Hotspur. 10 Kevin Keegan.
11 Gary Lineker. 12 Liverpool. 13 Jock Stein. 14 France.
15 England. 16 France. 17 Terry Venables. 18 Arsenal.
19 Chelsea. 20 Play-offs.

Quiz 43 Pot Luck 22

Answers – see page 49

LEVEL 1 ⚽

1 What is the second word in Peterborough's name?

2 Which country has Frank Stapleton played for?

3 What is the main colour of Leicester's home shirts?

4 Who plays home games at Oakwell?

5 Which Robbie was Liverpool's top scorer in 1995–96?

6 Which Derek of Rangers was Scottish Footballer of the Year in 1978?

7 Campbell and Calderwood were teammates at which club?

8 With which club did Stan Collymore make his League debut?

9 Which club did Gary Stevens join on leaving Everton?

10 Which Paul first captained England in June 1993?

11 Which Terry played 800+ league games, mostly for Southampton?

12 What country has Paul Mariner played for?

13 Which Peter was Newcastle's top league scorer in 1994–95?

14 Has there ever been an England international with the surname Bastard?

15 Which team does veteran politician Michael Foot support?

16 Which Gianni was known as Italy's "Golden Boy"?

17 Which Ian of Liverpool was PFA Player of the Year in 1995?

18 Which country has Gica Popescu played for?

19 Which was the first Scottish side that Stuart McCall played for?

20 Who scored an amazing chip goal in Euro 96 for the Czech Republic against Portugal?

Pot Luck 21 (see Quiz 41)
1 Southampton. 2 Andrei Kanchelskis. 3 Chelsea. 4 City.
5 Northern Ireland. 6 Cottee. 7 Bulgaria. 8 Arsenal. 9 Celtic.
10 Blue. 11 Allison. 12 The Quakers. 13 Crystal Palace.
14 Denmark. 15 Crystal Palace. 16 Perryman. 17 Green.
18 Tottenham Hotspur. 19 Russia. 20 Bull.

Answers

1 Which club did both Malcolm Allison and John Bond manage?

2 What changed from two to three in all games at the start of the 1981–82 campaign?

3 Which London team were hailed as "The Team of the Eighties"?

4 Which tycoon became Oxford chairman?

5 Which team was top of the First Division during 1981 but back in the Fourth Division by 1986?

6 Who won the 1982 World Cup?

7 What was the League Cup known as after a deal with the National Dairy Board?

8 Who retired as Liverpool boss after a season in which both the Championship and League Cup were won?

9 Garth Crooks and Steve Archibald played together at which club?

10 Which former England captain ended his playing days at Newcastle Utd?

11 Which Englishman was the top scorer in the 1986 World Cup finals?

12 Who did Wimbledon beat in their first FA Cup Final victory?

13 Which manager collapsed and died seconds before the end of the Wales v Scotland World Cup qualifying game?

14 On leaving Tottenham Hotspur, Chris Waddle moved to which country?

15 UEFA banned the clubs of which country from participation in European competitions?

16 Which host nation won the 1984 European Championship?

17 Which British manager took over at Barcelona?

18 Which team won the 1988–89 championship in the last minute of the season?

19 Kerry Dixon was Division 1 top scorer in 1984–85 with which team?

20 Which extra games were introduced to decide promotion?

1 Who plays at home at Fratton Park?

2 Which country won the 1992 European Championship?

3 Dave Bassett and Joe Kinnear have both managed which club?

4 What is the second word in Coventry's name?

5 Which country does Fabrizio Ravanelli come from?

6 Limpar and Rideout were teammates at which club?

7 Which country do Brondby come from?

8 With which club did Nigel Clough make his League debut?

9 Which club did Dan Petrescu join on leaving Sheffield Wednesday?

10 What colour are Wolves' home shirts?

11 Which Teddy was Tottenham Hotspur's top League scorer in 1995–96?

12 Who are The Cottagers?

13 Which Kenny of Liverpool won the Footballer of the Year award in 1983?

14 Which Mark was Sheffield Wednesday's top League scorer in 1994–95?

15 Which team does Jasper Carrott support?

16 Fullback Gary Stevens played three FA Cup Finals for which club?

17 Which country staged the World Cup finals when "Nessun Dorma" became an anthem?

18 What is Scotland's national football stadium called?

19 What make of crisps has Gary Lineker advertised?

20 Which Tony of Arsenal was PFA Young Player of the Year in 1987?

Answers

Pot Luck 24 (see Quiz 47)
1 Argyle. 2 Northern Ireland. 3 Red. 4 Leicester City.
5 Ghana. 6 McCoist. 7 Sweden. 8 Arsenal. 9 Arsenal.
10 Gillingham. 11 Sheffield Wednesday. 12 Scotland.
13 Benfica. 14 Red. 15 *Viz.* 16 Wimbledon. 17 Gigg Lane.
18 Norway. 19 Cottee. 20 Wallace.

1 Tim Sherwood led which club to the Premiership?

2 David Platt, Ray Parlour and Liam Brady have all played for which club?

3 Which French superstar was European Player of the Year three times in the 80s?

4 According to song, who was dreaming of Wembley with Tottenham Hotspur?

5 Which Billy was at the heart of Leeds' success in the 1960s and '70s?

6 Which English club did Kazimierz Denya join in the 70s?

7 Which former Liverpool skipper moved to Sampdoria?

8 Which midfield dynamo captained the West Germans in Italia 90?

9 Which Gary has played for Luton, Forest, Villa and Leicester?

10 Which London team did Stefan Schwartz play for?

11 What name is shared by Minto and Sellars?

12 Enzo Scifo has played for which country?

13 Which was Johnny Haynes' only English club?

14 Which-long serving Celtic and Scotland skipper first played back in 1982?

15 Michael Thomas has scored an FA Cup Final goal for which team?

16 What is the first name of West German 60s and 70s stalwart Overath?

17 Who was England's "Captain Marvel"?

18 Which club had the dream midfield of Ball, Harvey and Kendall?

19 Paul Ince was at which club when he made his England debut?

20 Has Robert Lee ever played for England?

Quiz 47 Pot Luck 24

Answers – see page 53

1 What is the last word in Plymouth's name?

2 Which country has Alan McDonald played for?

3 What colour are Liverpool's home shorts ?

4 Who plays home games at Filbert Street?

5 Where is Leeds Utd's Tony Yeboah from?

6 Which Ally was Scottish Footballer of the Year in 1992?

7 Which country hosted the 1992 European Championship?

8 With which London club did Niall Quinn make his league debut?

9 Which club did Anders Limpar leave to join Everton?

10 Which team is known as The Gills?

11 Chris Waddle and Des Walker were teammates at which club?

12 Which country has Andy Goram played for?

13 Which club plays at the Stadium of Light?

14 What colour are Belgium's home shirts?

15 Football character "Billy the Fish" appeared in which magazine?

16 Which London club did Hans Segers play for?

17 Where do Bury play?

18 What country has Liverpool's Bjornebye played for?

19 Which Tony was West Ham's top league scorer in 1994–95?

20 Which Rodney won a championship medal with Leeds in the 1990s?

Pot Luck 23 (see Quiz 45)
1 Portsmouth. 2 Denmark. 3 Wimbledon. 4 City. 5 Italy.
6 Everton. 7 Denmark. 8 Nottingham Forest. 9 Chelsea.
10 Old Gold. 11 Sheringham. 12 Fulham. 13 Dalglish.
14 Bright. 15 Birmingham City. 16 Everton. 17 Italy.
18 Hampden Park. 19 Walkers. 20 Adams.

Quiz 48 TV Pundits

LEVEL 1

1 Who formed a famous double act with Jimmy Greaves?

2 Which country did Sky man Andy Gray play for?

3 Who famously called a Polish keeper a "clown" on the box in 1973?

4 To four years either way, when did BBC TV first show *Match of the Day* on Saturday evening?

5 Which team does Des Lynam support?

6 Which club did Bob Wilson mainly play for?

7 Which commentator said, "They think it's all over... it is now!"?

8 Who, in the season Manchester Utd won their first double, said about them, " You don't win anything with kids"?

9 True or false – Jimmy Hill is a qualified referee?

10 Which club does Brian Moore support?

11 Who commentated at a Wembley Final presentation, "How apt that a man named Buchan should climb the 39 steps"?

12 Which former Tottenham Hotspur and Stoke striker reports for BBC?

13 Which impersonator features Des Lynam and Motty in his TV shows?

14 Which former presenter David went politically green?

15 Who was involved in tabloid headlines concerning sex-change Bond girl Caroline Cossey?

16 Who in 1977 became the youngest commentator on an FA Cup Final?

17 Who was a regular golfing partner of Kenny Dalglish?

18 Which pundit has been manager of Portsmouth?

19 Which *Match of the Day* expert became George Graham's assistant at Leeds?

20 Who declared Cantona was "nothing more than a brat" after a stamping incident against Norwich?

Answers

Midfield Men (see Quiz 46)
1 Blackburn Rovers. 2 Arsenal. 3 Michel Platini. 4 Osvaldo Ardiles. 5 Bremner. 6 Manchester City. 7 Graeme Souness. 8 Lothar Matthäus. 9 Parker. 10 Arsenal. 11 Scott. 12 Belgium. 13 Fulham. 14 Paul McStay. 15 Liverpool. 16 Wolfgang. 17 Bryan Robson. 18 Everton. 19 Manchester Utd. 20 Yes.

1   Who plays at home at Ewood Park?

2   Which Paul of Tottenham Hotspur was PFA Young Player of the Year in 1988?

3   Ron Atkinson and Gordon Strachan have both managed which club?

4   What is the second word in Crewe's name?

5   Which country has Frank Leboeuf played for?

6   Who was Aberdeen manager from 1978 to '86?

7   Which country do Panathinaikos come from?

8   With which club did David Batty make his League debut?

9   Which club did Lee Dixon join on leaving Stoke?

10 What colour are Wrexham's home shirts?

11 Which John was Tranmere's top League scorer in 1995–96?

12 What is Grimsby's nickname?

13 What is the colour of Italy's home shirts?

14 Which team does June Whitfield support?

15 Which Ian of Liverpool won the Footballer of the Year award in 1984?

16 Jeremy Goss and Ruel Fox were teammates at which club?

17 In which decade did Blackburn first play European soccer?

18 Which Scottish United does Lorraine Kelly support?

19 Which country does Branco play for?

20 Who brought a libel case against a paper involving his ex-wife Danielle?

Answers

Pot Luck 26 (see Quiz 51)
1 North. 2 The Republic of Ireland. 3 White. 4 Selhurst Park. 5 Marshall. 6 Strachan. 7 Chelsea. 8 QPR. 9 Nottingham Forest. 10 Leicester City. 11 White. 12 Wales. 13 Tottenham Hotspur. 14 Leeds Utd. 15 Yes. 16 Mark Hateley. 17 Keegan. 18 Red. 19 Aston Villa. 20 Liverpool.

1 Which non-league team beat Newcastle in February 1972?

2 Which Paul scored a 90s FA Cup winning goal for Everton?

3 Which London club won the FA Cup in 1981 and 1982?

4 Who was Des Walker playing for when he scored a Final own goal?

5 Dickie Guy was a goalkeeping hero with which 1970s non-league side?

6 Which United won the Scottish FA Cup for the first time in the 80s?

7 In which decade was the first Wembley Final?

8 Which Harry Redknapp team did a giant killing knocking out Manchester Utd in 1984?

9 Andy Linighan scored a last minute Final winner for which team?

10 Who beat Chelsea in the 1996 semi-finals?

11 Brian Flynn was boss as which club shocked Arsenal in 1992?

12 Cornishman Mike Trebilcock hit Final goals for which team in the 60s?

13 Ray Walker hit a screamer as which Midland team dumped Tottenham Hotspur in the 80s?

14 Arnold Muhren hit a Final goal for which club?

15 In 1989 Sutton United beat which First Division team 2–1?

16 Who was the first Frenchman to captain an FA Cup winning side?

17 Ray Crawford inspired which team to the ultimate giant killing by beating Leeds 3-2 in 1971?

18 In the 1980s, which South coast side were losing finalists the year they were relegated from the First Division?

19 What accounted for the 1990 Scottish Final score of Aberdeen 9 Celtic 8?

20 Geoff Thomas captained which London side in a 1990s Final?

1 What does the N stand for in PNE?

2 Which country has Liam Brady played for?

3 What is the main colour of Luton's home shirts?

4 Where do Crystal Palace play home games?

5 Which Ian was Ipswich's top scorer in 1995–96?

6 Which Gordon of Aberdeen was Scottish Footballer of the Year in 1980?

7 Ken Bates has been chairman of which London club?

8 With which club did Les Ferdinand make his league debut?

9 Which club did Stan Collymore leave to join Liverpool?

10 Which team is known as The Foxes?

11 What is the main colour of German home shirts?

12 Which country has Gary Speed played for?

13 Barmby and Anderton played together at which club?

14 Phil Masinga started in England with which club?

15 Can a goal be scored directly from a corner kick?

16 Which veteran striker moved from Rangers in Scotland to Rangers in London for £1.5 million at the end of 1995?

17 Which Kevin of Southampton was PFA Player of the Year in 1982?

18 What colour are Wales's home shirts?

19 Andy Townsend and John Fashanu were teammates at which club?

20 Ronnie Whelan made over 350 appearances for which club?

Answers

Pot Luck 25   (see Quiz 49)
1 Blackburn Rovers. 2 Gascoigne. 3 Coventry City.
4 Alexandra. 5 France. 6 Alex Ferguson. 7 Greece. 8 Leeds Utd. 9 Arsenal. 10 Red. 11 Aldridge. 12 The Mariners.
13 Blue. 14 Wimbledon. 15 Rush. 16 Norwich City.
17 1990s. 18 Dundee. 19 Brazil. 20 Graeme Souness.

LEVEL 1

1 Which team's ground is called St Andrews?

2 At which Park do Bolton play?

3 In the 90s Brighton have been dogged by the attempted sale of which ground?

4 At which Stadium was there crowd trouble at the Liverpool v Juventus European Cup Final of 1985?

5 Which club plays at Highbury?

6 Which side is at home if the venue is Ashton Gate?

7 Which London team has its ground situated in the Fulham Road?

8 What is Preston's ground called?

9 Who play at home at the Alfred McAlpine Stadium?

10 Which Scottish side were the first to boast an all-seater stadium?

11 Which stadium is situated in Sir Matt Busby Way?

12 Who plays at home at Boundary Park?

13 Which club has the Walker Steel stand on its ground?

14 Crystal Palace have extended ground-share to Wimbledon at which stadium?

15 Roker Park has been home for most of the 20th century to which team?

16 Which stadium has the Twin Towers?

17 At which Yorkshire club was there a fire tragedy in 1985?

18 Who plays at Vicarage Road?

19 The 1991 Liverpool and Nottingham Forest FA Cup semi-final was at which ground?

20 The Maracana Stadium is in which country?

1 Who plays at home at Craven Cottage?

2 Can a player be offside in his team's own half of the pitch when the ball is played?

3 Howard Wilkinson and George Graham have both managed which club?

4 What is the second word in Derby's name?

5 Which country has Tomas Brolin played for?

6 Which Paul of Arsenal was PFA Young Player of the Year in 1989?

7 Which country do Metz come from?

8 With which club did Nick Barmby make his league debut?

9 Which club did Kevin Richardson join on leaving Aston Villa?

10 Which Bob was WBA's top league scorer in 1995–96?

11 What colour are Barnsley's home shirts?

12 Which team is known as the Os?

13 Which England cricketer played for Scunthorpe?

14 Which hymn has been traditionally sung before the FA Cup Final?

15 Which team does Nick Hancock support?

16 What colour are the home shirts of Brazil?

17 Which Neville won the Footballer of the Year award in 1985?

18 Bobby Tambling is the career record scorer for which club?

19 Dave Bassett was manager at which Yorkshire club for eight years?

20 Darren Huckerby left which club to join Coventry City?

Quiz 54 World Cup
Answers – see page 64

1 Dunga was captain of which World Cup-winning country?

2 Which team knocked England out of the 1990 semi-finals?

3 Which President of FIFA gave his name to the original trophy?

4 Who was the manager of the 1990 West German trophy-winning team?

5 Goycochea played in a Final as goalkeeper for which country?

6 Which central American side shocked Scotland with a 1–0 win in 1990?

7 Prior to 1998 had the final stages ever been held in France?

8 Who was the Scottish boss for the trip to Argentina in 1978?

9 Which country knocked the Republic of Ireland out of the quarter-finals in 1990?

10 Which country was the only one beaten by the Republic of Ireland in the final stages of the 1994 tournament?

11 Which country did Lato play for?

12 When was the first ever Final played?

13 In which country was the first Final held?

14 Which Norman became the youngest scorer in final stages in 1982?

15 For which country did Oleg Salenko score the individual record of 5 goals in a game?

16 Which team made the Final in 1982, 1986 and 1990?

17 Which team were beaten finalists in 1994?

18 Which England goalkeeper retired from internationals after Italia 90?

19 In which decade were Sweden the host country?

20 For which country has Alexi Lalas played?

1 What does the letter P stand for in QPR?

2 Which country has Tony Cascarino played for?

3 What is the colour of Manchester City's home shirts?

4 Who plays at home at Tynecastle Park?

5 Which Andy was Huddersfield Town's top scorer in 1995–96?

6 Which team are "forever blowing bubbles"?

7 Who had trials with Bayern Munich before becoming a tennis champion?

8 With which club did fullback Rob Jones make his league debut?

9 Which club did Roy Wegerle leave to join Blackburn?

10 What is Lincoln City's nickname?

11 Which Andy of Rangers was Scottish Footballer of the Year in 1993?

12 Which country has Dave Phillips played for?

13 Which East Anglian side did John Bond manage?

14 Which Tottenham Hotspur defender shares his surname with a Scottish city?

15 Which England player is the son of a Jamaican international?

16 What colour are Argentina's home shirts?

17 Which John of Ipswich was PFA Player of the Year in 1981?

18 Who was the first player to win the league with different teams in consecutive seasons?

19 Des Walker and Roy Keane were teammates at which club?

20 Which club did Ray Clemence leave to join Tottenham Hotspur?

Answers

Pot Luck 27 (see Quiz 53)
1 Fulham. 2 No. 3 Leeds Utd. 4 County. 5 Sweden.
6 Merson. 7 France. 8 Tottenham Hotspur. 9 Coventry City.
10 Taylor. 11 Red. 12 Leyton Orient. 13 Ian Botham.
14 Abide With Me. 15 Stoke City. 16 Yellow. 17 Southall.
18 Chelsea. 19 Sheffield Utd. 20 Newcastle Utd.

1 Which 90s Chelsea skipper was unwise in his dealing with a London cabbie?

2 Who was made to serve 120 hours community service in 1995?

3 Why was Italian superstar Paolo Rossi banned in 1980?

4 Who got in trouble with the FA for narrating the video "Soccer Hard Men"?

5 The Sugar v Venables High Court rumpus concerned which club?

6 Which player appeared drunk on Terry Wogan's TV chat show?

7 In 1996, which country had the England squad played in prior to the reports of mid-air vandalism?

8 A 90s scandal forced Bernard Tapie out as President of which club?

9 Which star was tested positive for taking cocaine before a game for Napoli?

10 In 1995, who said, "I'm going to Gamblers' Anonymous, that's my night out now"?

11 Jan Molby was at which club when he was jailed for driving offences?

12 What part of a reporter's anatomy did Vinnie Jones bite in a Dublin bar?

13 At which Wembley event were Keegan and Bremner still fighting after being sent off?

14 Teammates Batty and Le Saux had a punch up at which club?

15 Which player went back to drink after England's Euro 96 defeat?

16 In 1995, who was banned for 12 months after a 'bung' enquiry?

17 Why was Arsenal's Sammy Nelson banned and fined in 1979?

18 Which Scottish player was nicknamed "Duncan Disorderly"?

19 Whose move to Lazio was delayed by a nightclub fracas?

20 Alan Cork reputedly had a hangover while playing in an FA Cup Final for which team?

Quiz 57 Pot Luck 29

Answers – see page 67

1 Who plays at home at Highfield Road?

2 At which club did Kevin Keegan make his first League appearance?

3 Ron Atkinson and Alex Ferguson have both managed which club?

4 What is the second word in Exeter's name?

5 Which country has John Collins played for?

6 Which Matt was PFA Young Player of the Year in 1990?

7 Which country do Werder Bremen come from?

8 With which club did Chris Waddle make his League debut?

9 Which club did Paul Warhurst join on leaving Sheffield Wednesday?

10 Which Tony was West Ham's joint top League scorer in 1995–96?

11 What colour are Bolton's home shorts?

12 Which team is known as the Reds or the Pool?

13 Which Clive of Tottenham Hotspur won the Footballer of the Year award in 1987?

14 Which team lost both the 1994 and 1995 Charity Shield games?

15 Which team does Bruce Forsyth support?

16 Which country does George Weah play for?

17 Which Scottish team won the Championship nine times in a row starting in 1966?

18 Martin Edwards has been chairman of which clubs?

19 Which London club has had a long time sponsorship with JVC?

20 What is the Neville brothers' father called?

Answers

Pot Luck 30 (see Quiz 59)
1 United. 2 England. 3 White. 4 Port Vale. 5 Kanchelskis.
6 Italy. 7 Rough. 8 Ipswich Town. 9 Cambridge Utd.
10 Arsenal and Tottenham Hotspur. 11 The Hatters.
12 Scotland. 13 Arsenal. 14 Armfield. 15 Manchester Utd.
16 Sweden. 17 McDermott. 18 Tottenham Hotspur.
19 Quinn. 20 Switzerland.

LEVEL 1

1 Who were the first British side to win the competition?

2 An Alan Smith goal won the trophy for which club?

3 Which English side won the 1990–91 trophy?

4 Which came first, the European Cup or the Cup Winners' Cup?

5 Which French team won the competition in 1996?

6 Sandy Jardine got a winners' medal with which club?

7 With which team did Alex Ferguson first win the trophy as a boss?

8 What colour home shirts did Manchester Utd wear when they beat Barcelona in a 1990s Final?

9 Who skippered West Ham's victorious team in the 1960s?

10 Which team did Peter Reid win the competition with?

11 Name the west London team won the trophy in 1971?

12 Eoin Jess scored four goals in the 1993–94 competition for which club?

13 To qualify, what is the trophy a team has to win in its domestic competition of the previous season?

14 Which home country have Crusaders represented in this tournament?

15 Did Celtic win the tournament in the 1970s and 1980s?

16 Who represented England in the 1996–97 tournament?

17 Which England international striker helped Barcelona in the 1989 Final?

18 Which Premier League team represented England in the 1995–96 tournament?

19 Which Welsh team hit a cricket score 12–0 in the early 1980s?

20 Have Ajax ever won the competition?

Answers

The 1990s (see Quiz 60)
1 Japan. 2 Bobby Moore. 3 Mick McCarthy. 4 Bosman.
5 Bobby Robson. 6 Faustino Asprilla. 7 Brighton. 8 Yugoslavia.
9 Shearer and Sutton. 10 Sunderland. 11 Arsenal.
12 Manchester Utd. 13 Graeme Souness. 14 Leeds Utd.
15 Graham Taylor. 16 Birmingham City. 17 Gary Lineker.
18 Barclays. 19 Rangers. 20 Maidstone Utd.

Quiz 59 Pot Luck 30

Answers – see page 65

1   What is the second word in Rotherham's name?

2   Which country has Mark Hateley played for?

3   What colour are Manchester Utd's home shorts?

4   Who plays home games at Vale Park?

5   Which Andrei was Everton's top scorer in 1995–96?

6   Serie A takes place in which country?

7   Which Alan of Partick was Scottish Footballer of the Year in 1981?

8   With which club did Alan Brazil make his league debut?

9   Which club did Dion Dublin leave to join Manchester Utd?

10   Which teams played in the 1991 all-London Charity Shield game?

11   What is Luton's nickname?

12   Which country has Jim Baxter played for?

13   David Rocastle played over 200 games for which London club?

14   Which Jimmy helped the FA to find a new England coach in 1996?

15   Which team does Mick Hucknall support?

16   What country has Thomas Ravelli played for?

17   Which Terry of Liverpool was PFA Player of the Year in 1980?

18   Irving Scholar was chairman of which London club?

19   Which Mick knocked in over 30 league goals for Newcastle in 1989–90?

20   Which country does Marc Hottiger play for?

LEVEL 1 ⚽

1 In which country did Gary Lineker finish his playing career?

2 Which former England skipper died of cancer in February 1993?

3 Who took over from Jack Charlton as manager of the Republic of Ireland?

4 Which Jean-Marc went to the European Court of Justice with a contractual dispute?

5 Which former England manager went to be boss of Barcelona?

6 Who moved from Parma to Newcastle for £7 million?

7 Which seaside club's last game of 1995–96 was abandoned after a crowd invasion?

8 Which war-torn country qualified but were excluded from the 1992 European Championship?

9 Who were Blackburn's "SAS" strikeforce?

10 Which Second Division side played Liverpool in the 1992 FA Cup Final?

11 A Steve Morrow goal gave which club League Cup success?

12 Which English club achieved two doubles in the 90s?

13 Which Liverpool manager had a triple heart bypass operation?

14 Which Yorkshire club was taken over by London-based group Caspian?

15 Which former England boss got the sack as manager of Wolves?

16 Where did Steve Bruce go to when he left Manchester Utd?

17 Which striker's son was diagnosed as having a rare form of leukaemia?

18 Which bank did not renew their sponsorship of the league?

19 Which team in 1991–92 won the Scottish League by 9 points?

20 Which side resigned from the league in August 1992?

Answers

European Cup Winners' Cup (see Quiz 58)
1 Tottenham Hotspur. 2 Arsenal. 3 Manchester Utd. 4 The European Cup. 5 Paris St Germain. 6 Rangers. 7 Aberdeen. 8 White. 9 Bobby Moore. 10 Everton. 11 Chelsea. 12 Aberdeen. 13 A national cup played on a knockout basis. 14 Northern Ireland. 15 No. 16 Liverpool. 17 Gary Lineker. 18 Everton. 19 Swansea City. 20 Yes, in 1987.

Quiz 61 Pot Luck 31

Answers – see page 71

LEVEL 1

1 Who plays at home at The New Den?

2 Marc Reiper first played in England for which club?

3 Dave Bassett and Howard Kendall have both managed which club?

4 What is the second word in Grimsby's name?

5 Which country has Martin Keown played for?

6 Which Lee of Manchester Utd was PFA Young Player of the Year in 1991?

7 Which country do Feyenoord come from?

8 With which club did Frank Stapleton make his League debut?

9 Which club did Pat Nevin join on leaving Everton?

10 Which Bryan was Forest's joint top League scorer in 1995–96?

11 What colour are Blackburn's home shorts?

12 Which team is known as The Citizens?

13 Tim Flowers and Neil Ruddock were in the same team at which club?

14 Dr Josef Venglos was manager of which English team?

15 Which team does Hugh Grant support?

16 Which country does Hristo Stoichkov play for?

17 Which Kenny of Forest won the Footballer of the Year award in 1978?

18 Who was West Ham manager from 1974–1989?

19 Dwight Yorke plays international soccer for which team?

20 Ray Wilkins and Andy Sinton were at which club together?

Answers

Pot Luck 32 (see Quiz 63)
1 United. 2 Northern Ireland. 3 Red. 4 Southend Utd.
5 Sturridge. 6 Denmark. 7 Aston Villa. 8 Wimbledon.
9 Newcastle Utd. 10 Manchester Utd. 11 Hateley. 12 England.
13 Oldham Athletic. 14 Barry Fry. 15 Crystal Palace.
16 Coventry City. 17 Brady. 18 Liverpool. 19 Brazil.
20 Coppell.

69

1 Which international stopper has played for Manchester Utd, Villa and Derby?

2 Ratcliffe and Mountfield were a partnership at which club?

3 Manuel Amaros played for which country?

4 Which Leeds defender was known as "The Giraffe"?

5 Which club did England fullback Eddie Hapgood play for?

6 Which fullback became Bryan Robson's assistant at Middlesbrough?

7 Which defender was supposed to "Bite Yer Legs"?

8 Which AC Milan sweeper is known as "Franco"?

9 At which club was the Butcher and Osman partnership?

10 Which John made a record number of appearance for Rangers before becoming boss?

11 Mike Duxbury won 10 England caps while at which League club?

12 Which country did Ronald Koeman play for?

13 Which club did Jimmy Armfield play for?

14 What forename links Leeds greats Madeley and Reaney?

15 What nickname did Chelsea's Ron Harris earn?

16 Djalma and Nilton Santos were fullbacks for which country?

17 Which country did Kevin Beattie play for?

18 Which defensive hardman is known as "Razor"?

19 Which Keith was involved in the 1996 televised bust up with Asprilla?

20 Frank Lampard was a great servant of which club?

1 What is the second word in Scunthorpe's name?

2 Which country has Nigel Worthington played for?

3 What colour are Middlesbrough's home shirts?

4 Who plays at home at Roots Hall?

5 Which Dean was Derby County's top scorer in 1995–96?

6 Which country has Kim Vilfort played for?

7 Curcic and Milosevic played together at which English club?

8 With which club did Vinnie Jones make his league debut?

9 Which club did Ruel Fox leave to join Tottenham Hotspur?

10 Which team is known as The Red Devils?

11 Which Mark of Rangers was Scottish Footballer of the Year in 1994?

12 Which country has Phil Neal played for?

13 Gunnar Halle first played in England for which club?

14 Who put his money into Peterborough in 1996?

15 Jim Cannon made a record number of appearances for which club?

16 Kevin Richardson and John Salako were together at which club?

17 Which Liam was PFA Player of the Year in 1979?

18 Which club did Mark Walters leave to join Southampton?

19 Which country did Socrates play for?

20 Which Steve has been Technical Director at Crystal Palace?

1 Which country finished third in the 1994 World Cup?

2 Which country does Bebeto play for?

3 Which country knocked the Republic of Ireland out of the 1994 World Cup finals?

4 What was the nickname of Italy's Schillaci?

5 The British-sounding Brown scored a World Cup Final goal for which country?

6 The NASL was founded in which country?

7 Which Jim was in goal for Scotland in the heroic draw in Russia in 1995?

8 Which country does Degryse play for?

9 Who beat North Korea 5–3 in an epic 1966 World Cup quarter-final?

10 Nemec, Nedved and Nemeck played in a European Championship Final for which country?

11 Which country finished second in the 1994 World Cup?

12 Which Bryan was in England's World Cup final squads in 1982, 86 and 90?

13 Which country does Blanc play for?

14 Who were the Republic of Ireland's opponents in the abandoned 1995 game?

15 Cesar Luis Menotti was manager of which World Cup winning country?

16 Turkyilmaz scored a penalty for Switzerland against which country in Euro 96?

17 Which club was David Platt with when he first played for England?

18 Why did Roberto Baggio did not impress in Euro 96?

19 Who was the Captain of the West German side that lost the World Cup Final in 1966?

20 Which English defender spent part of the 1990–91 season in prison?

Answers

Defenders (see Quiz 62)
1 Paul McGrath. 2 Everton. 3 France. 4 Jack Charlton.
5 Arsenal. 6 Viv Anderson. 7 Norman Hunter. 8 Baresi.
9 Ipswich Town. 10 Greig. 11 Manchester Utd. 12 Holland.
13 Blackpool. 14 Paul. 15 "Chopper". 16 Brazil.
17 England. 18 Neil Ruddock. 19 Curle. 20 West Ham Utd.

1 Who plays at home at Pittodrie?

2 Which team does violinist Nigel Kennedy support?

3 Peter Reid and Alan Ball have both managed which club?

4 What is the second word in Hartlepool's name?

5 Which country has Dean Saunders played for?

6 Which Ryan was PFA Young Player of the Year in 1992?

7 Which country do Maccabi Tel Aviv come from?

8 With which club did Teddy Sheringham make his League debut?

9 Which club did keeper Chris Woods join on leaving Norwich?

10 Which Robbie was Wimbledon's top League scorer in 1995–96?

11 What colour are Burnley's home shorts?

12 What is Mansfield's nickname?

13 Which city does David Beckham come from?

14 Which country has midfielder Luis Figo played for?

15 Which Emlyn of Liverpool won the Footballer of the Year award in 1977?

16 What colour are the home shorts of Holland?

17 Glenn Helder first played in England for which club?

18 Which Manchester Utd star appeared as a model on the catwalks of Paris in 1992?

19 In which city was Steve Coppell born?

20 Gary Megson has had two spells in charge of which East Anglian team?

LEVEL 1 ⚽

1 Which Denis has played for both sides in the Manchester derby?

2 Which England striker star Peter has played for both Liverpool and Everton?

3 Who are the opponents if Sheringham and Adams have scored in a north London derby?

4 Erik Bo Andersen scored a brace for which team in a derby game?

5 Which teams play in the derby by the River Trent?

6 Who has managed rivals Leicester City and Aston Villa in the 1990s?

7 Which overseas player has taken part in Manchester and Merseyside derby games?

8 Alex Miller has been boss of which team in a Scottish derby?

9 What flower is linked to games between teams from different sides of the Pennines?

10 Which side won both Merseyside FA Cup Finals of the 1980s?

11 Lou Macari has played for and managed which team with a great derby tradition?

12 Keith Curle has played for which blue-shirted team in a northern derby?

13 Which team were relegated after the 1974 Manchester derby?

14 Which two Scottish clubs have their grounds closest together?

15 Which Robbie scored in both Mersey League meetings in 1995–96?

16 Alan Oakes is a veteran of many clashes in which city?

17 Which Geordie Paul has played in Glasgow and London derby games?

18 Which Brian played for both Manchester City and Manchester Utd before joining the United management team?

19 Who are Norwich's traditional derby rivals?

20 Which derby traditionally takes place at the beginning of the year?

Answers

The Midlands (see Quiz 68)
1 WBA. 2 Red and white. 3 Gareth Southgate. 4 Nottingham Forest. 5 Peter Shilton. 6 Meadow. 7 Karen Brady. 8 Wolves. 9 Coventry City. 10 Mark McGhee. 11 Walsall. 12 "Bomber". 13 1950s. 14 WBA. 15 Derby, Nottingham Forest. 16 Graham. 17 Birmingham City. 18 Notts County. 19 Webb. 20 Peter Taylor.

1 Who plays at home at Turf Moor?

2 Oyvind Leonhardsen first played in England for which club?

3 Brady and Burns have both managed which club?

4 What is the second word in Hereford's name?

5 Which country has Eddie McGoldrick played for?

6 Which Andy of Newcastle was PFA Young Player of the Year in 1994?

7 Which country do Cagliari come from?

8 With which club did David May make his league debut?

9 Which club did David O'Leary join on leaving Arsenal?

10 Which Don was Wolves' top league scorer in 1995–96?

11 What colour are Bury's home shirts?

12 What is Millwall's nickname?

13 Which Kevin of Liverpool won the Footballer of the Year award in 1976?

14 What is the main colour of Bulgaria's home shirts?

15 Which team do the Gallagher brothers of Oasis support?

16 Matthew Simmons is the most famous – or infamous fan – of which club?

17 Which country did Luigi Riva play for?

18 Which Scottish side signed Paulo Di Canio from AC Milan?

19 Which club had Deehan, O'Neill and Megson as managers in 1995?

20 Peter Ndlovu plays for which country?

Answers

Pot Luck 33 (see Quiz 65)
1 Aberdeen. 2 Aston Villa. 3 Manchester City. 4 United.
5 Wales. 6 Giggs. 7 Israel. 8 Millwall. 9 Rangers. 10 Earle.
11 White. 12 The Stags. 13 London. 14 Portugal.
15 Hughes. 16 White. 17 Arsenal. 18 Eric Cantona.
19 Liverpool. 20 Norwich City.

1   Which team does comedian and chat show host Frank Skinner support?

2   What colour are the stripes on Stoke's home shirts?

3   Which Aston Villa player was in England's Euro 96 squad?

4   Which Midland club has a tree on its badge?

5   Which goalkeeper has played for Leicester City, Stoke City, Nottingham Forest and Derby County?

6   At which Lane do Notts County play?

7   Which club director said that she was, "More male than most men"?

8   Wagstaffe, Dougan and Richards have played for which team?

9   John Sillett led which team to FA Cup success?

10   In the 90s which manager walked out on Leicester City to go to Wolves?

11   Which team plays at the Bescot Stadium?

12   What was the nickname of WBA's long serving, high scoring, Tony Brown?

13   Aston Villa set a record with a seventh FA Cup win, but in which decade was this win?

14   Which club has had Bobby Gould and Ossie Ardiles as manager?

15   Which two Midland clubs did Brian Clough take to the championship?

16   What name is shared by former Wolves managers Taylor and Turner?

17   With which club did Trevor Francis begin his playing career?

18   With which club is Jimmy Sirrell associated as manager?

19   Which England midfielder Neil had two spells with Nottingham Forest?

20   Who was Clough's assistant in his early trophy-winning years?

Answers

Derby Games (see Quiz 66)
1 Law. 2 Beardsley. 3 Arsenal and Tottenham Hotspur.
4 Rangers. 5 Nottingham Forest and Notts County. 6 Brian
Little. 7 Andrei Kanchelskis. 8 Hibs. 9 Rose. 10 Liverpool.
11 Celtic. 12 Manchester City. 13 Manchester Utd.
14 Dundee and Dundee Utd. 15 Fowler. 16 Manchester.
17 Gascoigne. 18 Kidd. 19 Ipswich Town.
20 Celtic v Rangers.

Quiz 69 Pot Luck 35

1 What is the second word in Shrewsbury's name?

2 Which country has Chris Woods played for?

3 What colour are Norwich's home shorts?

4 Where do Birmingham play home games?

5 Which Dougie was Crystal Palace's top scorer in 1995–96?

6 Which Paul of Dundee Utd was Scottish Footballer of the Year in 1982?

7 Which country did Robert Rivelino play for?

8 With which club did Jason McAteer make his League debut?

9 Which club did Gary McAllister leave to join Leeds?

10 Which club was Matthew Harding connected with?

11 What is Newcastle United's nickname?

12 Which country has Ronnie Whelan played for?

13 The Chimes were traditionally heard at which club?

14 Which team did Michael Parkinson support as a boy?

15 Adidas awarded what type of Boot to Europe's leading scorer?

16 Which team does John Parrott support?

17 Which Peter of Nottingham Forest was PFA Player of the Year in 1978?

18 Which country does Craig Forrest play for?

19 Gazza recorded "Fog On The Tyne" with which group?

20 Which John was Wimbledon's top league scorer in 1989–90?

Answers

Pot Luck 36 (see Quiz 71)
1 Wolves. 2 Australia. 3 Norwich City. 4 City. 5 The Republic of Ireland. 6 Baggio. 7 Norway. 8 Arsenal. 9 Newcastle Utd. 10 Booth. 11 Red. 12 The Canaries. 13 Rod Stewart. 14 Manchester Utd. 15 Jennings. 16 Tottenham Hotspur. 17 Argentina. 18 Sheffield Wednesday. 19 Manchester City. 20 Aberdeen.

1 Charlie Nicholas scored two goals in a Final for which English team?

2 Which was established first, The Football League Cup or the Scottish League Cup?

3 Which Kenny played in six finals between 1978 and 1987 in England?

4 Which manager took Sheffield Wednesday to 1991 success against his former club Manchester Utd?

5 Which pools firm sponsored the Cup from 1986–90?

6 Clive Allen netted 12 times in the 1986–87 competition for which club?

7 Atkinson and Saunders were on target in a Final for which club?

8 Third Division Swindon caused a 60s shock by beating which team in the Final?

9 Jason McAteer was a losing finalist in 1995 with which team?

10 Dodds and Shearer were on target for which Scottish team?

11 Which drink's name was added to the trophy's name in the 1990s?

12 Howard Wilkinson was manager of which 1990s beaten finalists?

13 Marsh, Morgan and Lazarus were in which winning Third Division team?

14 Which Rovers had their first ever triumph in Scotland in 1995?

15 Which venue was used for English Finals in the 1980s?

16 Which team played in three out of four finals from 1989 to 1992?

17 York sensationally knocked out which giants in 1995–96?

18 Which club has won the Scottish League Cup most times?

19 John Sheridan got a winners' medal with which Yorkshire club?

20 Who was Nottingham Forest boss for the triumphs in the 1980s?

Quiz 71 Pot Luck 36

Answers – see page 77

1 Who plays at home at Molineux?

2 Which country does Mark Bosnich come from?

3 Walker and O'Neill have both managed which club?

4 What is the second word in Hull's name?

5 Which country has Steve Staunton played for?

6 Which Roberto was European Footballer of the Year in 1993?

7 Which country do Rosenborg come from?

8 With which club did David O'Leary make his league debut?

9 Which club did Dave Beasant join on leaving Wimbledon?

10 Which Scott was Aberdeen's joint top League scorer in 1995–96?

11 What colour are Manchester Utd's home shirts?

12 What is Norwich's nickname?

13 Who sang with the Scottish squad in the Euro 96 record?

14 Which team does Terry Christian support?

15 Which Pat of Tottenham Hotspur won the Footballer of the Year award in 1973?

16 Sedgley and Howells were teammates at which club?

17 Which country did Daniel Passarella play for?

18 Regi Blinker first played in England for which club?

19 In 1996 Phil Neal resigned as caretaker manager of which club?

20 Which club sold Steve Archibald to Tottenham Hotspur?

1 Who followed Dalglish as Blackburn manager?

2 Who has managed Watford and England?

3 Which club side did Don Revie manage in the 60s and early 70s?

4 In 1996 Trevor Francis became manager of which Midlands club?

5 Which manager's CV reads Wimbledon, Watford, Sheffield Utd and Crystal Palace?

6 Who is known as "The Bald Eagle"?

7 Which club did Joe Royle steer to an FA Cup Final victory over Manchester Utd?

8 Who was in charge of Manchester City when they were relegated in 1996?

9 Which club did Terry Venables manage before taking over the England team?

10 Which Mike has twice become manager of Norwich?

11 Brian Little followed Ron Atkinson at which club?

12 Which Scottish side was managed by Liam Brady?

13 Who returned from Turkey to become boss of Southampton?

14 Which club links Bobby Gould, Phil Neal and Ron Atkinson as managers?

15 Who took Bolton to the Premiership then left for Arsenal?

16 Who took over from Brian Clough at Nottingham Forest?

17 The 50s and 60s at Old Trafford were the years of which manager?

18 Which club made a statement saying that, "Mr Graham did not act in the best interests of the club"?

19 Which Herbert steered Arsenal to three Championships?

20 Terry Butcher took over at which Midlands team in 1990?

1 What is the second word in Southend's name?

2 Which country has Gordon Durie played for?

3 What is the main colour of Nottingham Forest's home shirts?

4 Who plays home games at Blundell Park?

5 Which tall striker was Coventry's top scorer in 1995–96?

6 Karel Poborsky plays for which national team?

7 Campbell and Keown were together at which club?

8 With which club did Gary Pallister make his League debut?

9 Which club did Eddie McGoldrick leave to join Arsenal?

10 Which Brian of Rangers was Scottish Footballer of the Year in 1995?

11 What is Notts County's nickname?

12 Which country has Kevin Moran played for?

13 Which team did Alf Garnett support?

14 Which striker Frank played over 200 games for both Arsenal and Manchester Utd?

15 Chris Waddle scored an FA Cup Final goal for which club in the 1990s?

16 Sasa Curcic first played in England for which club?

17 Which Andy of Villa was PFA Player of the Year in 1977?

18 What is the first name of Matteo who first played for Liverpool?

19 Which striker Chris became Tottenham Hotspur's record signing in June 1995?

20 Eric Gates played for which East Anglian club?

Quiz 74 The 1960s

Quiz 74 The 1960s

LEVEL 1

1. Which country did Joe Baker move from to play in Italy?
2. What was abolished on January 9th 1960 to affect all players?
3. Who scored a record six goals in an FA Cup tie only for the game to be abandoned?
4. Which Sir Stanley was elected president of FIFA?
5. Bobby Collins moved from Everton to start a revival of which club?
6. Who was the skipper of Tottenham Hotspur's double-winning team?
7. Ray Crawford was on target for which championship winning team?
8. Which founder members of the League resigned in 1962?
9. Which Brian moved after scoring 197 goals in 213 games for Middlesbrough?
10. Chile were the host nation for the World Cup in which year?
11. Ralph Brand and Jimmy Millar were scoring goals for which Scottish side in the early 1960s?
12. Jon Sammels was starring for which London club?
13. How did John White of Tottenham Hotspur tragically die?
14. Wishing to avoid the first £100,000 player tag, who did Tottenham Hotspur buy for £99,999?
15. Who were Scottish First Division champions for five years in a row?
16. Which country were hosts for the 1966 World Cup tournament?
17. Early 60s stars Ronnie Clayton and Bryan Douglas were with which Lancashire club?
18. England internationals from which club were revealed to have made money by betting on their club to lose?
19. Roger Hunt was scoring goals for which club?
20. Bell, Lee and Summerbee were sparkling for which team?

Answers

Red Card (see Quiz 76)
1 Graeme Souness. 2 Argentina. 3 Flitcroft. 4 Liverpool.
5 Never. 6 Roy Keane. 7 Hartson. 8 Two. 9 Russia.
10 Newcastle Utd. 11 Arsenal. 12 Holland. 13 Mullery.
14 Peter Shilton. 15 1960s. 16 Eric Cantona. 17 Wimbledon.
18 Paul Ince. 19 Babb. 20 Bergkamp.

1 Who plays at home at Hillsborough?

2 Which Marco was European Footballer of the Year in 1992?

3 Bonds and Redknapp have both managed which club?

4 What is the second word in Ipswich's name?

5 Which country has Henning Berg played for?

6 Which Gary of Everton won the Footballer of the Year award in 1986?

7 Which country do Benfica come from?

8 With which club did Des Walker make his league debut?

9 Which club did Steve Nicol join on leaving Notts County?

10 Which Julian was West Ham's joint top League scorer in 1995–96?

11 What colour are Manchester City's home shorts?

12 What is Oldham's nickname?

13 Which Guy has hit goals for Portsmouth, Aston Villa and Sheffield Wednesday?

14 Which country does Marcel Desailly play for?

15 Which team does veteran DJ John Peel support?

16 Which Chris was in goal as Sheffield Wednesday lost the 1993 FA Cup Final?

17 Teale and Townsend were together at which club?

18 What is the colour of Hungary's home shirts?

19 Alf Inge Haaland first played in England for which club?

20 How many games did Germany lose in Euro 96?

1 Which Rangers player/manager was sent off on his 1986 club debut?

2 In the 60s, who was Rattin playing for when sent off at Wembley?

3 In 1996, which Gary was sent off in the third minute of his home Blackburn debut?

4 Kevin Keegan was sent off in the Charity Shield playing for which team?

5 How many times was Gary Lineker sent off in his career?

6 Which Manchester Utd player was dismissed in the 1995 FA Cup semi-final against Crystal Palace?

7 Which Arsenal striker John celebrated New Year by getting sent off on Jan 1, 1997 after appearing as a substitute?

8 How many of the Argentinian side were sent off in the 1990 World Cup Final?

9 In which country was Colin Hendry sent off in a European Cup game?

10 With which league club was David Batty first sent off?

11 Lee Dixon was with which club when ordered off in an FA Cup semi-final against Tottenham Hotspur?

12 In the 1990 World Cup final stages who were Germany's opponents when two players were sent off in a notorious spitting incident?

13 Which Alan became the first England player to be sent off?

14 Which goalkeeper was sent off for the first time in his career in his 971st league game?

15 In which decade was the violent Chile v Italy World Cup "battle"?

16 Which Manchester Utd player was sent off twice in four days in 1994?

17 Vinnie Jones was first sent off while playing for which league club?

18 Which Englishman was sent off four times for Internazionale in 1996?

19 Which Phil was Liverpool's only player sent off in the 1994–95 season?

20 Which Dennis got his first red card in England in January 1997?

1 What is the second word in Stockport's name?

2 Which country has Florin Raducioiu played for?

3 What colour goes with blue on Oldham's home shirts?

4 Who plays home games at Vicarage Road?

5 Who won the FA Cup in 1970?

6 Which Charlie of Celtic was Scottish Footballer of the Year in 1983?

7 Paul Parker won the championship with which club?

8 With which club did Nigel Spink make his League debut?

9 Which club did Alan Smith leave to join Arsenal?

10 Ille Dumitrescu first played in England for which club?

11 Which team is known as "The Posh"?

12 Which country has Pat Bonner played for?

13 Which Franz was European Footballer of the Year in 1976?

14 Martin Edwards is connected with which club?

15 Cascarino and Wise were together at which club?

16 Which country has Paulo Maldini played for?

17 Which Pat of Tottenham Hotspur was PFA Player of the Year in 1976?

18 Van Hooijdonk and Cadete were together at which Scottish club?

19 Jan Molby first became a player/manager at which club?

20 At which club did Stone and Woan play in the same side?

Answers

Pot Luck 40 (see Quiz 79)
1 Middlesbrough. 2 Australia. 3 Liverpool. 4 Orient.
5 Scotland. 6 Bremner. 7 Spain. 8 Blackpool. 9 Everton.
10 Payton. 11 Blue. 12 The Pilgrims. 13 Papin. 14 Everton.
15 Chelsea. 16 Red. 17 Brazil. 18 Aston Villa. 19 Belfast.
20 Keith Gillespie.

Quiz 78 30 Somethings

LEVEL 1

Answers – see page 88

1 Which Colin starred in defence for Scotland in Euro 96?

2 Which veteran goalkeeper played his 1,000th League game in December 1996?

3 Which Arsenal striker notched League goal number 200 in 1997?

4 Which Ray was player/manager of QPR in his thirties?

5 Which 34-year old fullback played for England in Euro 96?

6 Which Liverpool scoring legend moved to Leeds in 1996?

7 Which Peter returned to Newcastle to complete a century of goals for the club?

8 Which Italian moved to Chelsea in May 1996?

9 Which veteran Liverpool defender was recalled to the England side in 1996, four years after his last international selection?

10 Which Bryan was Middlesbrough player/manager in his thirties?

11 Which veteran Everton goalkeeper won a 1995 FA Cup winner's medal?

12 Who started a new career with Derby at the age of 36?

13 Which fourty plus goalkeeper John turned out for Manchester City in 1994?

14 Which Brian was in Premiership-winning Manchester Utd sides in his thirties?

15 Who was Tottenham Hotspur's 38-year old keeper in the 1987 FA Cup Final?

16 Leslie Compton became the oldest player to make an international debut for which country?

17 Which Israeli international Ronny moved to Tottenham Hotspur after his thirtieth birthday?

18 Which midfielder Paul began his third spell at Sunderland in his 30s?

19 Who did veteran Tommy Hutchison play for in an FA Cup Final?

Answers

Club Colours (see Quiz 80)
1 Blue. 2 Arsenal. 3 Claret. 4 Blue. 5 White. 6 Red and blue.
7 Manchester Utd. 8 Liverpool, Manchester Utd. 9 White.
10 Blackpool. 11 White. 12 White. 13 White. 14 Leeds Utd.
15 Black. 16 Red. 17 Black and white. 18 White.
19 Internazionale. 20 Orange.

86

Quiz 79 Pot Luck 40

Answers – see page 85

1   Who plays at home at the Riverside Stadium?

2   Which country does Robbie Slater come from?

3   Dalglish, Souness and Evans have all managed which club?

4   What is the second word in Leyton's name?

5   Which country has Kevin Gallacher played for?

6   Which Billy of Leeds won the Footballer of the Year award in 1970?

7   Which country do Valencia come from?

8   With which seaside club did Alan Ball make his league debut?

9   Which club did Nick Barmby join on leaving Middlesbrough?

10   Which Andy was Barnsley's top league scorer in 1995–96?

11   What colour are Chelsea's home shirts?

12   What is Plymouth's nickname?

13   Which Jean-Pierre was European Footballer of the Year 1991?

14   Ablett and Hinchcliffe were together at which club?

15   Which team does Sebastian Coe support?

16   What colour are Wales's home shorts?

17   Which country did Jairzinho play for?

18   Charles and Wright were full-backs together at which club?

19   In which city are Glentoran based?

20   Which Newcastle winger was in the tabloids in 1996 for running up gambling debts of around £60,000?

Pot Luck 39 (see Quiz 77)
1 County. 2 Romania. 3 Red. 4 Watford. 5 Chelsea.
6 Nicholas. 7 Manchester Utd. 8 Aston Villa. 9 Leicester City.
10 Tottenham Hotspur. 11 Peterborough Utd. 12 The Republic
of Ireland. 13 Beckenbauer. 14 Manchester Utd. 15 Chelsea.
16 Italy. 17 Jennings. 18 Celtic. 19 Swansea City.
20 Nottingham Forest.

1   What colour are Everton's home shirts?

2   Which London club wear red home shirts with white sleeves?

3   What is the main colour of Aston Villa's home shirts?

4   What colour are Birmingham City's home shirts?

5   What colour along with blue is a major part of Blackburn's strip?

6   What colours are Barcelona's home shirts?

7   In the 1990s, which team changed their home shirts at half time in an away game at Southampton?

8   Which two teams who normally play in red met in the 1996 FA Cup Final?

9   What is the main colour of Ajax's home shirts?

10   Which north-west club wears tangerine home shirts?

11   What colour are Bolton's home shirts?

12   What colour are Real Madrid's home shirts?

13   What colour are Celtic's home shorts?

14   At which English club did Eric Cantona wear white as first choice kit?

15   What colour goes with red on AC Milan's home shirts?

16   What colour are Aberdeen's home shirts?

17   What colour are the stripes on Juventus's home shirts?

18   What colour are Rangers' home shorts?

19   Paul Ince wore a blue and black striped shirt with which club?

20   What colour are the home shirts of Dundee Utd?

Answers

Thirty Somethings (see Quiz 78)
1 Hendry. 2 Peter Shilton. 3 Ian Wright. 4 Wilkins. 5 Stuart Pearce. 6 Ian Rush. 7 Beardsley. 8 Gianluca Vialli. 9 Mark Wright. 10 Robson. 11 Neville Southall. 12 Paul McGrath. 13 Burridge. 14 McClair. 15 Ray Clemence. 16 England. 17 Rosenthal. 18 Bracewell. 19 Manchester City. 20 Pat Jennings.

Quiz 81 Pot Luck 41

Answers – see page 91

1 What is the second word in Stoke's name?

2 Which country did Emlyn Hughes play for?

3 What is the colour along with white and black on Plymouth's home shirts?

4 Who plays home games at Tannadice Park?

5 Which Carl was Charlton's top scorer in 1995–96?

6 Zeljko Kalac first played in England for which club?

7 Which Paul of Rangers was Scottish Footballer of the Year in 1996?

8 With which club did Dave Beasant make his League debut?

9 Which club did Robert Lee leave to join Newcastle?

10 Batty and McAllister were together at which club?

11 What is Portsmouth's nickname?

12 Which country has Colin Hendry played for?

13 Which Gerd of Bayern was European Footballer of the Year in 1970?

14 Darren Anderton played in an FA Cup semi-final for which Second Division club?

15 How many times did Arsenal win the championship with George Graham as boss?

16 What colour are Sweden's home shirts?

17 Which Colin was PFA Player of the Year in 1975?

18 Steven and Stevens were together at which Scottish club?

19 Which Gary played in every game when Leeds Utd were champions in 1992?

20 Which country has John Harkes play for?

Answers

Pot Luck 42 (see Quiz 83)
1 Manchester City. 2 Best. 3 Tottenham Hotspur. 4 City.
5 England. 6 Red. 7 Switzerland. 8 Tottenham Hotspur.
9 Chelsea. 10 Nogan. 11 White. 12 The Valiants.
13 Nottingham Forest. 14 Fleck. 15 Ruud Gullit. 16 Sheffield
Wednesday. 17 Jürgen Klinsmann. 18 Port Vale. 19 Shaka
Hislop. 20 Sunderland.

1 Which country does Rene Higuita play for?

2 Who was Manchester Utd's goalkeeper when they won the title in 1993 and 1994?

3 Which Coventry goalkeeper played in the 1987 FA Cup Final?

4 With which London club did Bob Wilson make his name?

5 Kevin Pressman and Chris Woods have both played for which club?

6 Which Dave has played for Wimbledon, Newcastle, Chelsea and Southampton?

7 Who played in his 1,000th game while with Leyton Orient in 1996?

8 Which Bobby was in goal when Blackburn went up to the top flight in the 1990s?

9 Who was Scotland's No 1 in Euro 96?

10 With which London club did Ian Walker make his League debut?

11 Which country did Frank Swift play for?

12 Peter Bonetti was a great servant for which London club?

13 Who played at international level with club colleague Tony Adams in his defence?

14 For which club has Bryan Gunn played 350 plus games?

15 Which country has Bruce Grobbelaar played for?

16 Which Tottenham Hotspur goalkeeper scored a freak goal in a Charity Shield game against Manchester Utd?

17 Which goalkeeper Andoni holds a record number of caps for Spain?

18 Branagan and Ward kept goal as which team went out of the Premiership in 1996?

19 Which country did Tony Waiters play for?

20 Which 1970s Partick goalkeeper Alan landed over 50 caps for his country?

Quiz 83 Pot Luck 42

Answers – see page 89

LEVEL 1 ⚽

1 Who plays at home at Maine Road?

2 Which George of Manchester Utd won the Footballer of the Year award in 1968?

3 Venables and Ardiles have both managed which club?

4 What is the second word in Lincoln's name?

5 Which country has John Salako played for?

6 What colour are Norway's home shirts?

7 Which country do Grasshopper Zurich come from?

8 With which club did Glenn Hoddle make his league debut?

9 Which club did Gianluca Vialli join on leaving Juventus?

10 Which Kurt was Burnley's top League scorer in 1995–96?

11 What colour are Nottingham Forest's home shorts?

12 What is Port Vale's nickname?

13 Chettle and Phillips were together at which club?

14 Which striker Robert returned to Norwich City in 1995 after an unhappy spell with Chelsea?

15 Which Dutch player with AC Milan was European Footballer of the Year in 1987?

16 Which team does politician Roy Hattersley support?

17 Which player said in 1995, "I would not have wanted to leave 'Spurs if Sugar had shown more ambition"?

18 John Rudge has had ten years plus as boss of which club?

19 Which goalkeeper cost Newcastle £1.5 million in August 1995?

20 Ord and Bracewell were together at which club?

Answers

Pot Luck 41 (see Quiz 81)
1 City. 2 England. 3 Green. 4 Dundee Utd. 5 Leaburn. 6 Leicester City. 7 Gascoigne. 8 Wimbledon. 9 Charlton Athletic. 10 Leeds Utd. 11 Pompey. 12 Scotland. 13 Müller. 14 Portsmouth. 15 Twice. 16 Yellow. 17 Todd. 18 Rangers. 19 McAllister. 20 USA.

91

1 Which German side won the UEFA Cup in 1996?

2 In which decade did the competition become an annual event?

3 Which Yorkshire side were in the Final in 1967, 1968 and 1971?

4 Have Watford ever taken part in the competition?

5 In the 1990s, is the Final one game or played over two legs?

6 In the first Final, England were represented not by a club but by which city?

7 Frank McLintock played for which London winners?

8 True or false – Manchester Utd have never taken part in the tournament?

9 When Tottenham Hotspur won the Cup in 1972, which English club did they play in the Final?

10 Which player later to manage the Republic of Ireland won a winners' medal in 1971?

11 Which Ipswich player created a record by scoring 14 goals in the tournament in 1980–81?

12 Who was the Ipswich manager at the time?

13 Which team knocked out Nottingham Forest in the 1996 quarter-finals?

14 Jeremy Goss was on target in 1993–94 for which club?

15 Who was Liverpool's scoring "Supersub" in the 1976 Final v Bruges?

16 Name the first Scottish team to have contested a Final.

17 Which club was Kevin Hector playing for when he scored seven goals in one game?

18 Which country has Borough United represented in the tournament?

19 True or false – Birmingham City were the first English League club to reach a Final of the competition?

20 Vialli was on the mark in the 1995 Final for which club?

1 Shipperley and Magilton were together at which club?

2 Which country did Garrincha play for?

3 What is the main colour of Portsmouth's home shirts?

4 The Manor Ground has been the home of which club?

5 Which John was Bolton's top scorer in 1995–96?

6 Striker Andy Booth moved from Huddersfield to which club in 1996?

7 Which Willie of Aberdeen was Scottish Footballer of the Year in 1984?

8 With which club did Viv Anderson make his League debut?

9 Which club did Kerry Dixon leave to join Chelsea?

10 Which northern team was nicknamed "The Lillywhites"?

11 Which Lothar was European Footballer of the Year in 1990?

12 Which country has Gary Kelly played for?

13 What colour are Northern Ireland's home shorts?

14 Fox and Calderwood were together at which club?

15 In 1996, which Ian had an on/off transfer from Norwich to Ipswich?

16 Which seaside club finished bottom of Division Three in 1996 but stayed in the League ?

17 Which Norman of Leeds was PFA Player of the Year in 1974?

18 Which Ron was the oldest Premiership boss in 1996?

19 Which north London team does Tom "Lofty" Watt follow?

20 Who were the first side to hit nine goals in a Premier League game?

Answers

Pot Luck 44 (see Quiz 87)
1 Luton Town. 2 True (in 1990–91). 3 Manchester City.
4 United. 5 Scotland. 6 Law. 7 Greece. 8 West Ham Utd.
9 Rangers. 10 White. 11 Yellow. 12 The Royals/Biscuitmen.
13 Blanchflower. 14 Colombia. 15 Wolves. 16 Blackburn
Rovers. 17 West Ham Utd. 18 Aberdeen. 19 Green.
20 Liverpool.

Quiz 86 Scottish Sides

Answers – see page 96

LEVEL 1

1 Willie Miller played over 550 games for which club?

2 Which United did Ally MacLeod manage before taking over the national team?

3 Which were the first Scottish team to win the European Cup?

4 Which side as known as "The Bairns"?

5 Which League sides have the word East in their name?

6 Which goalkeeper moved from Hibernian to Rangers for £1 million in 1991?

7 What is the colour of Hearts' home shirts?

8 Who were runners-up five times in six League seasons starting in 88–89?

9 At which ground do Queens Park play?

10 Which London club sold Richard Gough to Rangers?

11 'The Terrors" is the nickname of which club?

12 Which team did Alex McLeish take to runners-up spot in 1994–95?

13 Which club did Paul Elliott play for?

14 Which Rovers are known as "The Wee Rovers"?

15 Which side won the treble in 1992–93?

16 Which club plays at Dens Park?

17 With which club did Jim Leighton begin his career?

18 David Narey played over 600 games for which club?

19 Which team is known as "The Buddies"?

20 Kilmarnock play at which Park?

1 Who plays at home at Kenilworth Road?

2 Steve Bruce was once Manchester Utd's joint top League scorer. True or false?

3 Horton and Coppell have both managed which club?

4 What is the second word in Ayr's name?

5 Which country has Gordon Strachan played for?

6 Which Denis was European Footballer of the Year in 1964?

7 Which country do AEK Athens come from?

8 With which club did Paul Ince make his league debut?

9 Which club did Paul Gascoigne join on leaving Lazio?

10 Which veteran striker Steve was Hereford's top league scorer in 1995–96?

11 What colour are Norwich's home shirts?

12 What is Reading's nickname?

13 Which Danny of Tottenham Hotspur won the Footballer of the Year award in 1961?

14 Which country's fullback was shot dead after scoring an own goal in the 1994 World Cup tournament?

15 Which team does veteran rock singer Robert Plant support?

16 Warhurst and Wilcox were together at which club?

17 Alvin Martin has made 450+ appearances for which club?

18 Which was the first Scottish side that Dean Windass played for?

19 What colour is the Nigerian national kit?

20 The names Crown and Carlsberg have appeared on the red home shirts of which club?

Answers

Pot Luck 43 (see Quiz 85)
1 Southampton. 2 Brazil. 3 Blue. 4 Oxford Utd. 5 McGinlay.
6 Sheffield Wednesday. 7 Miller. 8 Nottingham Forest.
9 Reading. 10 Preston North End. 11 Matthäus. 12 The
Republic of Ireland. 13 White. 14 Tottenham Hotspur.
15 Crook. 16 Torquay Utd. 17 Hunter. 18 Atkinson.
19 Arsenal. 20 Manchester Utd.

1 Stan Bowles was a star at which London club?

2 Which country attracted Pele and Bobby Moore to end their careers?

3 Who did Ipswich Town beat to win the FA Cup for the first time?

4 Dave Needham and Kenny Burns were together at which club?

5 Which club was Steve Heighway playing for?

6 Which Welsh club did John Toshack join as player/manager?

7 Jack Charlton played his 600th game for which club?

8 In Barcelona the first European trophy triumph of which Scottish club was marred by crowd disturbances?

9 Which team signed Villa and Ardiles?

10 Lou Macari and George Graham joined which club?

11 Who was the boss who led Southampton to FA Cup glory?

12 Brian Little made his name playing for which club?

13 Which Argentinian was dubbed "the new Pele"?

14 Paul Allen became the youngest FA Cup Final player with which club?

15 Which manager bowed out after Liverpool's 1974 FA Cup Final triumph?

16 Who were you supporting if you were part of Ally's Army?

17 Which striker Andy went from Aston Villa to Wolves in a £1.5 million transfer?

18 Which Ron took over as England boss in the late 70s?

19 Bobby Moore played for which team against West Ham Utd in an FA Cup Final?

20 Which country did Don Masson play for?

Scottish Sides (see Quiz 86)

Answers

1 Aberdeen. 2 Ayr. 3 Celtic. 4 Falkirk. 5 Fife, Stirling.
6 Andy Goram. 7 Maroon. 8 Aberdeen. 9 Hampden Park.
10 Tottenham Hotspur. 11 Dundee Utd. 12 Motherwell.
13 Celtic. 14 Albion. 15 Rangers. 16 Dundee. 17 Aberdeen.
18 Dundee Utd. 19 St Mirren. 20 Rugby.

Quiz 89 Pot Luck 45

Answers – see page 99

LEVEL 1

1 What is the second word in Swindon's name?

2 Which country has Kenny Sansom played for?

3 What is the main colour of Port Vale's home shirts?

4 Who plays at home at Valley Parade?

5 Which Alan was Blackburn's top scorer in 1995–96?

6 Which Republic of Ireland player was known as "Chippy"?

7 Which Sandy of Hearts was Scottish Footballer of the Year in 1986?

8 With which club did Alan Shearer his League debut?

9 Which club did Denis Irwin leave to join Manchester Utd?

10 What is Rochdale's nickname?

11 What colour are Italy's home shorts?

12 Which country has Tommy Coyne played for?

13 Sellars and Ferdinand were together at which club?

14 In which country is the club Penarol?

15 Who resigned as Liverpool boss on February 22nd 1991?

16 Which Dutchman was European Footballer of the Year three times in the 1970s?

17 Which Alan became Fotball League secretary in the late 1950s?

18 Defenders Taggart and Bergsson were together at which club?

19 Who wrote the book titled *It's A Funny Old Life*?

20 At which club were Flitcroft and Lomas in the same side?

Pot Luck 46 (see Quiz 91)
1 Swansea City. 2 Red. 3 Leicester City. 4 Rangers. 5 The Republic of Ireland. 6 Charlton. 7 Germany. 8 Leicester City. 9 Middlesbrough. 10 Navy blue. 11 Rotherham. 12 Charlton. 13 Leeds Utd. 14 Italy. 15 Leeds Utd. 16 Derby County. 17 Bobby Robson. 18 Reading. 19 Brazil. 20 Port Vale.

97

1 Who scored for England in the 1990 World Cup semi-final?

2 A rare John Jensen goal in the 1992 European Championship Final helped beat which team?

3 Who is Rangers' all-time leading goal grabber?

4 In 1992–93 which Guy hit a record 42 goals for Portsmouth?

5 Who scored a goal for the "They think it's all over" commentary?

6 Mark Hughes scored twice in a European Cup Winners' Cup Final for which team?

7 Which two England players bagged a brace against Holland in Euro 96?

8 Basil Boli hit a European Cup Final winner for which French club?

9 Which Andy was the first man to hit five goals in a Premier League game?

10 Ian Porterfield scored an FA Cup winner for which club?

11 Which Ian set a post-war scoring record of FA Cup goals?

12 Nayim scored a last-minute European Cup Winners' Cup Final goal aginst which Arsenal goalkeeper?

13 Who was the first player to score 100 Premiership goals?

14 Ronnie Radford hit a much-televised screamer for which then non-league side as they beat Newcastle in the FA Cup?

15 Who scored an incredible 60 League goals in season 1927–28?

16 Who scored the extra time winner in the Euro 96 Final?

17 Who is Manchester Utd's all-time leading scorer?

18 Which Tony scored a screamer for Leeds v Liverpool in 1995?

19 Against which team did Gazza hit a Euro 96 Wembley wonder goal?

20 Who is Newcastle's all team leading scorer with 178 goals?

1 Who plays at home at the Vetch Field?

2 What colour are Portugal's home shirts?

3 Little, McGhee and O'Neill have all managed which club?

4 What is the second word in Berwick's name?

5 Which country has Ray Houghton played for?

6 Which Jack of Leeds won the Footballer of the Year award in 1967?

7 Which country do Fortuna Dusseldorf come from?

8 With which club did Gary Lineker make his league debut?

9 Which club did Fabrizio Ravanelli join on leaving Juventus?

10 What colour are Tottenham Hotspur's home shorts?

11 What club's nickname is The Merry Millers?

12 Which Bobby was European Footballer of the Year in 1966?

13 Palmer and Wetherall were together at which club?

14 Which country does Alessandro Del Piero play for?

15 Which team does Jeremy Paxman support?

16 Lionel Pickering pumped money into which club?

17 Which former England boss won a league title for PSV Eindhoven?

18 Quinn and Gooding were joint player/managers with which club?

19 Which country did Carlos Alberto play for?

20 Which team does ex-Take That member Robbie Williams support?

1 What colour are Newcastle's home shorts?

2 Where have Middlesbrough played most home games in the 20th century?

3 Sunderland won the FA Cup in the 70s under which boss Bob?

4 Which club are nicknamed the Quakers?

5 When Alan Shearer moved to Newcastle he was reunited with which former teammate?

6 Which Lennie was in charge at Middlesbrough before Bryan Robson?

7 Coventry's FA Cup Final scorer Keith Houchen was boss at which North Eastern club?

8 Who left Newcastle for Tottenham Hotspur for £2 million in July 1988?

9 Keegan and McDermott were teammates at which two clubs?

10 Which Lawrie went back to manage Sunderland after success with Southampton?

11 Who managed Middlesbrough and Newcastle Utd before becoming a national manager in the 1980s?

12 Which England midfielder Paul has signed three times for Sunderland?

13 Which Newcastle-born folk-hero was made an MBE in 1995?

14 Which goalkeeper holds Sunderland's league appearance record?

15 Peacock and Ferdinand both joined Newcastle from which club?

16 Which club had a ground with the Gallowgate End?

17 Which club did Newcastle sign Andy Cole from?

18 In 1995–96, which club managed only two league victories in the second half of the season?

19 An away defeat at which club is supposed to have prompted Keegan's decision to leave Newcastle in January 1997?

20 Which North-East team did the great Wilf Manion play for?

1 What is the second word in Wycombe's name?

2 Which country has Yordan Lechkov played for?

3 Along with navy blue what is the colour of Preston's home shirts?

4 Who plays at home at Gresty Road?

5 Which Dwight was Aston Villa's top scorer in 1995–96?

6 Which George was European Footballer of the Year in 1968?

7 Borrows and Burrows were fullbacks together at which club?

8 With which club did Tony Adams make his League debut?

9 Which club did David Speedie leave to join Blackburn?

10 What is Southampton's nickname?

11 Which Hamish of Dundee Utd was Scottish Footballer of the Year in 1985?

12 What colour are the Republic of Ireland's home shorts?

13 What country has Daniel Amokachi played for?

14 What was remarkable about the unfortunate collision that ended goalkeeper Chic Brodie's career?

15 Who has had "More clubs than Jack Nicklaus"?

16 Who was banned after video evidence showing a stamping incident involving John Spencer in 1995?

17 Fairclough and Stubbs were together at which club?

18 Paulo Futre joined West Ham from which club?

19 Which position did Dai Davies play?

20 Who was in charge of Bolton when they were relegated in 1996?

Answers

Pot Luck 48 (see Quiz 95)
1 Rangers. 2 Black. 3 Crystal Palace. 4 City. 5 The Republic of Ireland. 6 Howard Wilkinson. 7 Italy. 8 Newcastle Utd. 9 England. 10 Black. 11 Southend Utd. 12 Moore. 13 Holland. 14 Birmingham City. 15 Leyton Orient. 16 Manchester Utd. 17 Terry Venables. 18 West Ham Utd. 19 Keegan. 20 Arsenal.

Quiz 94 Internationals

Answers – see page 104

1 Republic of Ireland defender David O'Leary made a record number of appearances for which London club?

2 Which Welsh Mark has played for Norwich City and West Ham?

3 Which goalkeeper is Northern Ireland's most capped player?

4 Who in October 1991, became the youngest ever Welsh international?

5 Did George Best ever play in the finals of the World Cup?

6 Which English club was Roy Keane with when he made his Republic of Ireland debut?

7 Which Welsh goalkeeper holds most caps for his country?

8 Which club links internationals Staunton, Rush and Babb?

9 What surname is shared by Northern Ireland's former midfielders Jimmy and Sammy?

10 Which country has Eric Young played for?

11 Which striker has played for Arsenal, Manchester City and Sunderland?

12 Which Paul became the Republic of Ireland's most-capped player?

13 In which position did Welshman Jack Kelsey play?

14 Which John ended his career with the Republic of Ireland to concentrate on his job as Tranmere's player/manager?

15 Which great player Danny had a spell as boss of his country Northern Ireland?

16 Which club was Gary Speed with when he made his international debut?

17 Which country did Gerry Armstrong represent?

18 Which Frank has headed the Republic of Ireland's all-time scoring list?

19 Who was Welsh skipper for the 7–1 hammering by Holland in 1996?

20 Which Welshman called Hughes is the most capped of all time?

The 1980s (see Quiz 96)

Answers
1 Everton. 2 Diego Maradona. 3 Tottenham Hotspur. 4 It was made of artificial turf. 5 Aston Villa. 6 Alex Ferguson. 7 Rangers. 8 Manchester Utd. 9 Pat Jennings. 10 Liverpool. 11 Chris Waddle. 12 Charlton Athletic. 13 Kenny Dalglish. 14 The FA Cup. 15 Jack Charlton. 16 Hillsborough. 17 Taylor. 18 Tottenham Hotspur. 19 Woodcock. 20 Watford.

Quiz 95 Pot Luck 48

Answers – see page 101

1 Who plays at home at Ibrox Stadium?

2 What colour are Germany's home shorts?

3 Steve Coppell and Dave Bassett have both managed which club?

4 What is the second word in Brechin's name?

5 Which country has Niall Quinn played for?

6 Who took over as manager of Leeds Utd in 1988?

7 Which country do Napoli come from?

8 With which club did Paul Gascoigne make his League debut?

9 In the Sun headline "Yanks 2 Planks 0" who were the Planks?

10 What colour are Sunderland's home shorts?

11 Which club has the nicknames "The Shrimpers" and "The Blues"?

12 Which Bobby of West Ham Utd won the Footballer of the Year award in 1964?

13 Which country has Frank de Boer played for?

14 Millionaire David Sullivan is connected with which club?

15 Which London team does musician Julian Lloyd Webber support?

16 With which English club did Norman Whiteside begin his career?

17 Who was manager when Tottenham Hotspur won the FA Cup in 1991?

18 Moncur and Bishop were in the same team at which club?

19 Which Kevin was European Footballer of the Year in 1978?

20 Kevin Campbell first played in an FA Cup Final for which club?

1 Peter Reid won the Championship as a player with which club?

2 Who reckoned the "hand of God" had come to his aid?

3 Which First Division club was directly affected by the Falklands War?

4 What was different about the new pitch laid at QPR in 1981?

5 Allan Evans and Gordon Cowans played together with which club?

6 Which manager took Aberdeen to European Cup Winners' Cup glory?

7 Which club caused a storm by signing a Catholic?

8 Gidman and Albiston were together at which club?

9 Which great goalkeeper became the first player to appear in 1,000 senior matches in England?

10 Sammy Lee won the Championship with which club?

11 Who went to Marseille for a British record fee?

12 Former European Footballer of the Year Allan Simonsen signed for which English club?

13 Who won his 100th cap for Scotland?

14 What did Coventry City win for the first time in their history?

15 Which manager took the Republic of Ireland to the European Championship in 1988?

16 An inquiry under Lord Justice Taylor was set up after the disaster at which ground?

17 Which Gordon was secretary of the PFA?

18 Micky Hazard played in an FA Cup Final for which team?

19 Which striker Tony with a bird-surname played for England?

20 Luther Blissett was at which club when he was 1983–84 First Division top scorer?

Answers

Internationals (see Quiz 94)
1 Arsenal. 2 Bowen. 3 Pat Jennings. 4 Ryan Giggs. 5 No.
6 Nottingham Forest. 7 Neville Southall. 8 Liverpool.
9 McIlroy. 10 Wales. 11 Niall Quinn. 12 McGrath.
13 Goalkeeper. 14 Aldridge. 15 Blanchflower. 16 Leeds Utd.
17 Northern Ireland. 18 Stapleton. 19 Vinnie Jones.
20 Mark.

Quiz 97 Pot Luck 49

1 What is the second word in York's name?

2 Which country has Youri Djorkaeff played for?

3 What shapes are the colours on QPR's home shirts?

4 Who plays at home at Deepdale?

5 Which Ian was Arsenal's top scorer in the 1995–96 season?

6 Which Ronnie of Celtic was Scottish Footballer of the Year in 1967?

7 What is the nickname of Airdrieonians?

8 Uwe Rosler first played in England with which club?

9 Which club did Ray Wilkins join on leaving Paris St Germain?

10 In which city was George Best born?

11 What is Stockport's nickname?

12 Who plays at home at Ochilview Park?

13 Which Karl-Heinz was European Footballer of the Year in 1980?

14 What is the main colour of Denmark's home shirts?

15 Simon Barker has played 250 plus games for which club?

16 At which ground is the Holt End?

17 Which country has Faustino Asprilla played for?

18 Who was in charge of Northern Ireland from 1980 to 1993?

19 Which Frank was Manchester Utd's top League scorer in the early 1980s?

20 Ben Thatcher became the record signing for which London club?

1 Which Uwe scored 43 goals for West Germany in the 1950s, 60s and 70s?

2 Which London club did Jürgen Klinsmann play for in 1994–95?

3 Which country did Florian Albert play for?

4 With which club did Dennis Bergkamp begin his career?

5 Which Oleg was the first Russian to gain 100 caps?

6 Which London-born striker scored 44 goals in 57 games for England?

7 Who skippered Holland to the 1988 European Championship?

8 Which country did Marco Kempes play for?

9 Roberto Baggio moved from Fiorentina to which club in 1990?

10 Just Fontaine hit a record number of goals in a World Cup Finals tournament for which country?

11 Which Karl-Heinz was twice European Player of the Year?

12 Hristo Stoichkov moved to Spain in 1990 to which club?

13 Who was England manager when Gary Lineker played his last international game?

14 Which Cameroon striker played in the 1994 World Cup at the age of 42?

15 For which country did Hans Krankl score over 30 goals?

16 Which Gerd hit the 1974 World Cup winner for West Germany?

17 Which country did Steve Bloomer play for?

18 In 1995 George Weah moved to which Italian club?

19 Who became the first player to score a World Cup Final hat-trick?

20 Who took over as manager of Newcastle Utd in January 1997?

1 Who plays at home at Bramall Lane?

2 "The Minstermen" is the nickname of which club?

3 Howe and Wenger have both managed which club?

4 What is the second word in Dunfermline's name?

5 Which country has Brian Roy played for?

6 Which former Watford striker was transferred to AC Milan?

7 Which country do FC Porto come from?

8 Which team did Jimmy Case play for and later manage?

9 Which club did Mark Atkins join on leaving Blackburn?

10 What are Southend's colours?

11 What is Swansea's nickname?

12 Igor Stimac first played in England for which team?

13 At which club did Gascoigne and Lineker play together?

14 Which country does Georghe Hagi play for?

15 Which team does Desmond Morris support?

16 Which team play at the Amsterdam Arena?

17 What pattern is on the Croatian home shirts?

18 Which TV pundit is known as "The Chin"?

19 Which football boots did David Beckham endorse?

20 Which team does Cardinal Basil Hulme support?

Pot Luck 49 (see Quiz 97)
1 City. 2 France. 3 Hoops. 4 Preston North End. 5 Wright. 6 Simpson. 7 The Diamonds. 8 Manchester City. 9 Rangers. 10 Belfast. 11 County, or The Hatters. 12 Steinhousemuir. 13 Rummenigge. 14 Red. 15 QPR. 16 Villa Park. 17 Colombia. 18 Billy Bingham. 19 Stapleton. 20 Wimbledon.

Answers

The Medium Questions

This next selection of questions is getting a little more like it. For an open entry quiz then you should have a high percentage of medium level questions – don't try to break people's spirits with the hard ones, just make sure that people play to their ability.

Like all questions, this level of question can be classed as either easy or impossible depending on whether you know the answer or not, and although common knowledge is used as the basis for these questions there is a sting in the tail of quite a few.

Specialists are the people to watch out for, as those with a good knowledge of a particular subject will doubtless do well in these rounds so a liberal sprinkling of Pot Luck questions is needed to flummox them.

1 In which decade did Charlton Athletic first win the FA Cup?

2 What colour are Barnsley's home socks?

3 Which was Iain Dowie's first league club?

4 Which club was Teddy Sheringham with when he was Premier League leading scorer in 1992–93?

5 What is Wrexham's ground called?

6 Which England player was born on Guernsey in 1968?

7 Cyrille Regis and Kevin Richardson were in the same team at which club?

8 Which club did Peter Shilton join on leaving Stoke City?

9 Which club's nickname is The Saddlers?

10 Julio Iglesias was reserve team goalkeeper with which club?

11 In which decade was Ron Atkinson born?

12 Who was the regular keeper in QPR's 1995–96 relegation season?

13 Which country did Terry Mancini play for?

14 Which £13 million player was involved in a 1993 car crash?

15 Bob McKinlay set a league appearance record at which club?

16 Which team were beaten 2–1 by Arsenal in the 1993 FA Cup Final?

17 Which Colin became Middlesbrough manager in 1991?

18 Craig Short joined Everton from which club?

19 What is Chris Armstrong's middle name?

20 Chairman Francis Lee flew to Marbella to sign which holidaymaker as his club manager?

Answers

Pot Luck 2 (see Quiz 3)
1 Crystal Palace. 2 Red and black. 3 Middlesbrough.
4 Ruud Gullit and Mark Hughes. 5 Springfield Park.
6 Blackburn Rovers. 7 Chesterfield. 8 Sampdoria. 9 Bristol.
10 McNeill. 11 Eike Immel. 12 1920s. 13 Manchester City.
14 Clive Allen. 15 Wolves. 16 Wales. 17 Nigel Martyn.
18 David Pleat. 19 Paul. 20 1950s.

1 Which keeper Paul played 400+ times for Ipswich?

2 Who was Arsenal's regular keeper when they won the Premiership in 1988–89?

3 What was the nickname of Peru's Ramon Quiroga?

4 With which club did Neville Southall make his League debut?

5 Kevin Carr and Martin Thomas have both played for which club?

6 Bulgarian Boris (Bobby) Mikhailov first played in England for which club?

7 Which club did Jack Kelsey play for?

8 Who did David Seaman play for before his move to QPR?

9 Bernard Lama played for which country in Euro 96?

10 Which two clubs did Gordon Banks play for?

11 Which forename is shared by ex-keepers Grew and Wallington?

12 Which keeper along with Grobbelaar was involved in the alleged 1990s match fixing charges?

13 Who left Hibernian in 1991 to become Scotland's most expensive keeper?

14 Which ex-England keeper, working as a journalist, lost his life in the Munich air disaster?

15 Hans Van Breukelen first played for which English club?

16 Which keeper Steve of the 70s, 80s and 90s shares his name with a fruit?

17 Schmeichel played all but two games for Manchester Utd in 1993–94. Who played in those two games?

18 Who was in goal for Tottenham Hotspur in the 1991 FA Cup Final?

19 Who was the first keeper to skipper a World Cup winning side?

20 Terry Gennoe and Jim Arnold have played for which club?

Answers

The 1950s (see Quiz 4)
1 1950. 2 Switzerland. 3 Hungary. 4 Brian Clough.
5 Manchester Utd. 6 Juventus. 7 Derek Dooley. 8 1959.
9 1954–55. 10 February 1958. 11 Charles Buchan.
12 Norwich City. 13 Wolves. 14 Ferenc Puskas.
15 Manchester Utd. 16 Stanley Matthews. 17 Argentina.
18 Bert Trautmann. 19 Nat Lofthouse. 20 Polio.

LEVEL 2

1 Which team were beaten 1–0 by Manchester Utd in the replayed 1990 FA Cup Final?

2 What are the two main colours on Bournemouth's home shirts?

3 What was Colin Cooper's first league club?

4 The gate for a Paul Elliott benefit game in July 1995 was boosted by which two new Chelsea signings?

5 What is Wigan Athletic's ground called?

6 Kevin Moran and Colin Hendry were in the same team at which club?

7 Who are nicknamed The Spireites?

8 Which club did David Platt leave to join Arsenal?

9 In which city was Gary Mabbutt born?

10 Which Billy became Aston Villa manager in 1986?

11 Who played every game in goal in Manchester City's 1995–96 relegation season?

12 In which decade did Cardiff first win the FA Cup?

13 Eddie Large was a trainee at which club?

14 Which Tottenham Hotspur player was the First Division's leading scorer in 1986–87?

15 Derek Parkin set a league appearance record at which club?

16 Which country did Tony Norman play for?

17 Who was the regular goalkeeper in Crystal Palace's 1994–95 relegation season?

18 Luton Town chairman David Kohler demanded £300,000 compensation after which manager moved?

19 What is Teddy Sheringham's middle name?

20 In which decade was Dave Beasant born?

Answers

Pot Luck 1 (see Quiz 1)
1 1940s. 2 Red. 3 Luton Town. 4 Tottenham Hotspur.
5 Racecourse Ground. 6 Matt Le Tissier. 7 Aston Villa.
8 Nottingham Forest. 9 Walsall. 10 Real Madrid. 11 1930s.
12 Jurgen Sommer. 13 The Republic of Ireland. 14 Gianluigi
Lentini. 15 Nottingham Forest. 16 Sheffield Wednesday.
17 Todd. 18 Derby County. 19 Peter. 20 Alan Ball.

1   In what year did Portsmouth last win the Championship?

2   In which country was the 1954 World Cup Final played?

3   Which great national side included Grosics, Bozsik and Kocsis?

4   Who was the young Middlesbrough striker who made his England debut against Wales in 1959?

5   Who were the first English team to play in the European Cup?

6   Which Italian club did John Charles play for?

7   Who was the Sheffield Wednesday striker who had a leg amputated?

8   Tom Finney last played for England in which year?

9   What was the season when Chelsea won the Championship?

10   In which month was the Munich air disaster?

11   Who started the magazine *Football Monthly*?

12   Which Third Division giant-killers reached the 1959 FA Cup semi-final?

13   Which team did Slater and Clamp play for?

14   Which Hungarian player was nicknamed "The Galloping Major"?

15   Roger Byrne and Johnny Berry played for which team?

16   Which Blackpool and England player won the 1956 Footballer of the Year award?

17   In which country was Alfredo di Stefano born?

18   Who broke his neck in the 1956 FA Cup Final?

19   Who was nicknamed "The Lion Of Vienna"?

20   Which disease claimed the life of England defender Jeff Hall?

Answers

Keepers   (see Quiz 2)
1 Cooper. **2** John Lukic. **3** El Loco. **4** Bury. **5** Newcastle Utd.
6 Reading. **7** Arsenal. **8** Birmingham City. **9** France.
10 Leicester City and Stoke City. **11** Mark. **12** Hans Segers.
13 Andy Goram. **14** Frank Swift. **15** Nottingham Forest.
16 Cherry. **17** Gary Walsh. **18** Erik Thorstvedt.
19 Gianpietro Combi (1934, Italy). **20** Blackburn Rovers.

1 Which player with 430 games set a Wimbledon appearance record?

2 What colours are Brentford's home shirts?

3 What was Tony Daley's first league club?

4 To five years each way, when did Burnley first win the FA Cup?

5 Who plays at home at Plainmoor?

6 Which Phil became Bolton manager in 1985?

7 Which team are known as the Accies?

8 Which club did Richard Jobson join on leaving Oldham?

9 In which town was Nat Lofthouse born?

10 In which decade was Tommy Docherty born?

11 Which defender played in all Aston Villa's 1995–96 League games?

12 Dave Beasant and Andy Townsend were in the same team at which club?

13 Which club was Bob Latchford with when he was First Divison leading scorer in 1977–78?

14 Stan Boardman was once on the books of which club?

15 Which team were beaten 3–2 by Arsenal in the 1979 FA Cup Final?

16 Which Newcastle player was sent off in a 1996 Coca Cola quarter-final after clashing with Arsenal's Lee Dixon?

17 Francis Benali has played 200+ games for which club?

18 Which Tottenham Hotspur manager signed Jürgen Klinsmann?

19 Who was the regular goalkeeper for Ipswich in their 1994–95 relegation season?

20 Which country has Fredi Bobic played for?

Pot Luck 4 (see Quiz 7)
Answers

Pot Luck 4 (see Quiz 7)
1 Porterfield. 2 White. 3 Crewe Alexandra. 4 1960s.
5 Stockport County. 6 Newcastle Utd. 7 The Grecians.
8 Eintracht Frankfurt. 9 1911. 10 Little. 11 Billy Bonds.
12 Coventry City. 13 Australia. 14 David Seaman.
15 Manchester Utd. 16 WBA. 17 Doncaster Rovers.
18 Bryan Gunn. 19 England. 20 Malcolm.

Quiz 6 Transfer Trail

Answers – see page 116

LEVEL 2

1 Which striker was involved in Britain's first £300,000 transfer?

2 Who moved from Charlton in 1996 to become Britain's most expensive teenager?

3 Which club did Karel Poborsky leave to join Manchester Utd?

4 Who made 34 separate transfer requests to leave QPR?

5 Who became England's most expensive goalkeeper when he moved to Crystal Palace in 1989?

6 Which club did Alan Ball join on leaving Blackpool in 1966?

7 Which Scottish player has joined Ipswich Town on three occasions?

8 How much did Gianluca Vialli cost in a transfer fee when he joined Chelsea?

9 Which club did John Moncur leave to join West Ham United?

10 Who was the first British player to move for £1,000?

11 A £2.5 million fee set a record purchase for Notts County in 1992, when they bought which player?

12 Roberto Di Matteo joined Chelsea from which club?

13 A club record fee received stood for ten years when which player left Everton for Tottenham Hotspur in the mid 80s?

14 Which club did Ray Houghton leave to join Liverpool?

15 Roberto Baggio cost £10 million when he moved to AC Milan from where?

16 Which German international joined Celtic in July 1995?

17 Fernando Nelson moved from Sporting Lisbon to which club in 1996?

18 Stefan Schwarz left Arsenal for which club?

19 Which club did Emerson leave to join Middlesbrough?

20 Which club did Mark Draper leave to join Aston Villa?

Answers

Three Lions (see Quiz 8)
1 QPR. 2 Stanley Matthews. 3 Once. 4 Gary Stevens.
5 They all scored. 6 Sweden. 7 Two. 8 Dixie Dean. 9 Viv
Anderson. 10 Bobby Moore. 11 Nigeria. 12 Rangers.
13 Neil Webb. 14 Ian Wright. 15 Tom Finney. 16 David
Platt. 17 Ray Wilson. 18 Emlyn. 19 84. 20 Stuart Pearce.

114

Quiz 7 Pot Luck 4

Answers – see page 113

LEVEL 2

1 Which Ian became Chelsea manager in 1991?

2 What colour are the home shorts of both Bristol clubs?

3 What was Bruce Grobbelaar's first league club?

4 In which decade was Tony Adams born?

5 Who plays at home at Edgeley Park?

6 Which club was Malcolm Macdonald with when he was First Divison leading scorer in 1974–75?

7 What is the nickname of Exeter City?

8 Which club did Tony Yeboah leave to join Leeds?

9 To five years either way, when did Bradford City first win the FA Cup?

10 Which player and manager Brian was born in Peterlee in November 1953?

11 Who played 663 times to set West Ham Utd's League appearance record?

12 Kevin Gallacher and Paul Furlong were in the same team at which club?

13 Ned Zelic has captained which country?

14 Who was the only ever-present league player for Arsenal in 1995–96?

15 Which team was beaten 2–0 by Bolton in the 1958 FA Cup Final?

16 Bryan Robson was at which League club when he made his England debut?

17 Which club did comedian Charlie Williams play for in the 1950s?

18 Who was the regular keeper for Norwich City in their 1994–95 relegation season?

19 San Marino hit a goal in nine seconds in 1993 against which team?

20 What is Jason Wilcox's middle name?

Answers

Pot Luck 3 (see Quiz 5)
1 Alan Cork. 2 Red and white. 3 Aston Villa. 4 1914.
5 Torquay Utd. 6 Neal. 7 Hamilton Academical. 8 Leeds Utd. 9 Bolton. 10 1920s. 11 Alan Wright. 12 Chelsea.
13 Everton. 14 Liverpool. 15 Manchester Utd. 16 David Ginola. 17 Southampton. 18 Ossie Ardiles. 19 Craig Forrest.
20 Germany.

1 David Seaman was at which club when he made his international debut?

2 Who played his first England game in 1935 and his last in 1957?

3 How many times did Brian Little play for England?

4 In the 1986 World Cup which two England players in the squad had the same name?

5 What links the debuts of Alan Shearer, Robert Lee and Dennis Wise?

6 Gary Lineker played his last game against which country?

7 How many hat-tricks did Geoff Hurst score for England?

8 Who began his international career by scoring 2, 3, 2, 2, 3?

9 Who was the first black player to represent England in a full international?

10 Who was voted best defender in the world by journalists after the 1970 World Cup?

11 Steve McManaman first came on as a sub in November 1994, against which country?

12 Which club was Mark Walters with when he made his one and only England appearance?

13 In September 1987 who became the 1,000th England player?

14 Who hit his first England hat-trick in the 7–1 San Marino romp?

15 Who played left wing, right wing and centre forward and hit 30 goals?

16 In season 1992–93 who scored 9 goals in 10 England appearances?

17 Who was left back in the 1966 World Cup winning side?

18 Who is the most capped Hughes to play for England?

19 To five each way, how many times did Ray Wilkins play for England?

20 Which fullback has listed 'Anarchy in The UK' by the Sex Pistols as his favourite musical track?

---

1 In which decade did Bolton Wanderers first win the FA Cup?

2 What colour goes with amber on Cambridge United's home shirts?

3 Which was Trevor Steven's first League club?

4 Which Scottish captain was born in Motherwell in 1964?

5 Where do Shrewbury Town play at home?

6 Geoff Thomas and Eddie McGoldrick were in the same team at which club?

7 Which Brian became Leicester City manager in 1991?

8 Which club did Vinnie Jones join on leaving Chelsea?

9 What is Hereford United's nickname?

10 Which Brian of Celtic was Scottish Premier Divison leading scorer in 1983–84?

11 As a teenager Rod Stewart had trials with which club?

12 In which decade was Alan Ball born?

13 Who was the only League ever-present for Blackburn Rovers in the 1995–96 season?

14 Who holds the WBA League appearance record?

15 Which team were beaten 3–1 by Newcastle United in the 1955 FA Cup Final?

16 Which country did Alfred Strange play for?

17 Which English club did Jock Stein manage?

18 Which Scottish captain was born in Stockholm?

19 What is Ray Wilkins' middle name?

20 Who was the regular keeper for Sheffield Utd in their 1993–94 relegation season?

Answers

Pot Luck 6 (see Quiz 11)
1 1930s. 2 Blue. 3 Sunderland. 4 Neville Southall.
5 Scunthorpe Utd. 6 Southampton. 7 Shrewbury Town.
8 Brondby. 9 1950s. 10 Manchester Utd. 11 Francis.
12 Steve Pears. 13 Phelan. 14 Luther Blissett. 15 Leeds
United. 16 McDermott. 17 Vinnie Jones. 18 Mirandinha.
19 Iceland. 20 Robert.

Quiz 10 Alan Shearer

Answers – see page 120

LEVEL 2

1. Shearer hit the quickest goal of a game in Euro 96 against which side?

2. Against which country did Alan make his full international debut?

3. In which city was Shearer born?

4. Who was the Southampton boss when Alan made his League debut?

5. At Blackburn Rovers, Shearer said before a match he always ate chicken and what?

6. To five goals, how many League goals did Shearer score in his years at Southampton?

7. In what month was Shearer born?

8. Who was the last player before Alan to hit 30+ League goals in three consecutive seasons?

9. Which manager said that Alan was "so good it's frightening"?

10. Who were the regular numbers 7 and 11 who supplied Shearer in Blackburn Rovers's championship-winning season?

11. Who were the opponents when Shearer was first England skipper?

12. Which Southampton boss sold Shearer to Blackburn Rovers?

13. How many goals did Alan score in the season after he made his debut?

14. His last Blackburn Rovers goal was against which team?

15. Shearer's first Wembley game for Newcastle United was against who?

16. Who held the British transfer record before Shearer's '96 move?

17. How many games had he not scored for England before Euro 96?

18. Which other England regular was controversially sent off for a foul on Shearer in December 1996?

19. Discounting shoot-outs, how many goals did Alan score in Euro 96?

20. How many Blackburn Rovers hat-tricks did he hit in 1995–96?

Scottish Sides (see Quiz 12)
1 Jimmy McGrory. **2** Dunfermline. **3** Rangers. **4** Dumbarton.
5 Hibernian. **6** Stenhousemuir. **7** Aberdeen. **8** Rangers.
9 St Johnstone. **10** Third Lanark. **11** Livingston. **12** Airdrie.
13 Ross County. **14** Motherwell. **15** No. **16** The Gable
Endies. **17** Arbroath. **18** Norrie McCathie. **19** Aberdeen.
20 Stirling Albion.

Answers

1 In which decade did Arsenal first win the FA Cup?

2 What is the main colour of Carlisle Utd's home shirts?

3 What was Barry Venison's first league club?

4 Who was the only league ever-present for Everton in 1995–96?

5 Who plays at home at Glanford Park?

6 Which club was Kevin Keegan with when he was First Division leading scorer in 1981–82?

7 Which team are known as The Shrews?

8 Which club did Peter Schmeichael leave to join Manchester Utd?

9 In which decade was John Aldridge born?

10 Paul Parker and Clayton Blackmore were in the same team at which club?

11 Which Trevor became QPR manager in 1988?

12 Who was the regular keeper for Middlesbrough in their 1992–93 relegation season?

13 Which Mike of Manchester Utd won his only England cap in 1989?

14 With 415 games, who holds Watford's league appearance record?

15 Which team was beaten 1–0 by Sunderland in the 1973 FA Cup Final?

16 Which midfielder Terry was born in Kirby in December 1951?

17 Who was booked within five seconds of the start of the Chelsea v Sheffield Utd 1992 FA Cup tie?

18 Which Brazilian player joined Newcastle United in 1987?

19 Which country has Gudni Berggson played for?

20 What is Darren Anderton's middle name?

1 Who has scored most League goals for Celtic?

2 Which side is known as The Pars?

3 Alex Ferguson appeared in a Scottish Cup Final for which team?

4 Which team plays at Boghead Park?

5 Beating Dunfermline in the 1991 League Cup Final gave which club its first major trophy for 19 years?

6 Which side provided a great Scottish Cup shock by knocking Aberdeen out in 1995?

7 Which club broke their own transfer record to buy Paul Bernard from Oldham Athletic in 1995?

8 Which club got a 0–4 home drubbing from Juventus in the 90s?

9 Which League team comes from Perth?

10 Which club left the League in 1967?

11 What did Meadowbank Thistle change its name to?

12 Which team made their European debut in 1992?

13 Who joined the League in 1994 along with Caledonian Thistle?

14 Tommy Coyne joined which club when he left Tranmere Rovers?

15 Were Hibs founder members of the Scottish League?

16 What is the nickname of Montrose?

17 Which team holds the British record for a League victory?

18 Which Dunfermline player tragically died in the 1995–96 season?

19 Who beat Real Madrid in the 1983 European Cup Winners' Cup Final?

20 Who were the first Scottish club to play on artificial turf?

1 In which decade was Danny Blanchflower born?

2 What colour are Charlton's home shorts?

3 Which was Scott Sellars' first League club?

4 Steve Perryman set a League appearance record at which club?

5 Who plays at home at The McCain Stadium?

6 David White and Keith Curle were in the same team at which club?

7 Martin Peters had a short stay as boss of which club in 1981?

8 Which club did Pat Rice join on leaving Arsenal?

9 What is Swindon Town's nickname?

10 In which decade did Aston Villa first win the FA Cup?

11 In which Scottish city was Dave Mackay born?

12 Which club was John Charles with when he was First Divison leading scorer in 1956–57?

13 Chamberlain and Sutton shared the goalkeeping duties in the 1991–92 relegation season for which club?

14 Who said "That's life" when asked why a new England kit was launched soon after Christmas 1996?

15 Which Bill of Manchester Utd won his only England cap in 1954?

16 Who started his second spell as Stoke City boss in September 1994?

17 Which team were beaten 3–2 by Liverpool in the 1989 FA Cup Final?

18 Who was the only League ever-present for Nottingham Forest in 1995–96?

19 Which country did Zvonimir Boban play for in Euro 96?

20 The French player Prunier played twice in 1995–96 season for which Premiership side?

Answers

Pot Luck 8 (see Quiz 15)
1 1950s. 2 Blue and white. 3 Leicester City. 4 Brown.
5 Steve Cherry. 6 Rotherham Utd. 7 Steve McManaman.
8 Wimbledon. 9 The Gulls. 10 Oldham Athletic. 11 David James. 12 1930s. 13 Watford. 14 Swindon Town.
15 Branfoot. 16 Gidman. 17 Leeds Utd. 18 Howard.
19 England. 20 Mark Lawrenson.

1 Who scored for Nottingham Forest in the 1991 Final?

2 Paul Miller, Graham Roberts and Paul Price played for which 1980s finalists?

3 Who came off the bench to hit two goals in a Final for Crystal Palace?

4 To ten years either way, when did Manchester Utd first win the FA Cup?

5 Which club won the Scottish FA Cup three times in a row in the 1980s?

6 Who were the teams when there was a Rush on both sides in a Final?

7 Who were the first Welsh team to win the trophy?

8 At which ground was the first FA Cup Final played?

9 Who was Andy Gray playing for when he scored in an FA Cup Final?

10 Which player appeared in FA Cup Finals in the 1970s, '80s and '90s?

11 Brian Kilcline was skipper of which trophy-winning club?

12 Who was the first player to miss an FA Cup Final penalty?

13 Who was in goal for Manchester Utd in the Final replay against Crystal Palace in 1990?

14 In which decade did Liverpool first win the trophy?

15 To 5,000 either way what was the attendance of the first Scottish FA Cup Final between Queens park and Clydesdale?

16 Who was Southampton skipper in their 1970s triumph?

17 Who were the first team to win the FA Cup three years in succession?

18 Who won the first Scottish Final decided on penalties?

19 Who hit a hat-trick in the Matthews' Final?

20 Who scored Ipswich Town's 1978 winner against Arsenal?

LEVEL 2

1 In which decade did Blackpool first win the FA Cup?

2 What colour are the stripes on Chester's home shirts?

3 What was Peter Shilton's first League club?

4 Which Tony of WBA was First Divison leading scorer in 1970–71?

5 Who was the regular keeper for Notts County in their 1991–92 relegation season?

6 Who plays at home at the Millmoor Ground?

7 Which England attacking midfielder was born in Bootle in February 1972?

8 Which club did Andy Thorn leave to join Newcastle United?

9 What is Torquay's nickname?

10 Ian Marshall and Graeme Sharpe were in the same team at which club?

11 Steve McManaman and which other player were league ever-presents for Liverpool in 1995–96?

12 In which decade was Sir John Hall born?

13 Which team were beaten 2–0 by Everton in the 1984 FA Cup Final?

14 John Trollope set a league appearance record at which club?

15 Which Ian became Southampton manager in 1991?

16 Which John of Villa won his only England cap in 1977?

17 David Harvey played over 300 games for which club?

18 What is Nigel Clough's middle name?

19 Which country did Harry Daft play for?

20 Which ex-Liverpool star was boss at Oxford Utd for a short time in 1988?

1 Which Gray brothers were in the Leeds Utd team of the 1970s?

2 Striker Gary came back to League soccer with Barnet in the 1990s while brother Steve was scoring goals for which club?

3 What were the forenames of the Dutch Koeman brothers?

4 What were the names of QPR's Morgan twins of the 60s?

5 In which year did both Charlton brothers play their last international?

6 What was the name of Bill Shankly's brother who was also a soccer manager?

7 Who is Chris Casper's footballing father?

8 Which brothers Graham and Ray played at Chelsea in the 1970s?

9 Brothers Danny, Rodney and Ray Wallace were together at which club?

10 Who were the first brothers to be at an English double winning club?

11 What was the name of the Futcher twins?

12 What is the name of Elton John's footballing uncle?

13 Which of the Laudrup brothers did not play when Denmark won the European Championship?

14 Player/manager Ian Bowyer was in the same side as son Gary at which club?

15 What is the name of Clive Allen's dad who was also a Tottenham Hotspur player?

16 If dad John is the boss and son Kevin is a defender, what is the surname?

17 What was the name of Terry Hibbitt's soccer playing brother ?

18 Which brothers Mel and John played together for Wales in the 1950s?

19 What is the surname of strikers Allan, Frank and Wayne?

20 At which club did Eric Cantona's brother Joel make his English League debut?

Answers

FA & SFA Cup Finals (see Quiz 14)
1 Stuart Pearce. 2 Tottenham Hotspur. 3 Ian Wright. 4 1909.
5 Aberdeen. 6 Liverpool and Sunderland. 7 Cardiff City.
8 Kennington Oval. 9 Everton. 10 David O'Leary.
11 Coventry City. 12 John Aldridge. 13 Les Sealey.
14 1960s. 15 3,500. 16 Peter Rodrigues. 17 Blackburn Rovers.
18 Aberdeen. 19 Stanley Mortensen. 20 Roger Osborne.

1　Which Alan became Stoke City manager in 1989?

2　What colour are Chesterfield's home shirts?

3　Which was David Platt's first league club?

4　Which Scotland captain was born in Finnieston in 1950?

5　What is the name of York City's ground?

6　Which Roger was First Divison leading scorer in 1965–66?

7　Which country did Bob McNab play for?

8　Which club did Gordon Strachan join on leaving Aberdeen?

9　Which club are nicknamed The Chairboys?

10　In which decade did Blackburn Rovers first win the FA Cup?

11　Andy Sinton and Roy Wegerle were in the same team at which club?

12　Jim Montgomery set a League appearance record at which club?

13　Who was the only League ever present for Rangers in 1995–96?

14　In which city was Mark Hateley born?

15　Which Andy of Palace won his only England cap in 1991?

16　In which decade was Trevor Francis born?

17　Which team were beaten 3–2 by Coventry in the 1987 FA Cup Final?

18　Who was the regular keeper for Derby in their 1990–91 relegation season?

19　Which Glenn left as Watford boss in February 1996?

20　Which defender played 240 games for Wimbledon before going to Liverpool?

Answers

Pot Luck 10　(see Quiz 19)
1　Sheffield Wednesday. 2　Black. 3　Bristol Rovers. 4　1970s.
5　Wycombe Wanderers. 6　Shreeves. 7　Liverpool. 8　Paris St
Germain. 9　Queens Park. 10　1912. 11　Graham le Saux.
12　Stoke City. 13　Bolton Wanderers. 14　Tony Coton.
15　Gordon Marshall. 16　Marwood. 17　Tony Norman.
18　Preston North End. 19　Maurice. 20　Les Ferdinand.

1 Who scored the Republic of Ireland's goal against England in the 1988 Championship?

2 Who were England's scorers v Scotland in Euro 96?

3 Which country were the first ever winners of the competition?

4 In the qualifying tournament for Euro 96 which country finished top in the group that included the Republic of Ireland and Northern Ireland?

5 Who beat Italy in Euro 96 to stop them making the quarter-finals?

6 Which country played in the distinctive red and white chequered shirts in Euro 96?

7 Who was Scotland's number two keeper for Euro 96?

8 What number did Stuart Pearce go in the semi-final penalty shoot out?

9 Who was the first outfield player in a tournament-winning side to have played English League soccer?

10 Which England player missed the Euro 96 quarter-final after collecting two yellow cards in the tournament?

11 What was the scoreline in the Scotland v Switzerland Euro 96 game?

12 How many groups were in the Finals for the 1988 tournament?

13 Which country won the 1988 tournament?

14 Who was skipper of the victorious side in 1988?

15 Which country won the Fair Play Award in Euro 96?

16 Who was England's captain for the 1992 European Championship?

17 Which group did Germany play in in Euro 96?

18 Which German player became the first to score in consecutive Finals?

19 Who was the Russian keeper in the first ever Championship?

20 Who was manager of England's first team ever to enter the tournament?

Answers

Strikers (see Quiz 20)
1 Tranmere Rovers. 2 George Best. 3 Derby County. 4 Arthur Rowley. 5 Ipswich Town. 6 Ted MacDougall. 7 Jimmy Greaves. 8 Oldham Athletic. 9 Southampton. 10 Matt Le Tissier. 11 Simon Garner. 12 Jimmy Greaves. 13 Bristol City. 14 Middlesbrough. 15 10. 16 Bolton Wanderers. 17 Jackie Milburn. 18 Hector. 19 Peterborough. 20 Faustino Asprilla.

1 Carlton Palmer and Paul Warhurst were in the same team at which club?

2 What colour are Port Vale's home shorts?

3 What was John Scales' first league club?

4 In which decade was Juninho born?

5 Who plays at home at Adams Park?

6 Which Peter became Tottenham Hotspur manager in 1991?

7 Burrows, Thomas and Wright appeared in an FA Cup Final team for which club?

8 Which club did Ray Wilkins leave to join Rangers?

9 Which Scottish club is nicknamed the Spiders?

10 To five either way, in which year did Barnsley first win the FA Cup?

11 Which England player was born on Jersey in 1968?

12 Eric Skeels set a League appearance record at which club?

13 Which club was Frank Worthington with when he was First Division leading scorer in 1978–79?

14 Which keeper can list Birmingham, Watford and Sunderland among his clubs?

15 Who was the only league ever-present for Celtic in 1995–96?

16 Which Brian of Arsenal won his only England cap in 1988?

17 Who was the regular keeper for Sunderland in their 1990–91 relegation season?

18 Which team were beaten 3–2 by West Ham Utd in the 1964 FA Cup Final?

19 What is Roy Keane's middle name?

20 Which striker – who has since played for England – was loaned to Istanbul side Besiktas in 1989?

Answers

Pot Luck 9 (see Quiz 17)
1 Ball. 2 Blue. 3 Crewe Alexandra. 4 Danny McGrain.
5 Bootham Crescent. 6 Hunt. 7 England. 8 Manchester Utd.
9 Wycombe Wanderers. 10 1880s. 11 QPR. 12 Sunderland.
13 Alan McLaren. 14 Liverpool. 15 Gray. 16 1950s.
17 Tottenham Hotspur. 18 Peter Shilton. 19 Roeder.
20 John Scales.

1 At which club has John Aldridge scored his highest number of goals?

2 Which player, recognised as a winger, hit 147 goals in 411 league games for Manchester Utd?

3 Where did Dean Saunders move to when he left Oxford Utd?

4 Who holds the career record for League goals, with 434 strikes?

5 Chris Kiwoyma has been leading scorer with which club?

6 Who scored nine goals in a 1970s FA Cup match against Margate?

7 Who scored debut goals for Chelsea, Tottenham Hotspur, West Ham Utd and England?

8 Who was Frankie Bunn playing for when he hit a record six in a League Cup game?

9 Phil Boyer was Division One top scorer in the 1980s when he was at which club?

10 Who won the "Match Of The Day" Goal of the Season in 1995 for a 35-yard chip shot against Blackburn Rovers?

11 Who has scored most goals in a career for Blackburn Rovers?

12 Who holds Chelsea's record of 41 goals in a season?

13 Which club did John Atyeo score 314 League goals for?

14 George Camsell hit 59 goals in a season for which club?

15 Joe Payne holds the old Third Division (South) record of goals in a game. How many did he strike?

16 Which club was Frank Worthington with when he was the First Divison's top scorer?

17 Who has scored most goals in a career for Newcastle Utd?

18 Which Kevin was a scoring machine for Derby County in the 1970s?

19 Who was Terry Bly playing for when he hit 52 goals in 1960–61?

20 Who was the first Colombian striker to play in English soccer?

Euro Championship (see Quiz 18)

Answers
1 Ray Houghton. 2 Shearer and Gascoigne. 3 USSR.
4 Portugal. 5 Czech Republic. 6 Croatia. 7 Jim Leighton.
8 Third. 9 Arnold Muhren. 10 Paul Ince. 11 1–0 to Scotland.
12 Two. 13 Holland. 14 Ruud Gullit. 15 England.
16 Gary Lineker. 17 Group C. 18 Gerd Müller. 19 Lev Yashin. 20 Alf Ramsey.

1 Tony Barton followed Ron Saunders as boss of which club?

2 Which country did Tony Galvin play for?

3 Which was Steve Bould's first League club?

4 In which decade was Duncan Edwards born?

5 Who plays at home at East End Park?

6 The resignation of director Richard Thompson in May 1996 meant that which club was up for sale?

7 Charlie Aitken set a League appearance record at which club?

8 Which club did Dave Beasant join on leaving Chelsea?

9 Which team were beaten 4–1 in the first post-World War Two FA Cup Final?

10 Tommy Coyne was at which club when he made his international debut?

11 Which 38-year old goalkeeper was released by Southampton in May 1996?

12 Who moved from Barnsley to Nottingham Forest in 1991 to set a club record for transfer fee received?

13 What colour are Aberdeen's home shorts?

14 In which decade did Chelsea first win the FA Cup?

15 Which Republic of Ireland defender was born in Lambeth, London in 1970?

16 Which Adrian became manager of Burnley in March 1996?

17 Which club did Mervyn Day leave to join Aston Villa?

18 Who was stripped of the captaincy of the Republic of Ireland in 1996 for holidaying without informing his boss?

19 Which Ted became secretary of the FA in September 1973?

20 Mel Sterland and Tony Dorigo were in the same team at which club?

Pot Luck 12 (see Quiz 23)

Answers

1 Swansea City. 2 1940s. 3 Tottenham Hotspur. 4 Manager of Wales. 5 David Batty. 6 Creaney. 7 Gold. 8 Birmingham City. 9 Leyton Orient. 10 David O'Leary. 11 Wales. 12 1980s. 13 Arsenal. 14 Bristol City. 15 Everton. 16 Fry. 17 Liverpool. 18 Leeds United. 19 Ipswich Town. 20 Rune Hauge.

Quiz 22 Nicknames

Answers – see page 132

1 Which two Athletics have the same nickname?

2 The Bankies is the nickname of which club?

3 Who was known in France as "El Magnifico" ?

4 Which club supposedly got their nickname in 1934 as fans responded to the smart and stylish new kit worn by the players?

5 Which England player was known as "Crazy Horse"?

6 The Ironsides is an old nickname of which club?

7 Which club are known as The Loons?

8 Who was the striker known as "Supermac"?

9 Which team have a nickname linked with fictional litter collecting creatures on a real common?

10 Oxford and Cambridge share which nickname?

11 Who was dubbed "Mighty Mouse"?

12 What is Dumbarton's nickname?

13 Who are the Doonhammers?

14 Which player was known as "Glenda"?

15 Which international star was known as "The Little Bird"?

16 Who is "The Divine Ponytail"?

17 The Glaziers is a long standing nickname for which team?

18 Which Sheffield Wednesday striker was nicknamed "Bronco"?

19 Who was nicknamed "The Black Panther" after the 1966 World Cup?

20 Who liked to be called Bill Dean and hated his nickname?

Answers

The 1960s (see Quiz 24)
1 Stanley Matthews. 2 Chile. 3 Brazil and Czechoslovakia.
4 Alf Ramsey. 5 David Webb. 6 George Best. 7 Pat Jennings.
8 John White. 9 Burnley. 10 Bobby Charlton. 11 Real Madrid.
12 Johnny Haynes. 13 Gordon Banks. 14 Bill Nicholson. 15 Dave Mackay. 16 Pickles. 17 European Cup. 18 Allan Clarke.
19 Alf Ramsey. 20 Jimmy Greaves.

LEVEL 2

1 Who was keeper Roger Freestone playing for when he scored two penalty goals in 1995–96?

2 In which decade was commentator Barry Davies born?

3 Which was Mark Bowen's first League club?

4 Atkinson, Kendall and Walker were in contention for which management job in August 1995?

5 Who moved from Blackburn Rovers in 1996 for £3,750,000 to set a club record for transfer fee received?

6 Which Gerry went from Portsmouth to Manchester City in 1995?

7 What colour are Dumbarton's home shirts?

8 Which club did David Seaman leave to join QPR?

9 Who plays at home at Brisbane Road?

10 Who holds the Arsenal league appearance record?

11 Which country did George Berry play for?

12 In which decade did Coventry City first win the FA Cup?

13 Don Howe followed Terry Neill as boss of which club?

14 Which club did Rob Newman leave to join Norwich City?

15 Which team were beaten 1–0 by Manchester Utd in the 1985 FA Cup Final?

16 Which Barry became manager of Birmingham City in 1993?

17 In which city was John Aldridge born?

18 Terry Yorath was at which club when he made his international debut?

19 Frank Yallop and Neil Thompson were fullbacks at which club?

20 Who was the Norwegian agent in the George Graham 'bung' case?

Quiz 24 The 1960s

Answers – see page 130

LEVEL 2

1 Who retired from football, aged 50, in April 1965 ?

2 Which country was the venue for the 1962 World Cup?

3 Which teams played in the 1962 World Cup Final?

4 Who was manager of Ipswich Town's championship winning team?

5 Who scored Chelsea's winner against Leeds Utd in the replayed FA Cup Final of 1969–70?

6 Which Manchester Utd star was named European Footballer of the Year in 1968?

7 Which goalkeeper scored a goal in the 1967 Charity Shield match?

8 Which famous player was killed by lightning on a golf course in 1965?

9 Which Lancashire side won the championship in 1960?

10 Who became England's all-time leading scorer when he netted against Sweden in 1968?

11 Which club won the first World Club Championship in 1960?

12 Who became Britain's first £100-a-week footballer?

13 Who was keeper for the losing Leicester City side in the 1961 FA Cup Final?

14 Which manager bought Jimmy Greaves back from Italy?

15 Returning from a broken leg, which Scottish star broke his leg in his comeback game in 1964?

16 What was the name of the dog who found the stolen World Cup in 1966?

17 What trophy was won with Celtic's 200th goal of the season in 1967?

18 Which Leeds Utd player was nicknamed "Sniffer"?

19 Which manager was knighted in the 1967 New Year's Honours List?

20 In the 1966 World Cup quarter-finals which injured player did Geoff Hurst replace?

Answers

Nicknames (see Quiz 22)
1 Oldham and Wigan. The Latics. 2 Clydebank. 3 David Ginola. 4 Peterborough, The Posh. 5 Emlyn Hughes. 6 Middlesbrough. 7 Forfar. 8 Malcolm Macdonald. 9 The Wombles, Wimbledon. 10 The Us. 11 Kevin Keegan. 12 The Sons. 13 Queen of the South. 14 Glenn Hoddle. 15 Garrincha. 16 Roberto Baggio. 17 Crystal Palace. 18 David Layne. 19 Eusebio. 20 "Dixie" Dean.

Quiz 25 Pot Luck 13

Answers – see page 135

LEVEL 2

1 Who was Jimmy Case playing for when he knocked his old club Liverpool out of the FA Cup in a 1980s shock result?

2 In which decade did Derby County first win the FA Cup?

3 Which was Mark Draper's first League club?

4 Who plays at home at Somerset Park?

5 John Aldridge was at which club when he made his international debut?

6 In which city was the draw for the qualifying rounds of the 1998 World Cup made?

7 Who moved from Birmingham City in February 1996 for £1,100,000 to set a club record for transfer fee received?

8 Which club did Ray Wilkins join on leaving Manchester Utd?

9 Which team were beaten 2–1 by Manchester Utd in the 1977 FA Cup Final?

10 Which country did Ashley Grimes play for?

11 What colour goes with black on Barnet's home shirts?

12 In which decade was Faustino Asprilla born?

13 Derek Fazackerley set a League appearance record at which club?

14 Shearer and Ferdinand first formed a strike-force for which team?

15 Gareth Southgate and Chris Coleman were in the same team at which club?

16 Which Roy became manager of Bolton Wanderers in 1995?

17 Where was Tony Adams born?

18 Terry Cooper followed Lou Macari as boss of which club?

19 Which club did Mike Phelan leave to join Manchester Utd?

20 Which Blackburn Rovers and England defender suffered a long-term injury against Middlesbrough in December 1995?

Answers

Pot Luck 14 (see Quiz 27)
1 Paul Gascoigne. 2 60. 3 Carlisle United. 4 1906.
5 Swansea. 6 Blackburn Rovers. 7 Jimmy Armfield. 8 Crystal Palace. 9 Alloa. 10 Kevin Richardson. 11 Arsenal. 12 Case.
13 Scotland. 14 White. 15 1940s. 16 Chelsea.
17 Manchester City. 18 Nottm Forest. 19 Chester.
20 Trevor Sinclair.

Quiz 26 Midlands & The North

1 Which famous comedian and TV personality is a supporter of WBA?

2 Which team were originally known as Small Heath Alliance?

3 Who did Blackburn Rovers play in the 1994 Charity Shield match?

4 Which club did Danny Blanchflower play before he joined Tottenham Hotspur?

5 Name the two goalkeepers in the 1983 Manchester Utd v Liverpool FA Cup Final?

6 Which international star moved to Bari in August 1992?

7 Gordon Banks won the League Cup with which different clubs?

8 Alan Hudson and Geoff Hurst both played for which Midlands team?

9 Which Midlands' star made a goalscoring England debut against Scotland in 1989?

10 Who was manager of Stockport at the start of the 1996–97 season?

11 Who scored a hat-trick for Blackpool in the 1953 FA Cup Final?

12 Which club dropped from First to Fourth Divisions between 1984–86?

13 What was the nickname of Aston Villa's 1930s player Thomas Waring?

14 In 1960 the Blackpool v Bolton game achieved a first. What was it?

15 Which player did Real Madrid sign from WBA for £1 million in 1979?

16 Who created the first £10,000 transfer fee joining Arsenal from Bolton?

17 Which Aston Villa forward won the Young Player of the Year award in 1977?

18 Who played for Arsenal and Everton and managed Aston Villa, Manchester City and England?

19 What happened to Manchester City in 1938 after being champions in 1937?

20 Which club did Bobby Charlton manage between 1973 and 75?

Answers

European Cup (see Quiz 28)
1 AC Milan. 2 Trevor Francis. 3 Manchester Utd. 4 Wembley.
5 Bobby Charlton. 6 Aston Villa. 7 Marseille. 8 Tommy
Gemmell. 9 Leeds United. 10 1956. 11 Terry McDermott.
12 Yes, in 1992. 13 It was the first Final to be replayed.
14 Eintracht Frankfurt. 15 Rome. 16 Panathinaikos.
17 Kenny Dalglish. 18 Wembley. 19 Brian Clough.
20 Steaua Bucharest.

1 Who in December 1995 got booked for "showing" the referee a yellow card after it fell from his pocket?

2 To one year each way, how old was Jack Charlton when he stood down as manager of the Republic of Ireland?

3 With which club did Peter Beardsley make his League debut?

4 To five years each way, when did Everton first win the FA Cup?

5 In which city was Ivor Allchurch born?

6 Kenny Dalglish followed Don Mackay as boss of which club?

7 Who holds the league appearance record for Blackpool?

8 Which club did Iain Dowie leave to join Southampton?

9 Which Scottish side plays at home at Recreation Park?

10 Who, in December 1995, got sent off playing for Coventry City on his return to his former club Aston Villa?

11 Paul Davis and Anders Limpar were in the same team at which club?

12 Which Jimmy became manager of Brighton in November 1995?

13 Which country did Adam Blacklaw play for?

14 What colour are Blackpool's home shorts?

15 In which decade was Roy Evans born?

16 Which team were beaten 2–1 by Tottenham Hotspur in the 1967 FA Cup Final?

17 Colin Bell was at which club when he made his international debut?

18 Which club did Lee Chapman leave to join Leeds Utd the first time?

19 Which Sir Norman produced the 1980s report "The State of Football"?

20 Who moved from Blackpool in August 1993 for £750,000 to set a club record for transfer fee received?

Pot Luck 13 (see Quiz 25)
1 Brighton. 2 1940s. 3 Notts County. 4 Ayr Utd. 5 Oxford Utd. 6 Paris. 7 Liam Daish. 8 AC Milan. 9 Liverpool. 10 The Republic of Ireland. 11 Amber. 12 1960s. 13 Blackburn Rovers. 14 England. 15 Crystal Palace. 16 McFarland. 17 Romford. 18 Birmingham City. 19 Norwich City. 20 Graeme Le Saux.

1 Who in 1963 became the first Italian team to win the trophy?

2 Who scored the Nottingham Forest match winner in the 1979 Final?

3 Which side represented England for the first time in 1956–57?

4 What was the venue for the Manchester Utd v Benfica 1968 Final?

5 Which English player scored twice in the 1968 Final?

6 Which Midlands team won the 1982 Final?

7 Which French team had the trophy subsequently taken away after winning the Final in 1993?

8 Who scored Celtic's first goal in the 1967 Final triumph?

9 In 1975 which team became the second English side to reach a Final?

10 In which year was the first ever European Cup Final played?

11 Who scored Liverpool's first goal in a European Cup Final?

12 Have Barcelona ever won the trophy?

13 When Bayern Munich won the trophy in 1974 what was special about the Final?

14 Who did Real Madrid beat in their famous 7–3 victory in 1960?

15 Which city hosted the 1968 European Championship Final?

16 Which Greek side reached the semi-finals in 1996?

17 Who scored Liverpool's match-winning goal of the 1978 Final?

18 At which stadium did that match take place?

19 Who was manager of the Nottingham Forest team when they first won the trophy?

20 Who were the first Romanian team to win the European Cup?

1 Kevin Sheedy was at which club when he made his international debut?

2 Where was John Barnes born?

3 Which was Colin Hendry's first League club?

4 In which decade was Garrincha born?

5 Which team were beaten 4–2 by Manchester Utd in the 1948 FA Cup Final?

6 Which Joe became manager of Bristol City in November 1994?

7 Which 46-year-old physiotherapist became Arsenal manager?

8 Which club did Peter Beardsley join on leaving Liverpool?

9 Airdrieonians and Clyde have shared which ground?

10 Who moved from Bolton to Celtic in 1994 to set a club record for transfer fee received?

11 Which country did Ralph Coates play for?

12 In which decade did Huddersfield Town first win the FA Cup?

13 What colour are Barcelona's home shorts?

14 Howard Wilkinson followed Billy Bremner as boss of which club?

15 In 1985 which Harry died while watching Everton, a club he had once managed ?

16 Eddie Hopkinson set a League appearance record at which club?

17 Regis and Atkinson were the strike force at which club?

18 Who won his 100th Scottish cap in March 1986?

19 Which club did Mike Milligan leave to join Everton?

20 At which club did former England boss Bobby Robson begin his playing career?

Pot Luck 16 (see Quiz 31)
Answers
1 Liverpool. 2 Chris Woods. 3 Nottm Forest. 4 Red. 5 1900.
6 Nigel Martyn. 7 Hull City. 8 Wrexham. 9 Leeds.
10 Oldham Athletic. 11 Alan Harris. 12 Arsenal. 13 1940s.
14 Blackburn Rovers. 15 Millwall. 16 Billy McNeill.
17 Hollins. 18 The Republic of Ireland. 19 Manchester Utd.
20 Leicester City.

Quiz 30 Gary Lineker

Answers – see page 140

LEVEL 2

1 How many international goals did Gary Lineker score?

2 Who was the boss who took him to Everton in 1985?

3 Who were the opponents for the World Cup hat-trick in Mexico?

4 What is Gary's starsign?

5 At which club did he hit his best League goals total of 30 in a season?

6 Who was in charge of Barcelona when Lineker went there?

7 How many goals did Gary score in the World Cup in Italy in 1990?

8 What is Gary Lineker's middle name?

9 What was the only major European club trophy that Lineker won?

10 Which Gordon was his regular strike partner in his last League season in England?

11 Gary scored all four of England's goals in games against Malaysia and which other country?

12 How many red cards did he receive in his career?

13 Who went on when Gary was substituted in his last international?

14 Who saved his penalty in an FA Cup Final?

15 Who was in charge of Tottenham Hotspur when Lineker went there?

16 Top scorer in the 1986 World Cup final stages, he had hit how many goals?

17 Who is Gary's long-standing pal in the snooker world?

18 Which Frank was Leicester boss at the time of Gary's 1979 League debut?

19 Which university awarded Lineker an honorary Master of Arts degree in 1991?

20 At which club was Gary playing when he retired from soccer?

Answers

Quote, Unquote (see Quiz 32)
1 The Hillsborough tragedy 1989. 2 Gary Lineker. 3 Barry Fry.
4 Jack Charlton. 5 Hall. 6 Tommy Docherty. 7 Ian Rush.
8 Rod Stewart. 9 Brian Clough. 10 Alex Ferguson. 11 Dave
Bassett. 12 Beat them. 13 USA. 14 Kenny Dalglish.
15 Altrincham. 16 Stan Flashman. 17 Brian Clough.
18 Karen Brady. 19 Graeme Souness. 20 Graham Taylor.

138

1 Craig Johnston scored an FA Cup Final goal for which club?

2 Who in July 1986 moved to Rangers for £600,000, a new record fee for a keeper ?

3 What was Steve Hodge's first League club?

4 What colour are Benfica's home shirts?

5 To ten years either way, when did Bury first win the FA Cup?

6 Who moved from Bristol Rovers in November 1989 to set a club record for transfer fee received?

7 Who plays at home at Boothferry Park?

8 Which club did Joey Jones leave to join Liverpool?

9 In which city was David Batty born?

10 Andy Goram was at which club when he made his international debut?

11 Who was Terry Venables's assistant at Barcelona?

12 Which team were beaten 1–0 by Ipswich in the 1978 FA Cup Final?

13 In which decade was Geoff Hurst born?

14 Alan Wright and Scott Sellars were in the same team at which club?

15 Which club did Wimbledon buy John Fashanu from?

16 Who holds the League appearance record at Celtic?

17 Which John became manager of Chelsea in March 1985?

18 Which country did Mick Robinson play for?

19 Ron Atkinson followed Dave Sexton as boss of which club?

20 Which club did Gary McAllister leave to join Leeds Utd?

---

1 After what event did Kenny Dalglish say, "Football is irrelevant now"?

2 Who said, "I'm not as nice as all that. In fact I swore last week"?

3 Who said, "If ...Liverpool is a danger to your health, try managing Barnet"?

4 After a check up and brain scan, who said, "It proves that I do have a brain"?

5 Which Stuart on Radio 5 said, "Lee Sharpe has got dynamite in his shorts"?

6 Barnes' problem is that he gets injured on *Question of Sport*!" Who said this?

7 "His goals do the talking, but so far he hasn't spoken very much"? Who was the Juventus president talking about?

8 Which soccer-mad pop singer said after the birth of his daughter, "It's like seeing Scotland score a goal. You never got used to it"?

9 Which manager, when he heard about Souness having heart surgery, said, "My heart goes out to Graeme Souness"?

10 Who said, "The Old Trafford job was one I simply could not turn down"?

11 Who said on promotion to the top flight, "Contrary to popular opinion I don't tell my players to kick the opposition in the nuts"?

12 Complete the quote from the Danish Foreign Minister after Denmark opted out of the Maastricht Treaty and won Euro 92, "If you can't join them ..."?

13 "Played them on the wrong day," – Graham Taylor's said after loss to who?

14 Who said in 1997, "The temptation of a job like this was too much"?

15 Which club was called "the Manchester Utd of non League football"?

16 Who was Barry Fry talking about: "If you didn't know him, you'd think he was an ignorant pig"?

17 Who said, "The Trent is lovely, too. I've walked on it for 18 years"?

18 Which lady said,"everyone thinks I earned this job between the sheets"?

19 "The best players will be signed, no matter what they are," was the response of which manager to Catholic/Protestant controversy?

20 Who said, "This is a bloody awful job"?

Answers

Gary Lineker (see Quiz 30)
1 48. 2 Howard Kendall. 3 Poland. 4 Sagittarius.
5 Everton. 6 Terry Venables. 7 Four. 8 Winston.
9 European Cup Winners' Cup. 10 Durie. 11 Spain.
12 None. 13 Alan Smith. 14 Mark Crossley. 15 Terry
Venables. 16 Six. 17 Willie Thorn. 18 McLintock.
19 Leicester. 20 Nagoya Grampus 8.

1 Jock Stein followed Jimmy Armfield as boss of which club?

2 In which decade did Leeds United first win the FA Cup?

3 Which was Tony Dorigo's first League club?

4 Which country did Paul Bodin play for?

5 Who said on revealing his new haircut in 1994 at the World Cup Finals, "I asked for a Valderrama and they gave me a Val Doonican"?

6 Kevin Wilson and Clive Allen were in the same team at which club?

7 In which decade was Des Lynam born?

8 Which club did Gary Taggart join on leaving Barnsley?

9 Who plays at home at Twerton Park?

10 Peter Barnes was at which club when he made his international debut?

11 Which Terry became manager of Coventry City in 1990?

12 What was the score in the drawn Manchester Utd v Brighton FA Cup Final of 1983?

13 What colour are Hearts' home shirts?

14 Brondby knocked which English team out of the UEFA Cup in 1995?

15 Tony Blair is a fan of which team?

16 Which club did Stephen Pears leave to join Middlesbrough?

17 Willie Miller set a League appearance record at which club?

18 Where was Raich Carter born?

19 Who moved from Bradford in 1995 to Wolves to set a club record for transfer fee received?

20 Kevin Campbell and Chris Bart-Williams both moved on the same day to which club?

Answers

Pot Luck 18 (see Quiz 35)
1 Charlton Athletic. 2 Recreation Ground. 3 West Ham Utd.
4 1950s. 5 Scotland. 6 Millwall. 7 Michel Platini. 8 Crewe Alexandra. 9 Green. 10 Mark Lawrenson. 11 Blackburn Rovers. 12 Fulham. 13 Dublin. 14 Wimbledon. 15 Everton.
16 Smith. 17 Never. 18 Crystal Palace. 19 South Africa.
20 Alan Shearer.

1 Which French club did Mo Johnston play for?

2 How much, to the nearest million pounds, did Marseille pay for Trevor Steven?

3 What is the main stadium used for French home internationals?

4 David Ginola and George Weah have played for which French club?

5 Which team lost in the Final of the 1992 European Cup Winners' Cup?

6 At what stage did France get knocked out of the 1994 World Cup?

7 Which French keeper joined Sunderland in 1996?

8 How many different clubs in France did Eric Cantona play for before coming to England?

9 At which Italian club did Michel Platini end his career?

10 At which ground do Marseille play?

11 Which team are known as The Greens – Les Verts?

12 Which Arsenal and England player moved to Le Havre in the early 1990s?

13 Which Manuel holds the appearance record for France?

14 Which club won the 1996 European Cup Winners' Cup?

15 Which French club did Chris Waddle play for?

16 Which team scored within 27 seconds against France in the 1982 World Cup?

17 Which two English internationals helped Monaco to the Championship in 1988?

18 In which country did France first win the European Championship?

19 Which French Player of the Year in 1994 moved to England in 1995?

20 For which club has Eric Cantona made most appearances?

Scottish Internationals (see Quiz 36)
1 Andy Roxburgh. 2 1990. 3 Denis Law & Kenny Dalglish.
4 Archie Gemmill. 5 1958. 6 Hughie Gallacher. 7 3–2 to
Scotland. 8 Ally McCoist. 9 Denis Law. 10 Leeds (Gary
McAllister was involved). 11 Pat Nevin. 12 Fullback. 13
Dundee Utd. 14 Alex Ferguson. 15 Aberdeen. 16 8. 17 1984.
18 Celtic & Albion Rovers. 19 First goalless draw. 20 Leeds.

Quiz 35 Pot Luck 18

Answers – see page 141

LEVEL 2

1   Sam Bartram set a League appearance record at which club?

2   Which ground do Chesterfield play at?

3   What was Ray Houghton's first League club?

4   In which decade was Sam Hamman born?

5   Which country did Jimmy Crapnell play for?

6   Mick McCarthy followed Bruce Rioch as boss of which club?

7   Who resigned as coach of France in July 1992?

8   Which club did David Platt leave to join Aston Villa?

9   What is the main colour of Hibernians' home shirts?

10 Who moved from Brighton to Liverpool in 1981 to set a club record for transfer fee received?

11 Which club withdrew from a £3 million bid for Geoff Thomas in 1992?

12 Which team were beaten 2–0 by West Ham Utd in the 1975 FA Cup Final?

13 In which city was Liam Brady born?

14 Terry Phelan was at which club when he made his international debut?

15 Tony Cottee and Peter Beardsley were in the same team at which club?

16 Which Alan became manager of Crystal Palace in March 1993?

17 In which decade did Leicester City win the FA Cup before the 1990s?

18 Which club did Kenny Sansom leave to join Arsenal?

19 In July 1992, which country was re-elected to FIFA after an absence of 18 years?

20 On July 26, 1992 the move of which player to Blackburn Rovers broke the British transfer record?

Answers

Pot Luck 17 (see Quiz 33)
1. Leeds Utd. 2 1970s. 3 Aston Villa. 4 Wales. 5 Andy Townsend. 6 Chelsea. 7 1940s. 8 Bolton Wanderers.
9 Bristol Rovers. 10 Manchester City. 11 Butcher. 12 2–2.
13 Maroon. 14 Liverpool. 15 Newcastle Utd. 16 Manchester Utd. 17 Aberdeen. 18 Sunderland. 19 Dean Richards.
20 Nottingham Forest.

1 Who did Craig Brown replace in charge of the Scottish team?

2 In which year did Scotland last play Brazil in a World Cup tournament?

3 Which two players are joint top scorers for Scotland?

4 Which Scottish player scored a brilliant solo goal against Holland in a 1978 World Cup match?

5 When did Scotland first qualify for the World Cup finals?

6 Who scored 23 goals in only 20 games for Scotland?

7 What was the score of Wembley's England v Scotland game in 1967?

8 Which Scottish international won Europe's Golden Boot award in 1992?

9 Who retired from international soccer after the 1974 World Cup game against Zaire?

10 In 1995 which English club was incensed when their player was injured against Sweden?

11 Which Scottish Pat was on Tranmere's books at the start of 1996–97?

12 In which position did Ray Stewart play?

13 Duncan Ferguson was with which club when he made his international debut?

14 Who was Scotland's caretaker manager in the mid 80s?

15 In which city was Denis Law born?

16 To five each way, how many times did Alex James play for Scotland?

17 To one either way, in which year was Paul McStay first capped?

18 Which two Scottish clubs did Jock Stein play for?

19 What was notable about the draw between England and Scotland in the 1970s Home International Championship?

20 Which club links McQueen, McAllister and Lorimer?

Answers

French Connection (see Quiz 34)
1 Nantes. 2 Five. 3 Parc des Princes. 4 Paris St Germain.
5 Monaco. 6 They failed to qualify. 7 Lionel Perez. 8 Five.
9 Juventus. 10 Stade Velodrome. 11 St Etienne. 12 Graham Rix. 13 Amaros. 14 Paris St Germain. 15 Marseille.
16 England. 17 Mark Hateley and Glenn Hoddle. 18 France.
19 David Ginola. 20 Manchester Utd.

Quiz 37 Pot Luck 19

Answers – see page 147

1 How many home League games did Manchester United lose in 1995–96?

2 Where does the Alexandra come from in Crewe's name?

3 Which was Denis Irwin's first League club?

4 In which decade did Ipswich Town first win the FA Cup?

5 Ossie Ardiles followed Jim Smith as boss of which club?

6 Which country did Gary Waddock play for?

7 Who plays at home at the Pulse Stadium?

8 Which club did Ian Rush join on leaving Liverpool for the first time?

9 Which club was Roger Stanislaus with when he failed a random drug test?

10 Who moved from Bristol City in March 1993 to set a club record for transfer fee received?

11 What is the main colour of Walsall's home shirts?

12 Which team were beaten 4–3 by Blackpool in the 1953 FA Cup Final?

13 In which decade was Ron Greenwood born?

14 Jim Cannon set a League appearance record at which club?

15 Which Bolton Wanderers boss got the sack on 2nd January 1996?

16 Which club did David Phillips leave to join Nottingham Forest?

17 Which Colin became manager of Everton in 1987?

18 In which city was Les Ferdinand born?

19 Kevin Moran was at which club when he made his international debut?

20 Eric Cantona and Steve Hodge were in the same team at which club?

Answers

Pot Luck 20 (see Quiz 39)
1 Arsenal. 2 Aberdeen. 3 Bradford City. 4 Blackburn Rovers.
5 Plymouth. 6 Colchester United. 7 Manchester City.
8 Barnsley. 9 San Marino. 10 Celtic. 11 White. 12 1960s.
13 Manchester Utd. 14 Bolton Wanderers and Sheffield United.
15 QPR. 16 Wales. 17 Adams. 18 1920s. 19 Norwich
City. 20 Dion Dublin.

145

Quiz 38 Going Up
Answers – see page 148

LEVEL 2

1 Which former Liverpool player was Blackburn Rovers's top scorer in their 1992 promotion season?

2 Kernaghan and Slaven played for which promoted team?

3 Who did Bolton beat 3–2 in the thrilling 1995 play-off Final, having trailed 2–0 at one stage?

4 Which manager John took Ipswich Town up as Second Division Champions?

5 Ian Marshall's goals helped which club to the top flight in 1991?

6 To two years each way, when did Liverpool last gain promotion?

7 Which team lost a play-off Final yet still went up in 1990?

8 Vinnie Jones and Mel Sterland were part of which promoted team?

9 Which 1960s team won the Championship directly after promotion?

10 Which 1970s team won the Championship directly after promotion?

11 Which boss who took Newcastle United into the Premier League?

12 Which team got promotion via the play-offs in their first season in the League in 1993–94?

13 A Mike Newell play-off Final goal took which club into the Premier League?

14 Which City were Second Division Champions in 1971 and 1980?

15 Chris Waddle was an ever-present in which promoted 1980s side?

16 Which United were Third Division Champions in 1984 and Second Division Champions the following season?

17 Who was the Sheffield Wednesday boss in the 1990–91 season?

18 Maurice Malpass was assistant manager and a player for which team on the up in 1996?

19 Neil Warnock took which side up to the top flight in 1991?

20 Marco Gabbiadini was top scorer for which team on the up in 1990?

Going Down (see Quiz 40)
1 Sheffield Weds. 2 Manchester Utd. 3 Lincoln City. 4 1960s.
5 Mark McGhee. 6 Charlton. 7 Falkirk. 8 West Ham United.
9 Newport County. 10 John Gorman. 11 Luton Town.
12 Dave Bassett. 13 1960s. 14 Sheffield Weds. 15 Halifax
Town. 16 Ipswich Town. 17 Southport. 18 Never.
19 Norwich City. 20 Alan Ball.

Quiz 39 Pot Luck 20

1 Which London club has a fanzine called *The Gooner*?

2 Alphabetically, which is the first Scottish League team?

3 What was Phil Babb's first League club?

4 Which team were beaten 3–0 by Wolves in the 1960 FA Cup Final?

5 In which city was Trevor Francis born?

6 Who plays at home at Layer Road?

7 Alan Oakes set a League appearance record at which club?

8 Which club did Gary Taggart join on leaving Manchester City?

9 Which team did Wales beat 5–0 in their first game in the 1998 World Cup campaign?

10 Chris Morris was at which club when he made his international debut?

11 What colour goes with black stripes on Swansea's home shirts?

12 In which decade did Liverpool first win the FA Cup?

13 Mal Donaghy and Denis Irwin were in the same team at which club?

14 Nathan Blake and Mark Patterson swapped over between which clubs?

15 Which club did Paul Parker leave to join Fulham?

16 Which country did Kenny Jackett play for?

17 Which Micky became manager of Fulham in February 1996?

18 In which decade was Jimmy Hill born?

19 Dave Stringer followed Ken Brown as boss of which club?

20 Who moved from Cambridge in 1992 to Manchester Utd to set a club record for transfer fee received?

Quiz 40 Going Down

Answers – see page 146

LEVEL 2

1 Pressman and Turner were the keepers as which club went down?

2 Who went down in 1974 after 37 years in the top flight?

3 In the 1980s, which club was the first to be automatically demoted from the League?

4 In which decade were Fulham last in the top flight in England?

5 Who was boss when Leicester City went down in 1994–95?

6 Robert Lee missed just one League game as which side went down?

7 Which team were relegated from the Scottish Premier League in 1993 and again in 1996?

8 Parris and Potts played for which relegated side?

9 Which Welsh club was finally wound up in February 1989?

10 Who was boss when Swindon Town went down in 1994–95?

11 Mark Pembridge played every 1992 game as which team went down?

12 In 1994, after going down, which boss said, "If you continually play Russian roulette eventually you're going to get the bullet"?

13 In which decade did Blackpool last play in the top division?

14 In 1990 which Sheffield team went down while the other went up?

15 Which Yorkshire team went out of the League in 1993?

16 Which team went down two seasons after winning the championship in the 60s?

17 Which seaside club went out of the League in 1978?

18 How many times were Aberdeen relegated in the 50 years following the Second World War?

19 Robins and Ekoku started the season as strikers, but left before which club went out of the Premiership?

20 Who was Portsmouth's manager when they went down from the top flight in 1988?

Answers

Going Up (see Quiz 38)
1 David Speedie. 2 Middlesbrough. 3 Reading. 4 Lyall.
5 Oldham Athletic. 6 1962. 7 Sunderland. 8 Leeds Utd.
9 Ipswich Town. 10 Nottingham Forest. 11 Kevin Keegan.
12 Wycombe Wanderers. 13 Blackburn Rovers. 14 Leicester.
15 Newcastle Utd. 16 Oxford. 17 Ron Atkinson. 18 Dundee
Utd. 19 Notts County. 20 Sunderland.

Quiz 41 Pot Luck 21

Answers – see page 151

LEVEL 2

1 Who won the last FA Cup Final before the Second World War?

2 Bobby Saxton followed Howard Kendall as manager of which club?

3 Which was Stuart Pearce's first League club?

4 Which country did David Langan play for?

5 Which team plays at home in front of the Kippax Stand?

6 In which decade was Daniel Amokachi born?

7 Gordon Davies set a most League goals in total record at which club?

8 Which club did Niall Quinn join on leaving Manchester City?

9 Which Bobby became Wimbledon manager in 1987?

10 Ashley Ward joined Derby County from which club?

11 What is Ian Rush's middle name?

12 Which club has a fanzine called *Gulls Eye*?

13 Which keeper Peter was with Stoke City throughout the entire 1980s?

14 In what decade did Manchester Utd first win the FA Cup?

15 Which club did Mel Sterland leave to join Rangers?

16 Peter Cormack was an FA Cup winner with which club?

17 In which city was Andy Hinchcliffe born?

18 Who plays at home at Sincil Bank?

19 Which England player set a League appearance record for Ipswich Town?

20 Which Colin was Minister for Sport in the 1980s?

Pot Luck 22 (see Quiz 43)

Answers

1 Leicester City. 2 1940s. 3 Wimbledon. 4 Watford.
5 Coventry City. 6 Ipswich Town. 7 Jimmy Case.
8 Birmingham City. 9 1900s. 10 Norwich City. 11 White.
12 Liverpool. 13 Leeds United. 14 The club flag. 15 Mills.
16 Birmingham City. 17 Andrew. 18 Scotland. 19 King.
20 Hereford United.

1 Which sport was played professionally by Ryan Giggs' father?

2 Which Scottish club bought Lee Martin?

3 Which Manchester Utd manager signed Gordon Strachan?

4 Which ex-United player became Jack Charlton's assistant with the Republic of Ireland?

5 A win in the final game of the 1994–95 season would have made United Premiership winners. Which team held them to a draw?

6 Who was the 1970s favourite "Pancho"?

7 How many times did Bryan Robson win the FA Cup as United skipper?

8 Which Dutch master joined United from Ipswich Town?

9 To one year either way, when did Bobby Charlton first play for United?

10 In which country was Gary Bailey born?

11 How many Championships did Sir Matt Busby win for United?

12 Which club did Graeme Hogg move to from United?

13 Who beat Manchester United at Old Trafford in their first European defeat of the 1990s?

14 Pat Crerand became assistant to which United manager?

15 In the 1960s David Herd left which club to join United?

16 1970s international centres Ron and Wyn share what surname?

17 Which player moved to Vancouver Whitecaps in the early 1980s and then came back to collect over 50 England caps?

18 Who followed Sir Matt as United boss?

19 Which keeper did Alec Ferguson sign from his former club Aberdeen?

20 What was Robson's shirt number for most of his United career?

Answers

The 1970s (see Quiz 44)

1 Brian Clough. 2 Alberto Tarantini. 3 Bremner + Keegan.
4 Don Revie. 5 Bobby Moore. 6 Aberdeen. 7 Hereford United.
8 Frank McLintock. 9 Ipswich Town. 10 Kevin Keegan.
11 Carlos Alberto. 12 Ibrox Park. 13 Ally MacLeod.
14 Nottingham Forest. 15 Billy Bremner. 16 Cyprus.
17 Gordon Banks. 18 Bobby Charlton. 19 West Ham Utd.
20 David Fairclough.

1. Which team were beaten 1–0 by Man City in the 1969 FA Cup Final?

2. In which decade was Pat Jennings born?

3. What was Alan Cork's first League club?

4. Graham Taylor followed Glenn Roeder as manager of which club?

5. Swan Lane and Thackhall Street lead to which club's ground?

6. Which club was Kevin Beattie with when he first played international soccer?

7. Which 41-year-old hung up his boots in November 1995 after a serious neck injury in a reserve team game?

8. Which club did Paul Furlong join on leaving Chelsea?

9. In what decade did Manchester City first win the FA Cup?

10. Which club has a fanzine called *I Can Drive A Tractor*?

11. What is the main colour of Stockport County's home shirts?

12. In which city was Michael Branch born?

13. Which club did Mervyn Day leave to join Aston Villa?

14. What did Souness place in the centre of the pitch after his team won the Turkish Cup Final?

15. Which Mick became Stoke City manager in 1985?

16. Steve Claridge joined Leicester City from which club?

17. What is Peter Beardsley's middle name?

18. Which country did Arthur Albiston play for?

19. Which John went upstairs at Tranmere Rovers when John Aldridge took over team affairs?

20. Which club plays at home at Edgar Street?

Answers

Pot Luck 21 (see Quiz 41)

1 Portsmouth. 2 Blackburn Rovers. 3 Coventry City. 4 The Republic of Ireland. 5 Manchester City. 6 1970s. 7 Fulham. 8 Sunderland. 9 Gould. 10 Norwich City. 11 James. 12 Brighton. 13 Fox. 14 1900s. 15 Leeds Utd. 16 Liverpool. 17 Manchester. 18 Lincoln City. 19 Mick Mills. 20 Moynihan.

Quiz 44 The 1970s

Answers – see page 150

LEVEL 2

1 Who was John McGovern referring to when he said, "I can only say he makes you want to play for him"?

2 Which Argentinian player joined Birmingham City in October 1978?

3 Which two players were sent off in the 1975 Charity Shield?

4 Who succeeded Alf Ramsey as England boss?

5 Which England player made his 100th appearance against Scotland in 1973?

6 Rangers and Celtic won the Scottish FA Cup each season in the 70s apart from 1970, when which team triumphed?

7 Which non-League side defeated Newcastle Utd in a third round 1971–72 FA Cup replay?

8 Who was Footballer of the Year in his club's double-winning season?

9 Geddis and Talbot played for which 1970s FA Cup winners?

10 Which player returned from Hamburg to play for Southampton?

11 Who was skipper of Brazil's 1970 World Cup team?

12 At which Scottish ground did 66 people die in a New Year's Day tragedy in 1971 ?

13 Which manager took Scotland to the 1978 World Cup finals?

14 Which English club ended Liverpool's European Cup reign in 1978?

15 Who was the Leeds Utd player banned by the Scottish FA from playing for his country in 1975?

16 Against which country did Malcolm Macdonald score 5 goals?

17 Which international keeper lost an eye in a car crash in 1972?

18 Who resigned as Preston North End's manager in 1975 after transfer disputes?

19 Mervyn Day played in goal for which 1970s FA Cup-winning team?

20 Which Liverpool player was nicknamed "Supersub" by the media?

Manchester Utd (see Quiz 42)
1 Rugby League. 2 Lee Martin. 3 Ron Atkinson. 4 Maurice Setters. 5 West Ham Utd. 6 Stuart Pearson. 7 Three. 8 Arnold Muhren. 9 1956. 10 England (in Ipswich). 11 Five. 12 Portsmouth. 13 Juventus. 14 Tommy Docherty. 15 Arsenal. 16 Davies. 17 Peter Beardsley. 18 Wilf McGuinness. 19 Jim Leighton. 20 7.

Quiz 45   Pot Luck 23

1   With 700+ games, which player set a League appearance record for Southampton?

2   Liam Brady followed Barry Lloyd as manager of which club?

3   Which was Alan Wright's first League club?

4   Who plays at home at the Abbey Stadium?

5   Which club has a fanzine called *United We Stand*?

6   Pat Nevin and Kevin Sheedy were in the same side at which club?

7   In which decade did Nottingham Forest first win the FA Cup?

8   Which club did David Platt join on leaving Aston Villa?

9   Which country did Chris Hughton play for?

10   Which manager said, "Newcastle supporters have, in the last few years, been through thick and thin"?

11   What colour are Brighton's home shorts?

12   Which team were beaten 1–0 by Celtic in the 1995 Scottish FA Cup Final?

13   Which club did Paul Rideout leave to join Everton?

14   In which decade was Tom Finney born?

15   Which Danny became boss of Barnsley in June 1994?

16   Who moved from Portsmouth for £2 million in May 1992 to set a club record for a transfer fee received?

17   Viv Anderson was with which club when he made his international debut?

18   How much did the transfer of Ruud Gullit cost Chelsea?

19   Which Danish midfielder was loaned from Liverpool to Barnsley in 1995?

20   Which Canadian side did Peter Beardsley play for?

1 At which club did Peter Reid start his playing career?

2 Which midfielder Gordon was awarded an OBE in 1993?

3 At QPR which ex-England midfielder followed another ex-England midfielder as manager?

4 Tim Sherwood moved to Norwich City from which club?

5 How old was Duncan Edwards when he made his League debut?

6 Which WBA and Manchester Utd player was forced to retire through injury in 1988?

7 Which country did Gerry Daly play for?

8 Which England midfielder scored the only goal in the World Cup quarter-final against Belgium in Bologna in 1990?

9 Which team did Robert Lee support as a boy?

10 To 10 each way how many League games did Glenn Hoddle play for Chelsea?

11 At which club did Bobby Charlton end his playing career?

12 Which midfielder did Ron Atkinson call "The Crab" because he was always moving sideways?

13 In what year did Paul McStay make his international debut?

14 Which country did Barry Hole play for?

15 Which club honours did Johnny Haynes gain in his 18 years at Fulham?

16 Which midfielder did Glenn Hoddle make skipper of Chelsea?

17 Which club did Roy Keane turn down when he joined Manchester Utd?

18 Which injury forced Bryan Robson out of the 1986 World Cup?

19 Which English midfielder scored in a World Cup Final?

20 Which England midfielder's autobiography was called *Rock Bottom*?

Answers

Viva España (see Quiz 48)
1 Estadio Santiago Bernabeu. 2 Real Sociedad. 3 0–0.
4 Barcelona. 5 The Vulture. 6 Seville. 7 Miguel Angel Nadal.
8 Suarez. 9 Archibald. 10 White. 11 Espanol. 12 Clemente.
13 Valencia. 14 John Toshack. 15 Laurie Cunningham.
16 Mexico. 17 Barcelona. Gary Lineker & Mark Hughes.
18 Julio Salinas. 19 Real Madrid. 20 Pope John Paul II.

1 Which future England manager won a championship medal with Tottenham Hotspur in 1951?

2 Howard Kendall followed Mel Machin as manager of which club?

3 With which club did Graeme Souness make his League debut?

4 Playing from the 1940s to the 1960s who set a League appearance record for Sheffield Utd?

5 Alan Devonshire made his international debut while at which club?

6 To five years, when did Newcastle Utd first win the FA Cup?

7 Who moved from Crewe Alexandra for £600,000 in October 1991 to set a club record for a transfer fee received?

8 Who teamed up with Henry Cooper to advertise Brut?

9 In which prison did Duncan Ferguson do time?

10 In which city was Tommy Docherty born?

11 Who plays at home at Home Park?

12 Which Ray became boss of Barnet in January 1994

13 Which club did Nigel Worthington leave to join Leeds Utd?

14 In which decade was Robert Lee born?

15 Which club has a fanzine called *Loadsamoney*?

16 What is Keith Gillespie's middle name?

17 Brian Marwood and Martin Hayes were in the same side at which club?

18 Which team were beaten 3–1 by Wolves in the 1949 FA Cup Final?

19 What colour are Portsmouth's home shorts?

20 Which country did Mike Bailey play for?

1 Real Madrid play at which stadium?

2 Which Spanish club did John Aldridge play for?

3 What was the half-time score in the England v Spain Euro 96 game?

4 Which team won the Spanish league in 1991, '92, '93 and '94?

5 What was the nickname of 1980s striker Emil Butragueno?

6 Real Betis come from which city?

7 In Euro 96, David Seaman produced a penalty shoot-out save to deny which Spanish player?

8 Which Luis was the last Spanish European Footballer of the Year before the 1990s?

9 Which Scottish Steve played for Barcelona in the 80s?

10 What colour are Real Madrid's home socks?

11 At which club did Alfredo di Stefano end his playing career?

12 Which Javier was in charge of Spain for Euro 96?

13 Which club did Zubizarreta move to from Barcelona?

14 Which Welshman managed Real Madrid and Real Sociedad?

15 Which former England player died in a car crash in Madrid in July 1989?

16 Which country did Real Madrid's scoring star Hugo Sanchez play for?

17 At which club did an English and a Welsh international link up?

18 Who had a goal disallowed for offside against England in Euro 96?

19 Castilla are the nursery side of which club?

20 Which special person was enrolled as member No. 108,000 at Barcelona?

1 Martin Dobson made his international debut while at which club?

2 Which Gary became boss of Blackpool in July 1996?

3 Which was Neil Webb's first League club?

4 Paul Groves was an ever-present for which team in 1995–96?

5 Ossie Ardiles followed Jim Smith as manager of which club?

6 Barry Kitchener set a League appearance record for which club?

7 Which club signed a reputed £60 million kit deal with Umbro in February 1996?

8 Which club did Derek Mountfield join on leaving Everton?

9 Which country did Noel Brotherston play for?

10 Who was fined in 1996 for a newspaper article criticising Ruud Gullit?

11 Who plays at home at the Field Mill Ground?

12 Which team were beaten 1–0 by Dundee Utd in the 1994 Scottish FA Cup Final?

13 Which club did Dean Yates leave to join Derby County?

14 In which decade was Bobby Gould born?

15 Which club has a fanzine called *Talking Bull*?

16 What is Andy Cole's middle name?

17 Geraint Williams and Dean Saunders were in the same side at which club?

18 Who moved from Oldham Athletic for £1,700,000 in February 1992 to set a club record for a transfer fee received?

19 What colour are Brentford's home shorts?

20 At which ground do Linfield play?

Quiz 50 FA and SFA Cup

LEVEL 2

1 Danny Wilson played in an FA Cup Final for which side?

2 How many times did Arsenal win the FA Cup in the 1980s?

3 Chris Waddle scored a wonder goal for which underdogs to knock out Everton in the 4th round in 1997?

4 For which team did Steve Archibald play in an FA Cup Final?

5 Which Chelsea player has scored in every round, including the Final?

6 In the 1980s, who scored for both sides in an FA Cup Final?

7 Webb and Wallace lined up together for which trophy-winning team?

8 Who were the winners in the Scottish FA Cup record score of 36–0?

9 And which team was on the receiving end of that thrashing?

10 Which club was Peter Beardsley with when he first won the FA Cup?

11 Which non-League side hit a last minute goal to draw at Coventry in 1997?

12 Which player has scored most FA Cup goals in total since 1945?

13 How many 1980s FA Cup Finals did Graeme Sharp take part in?

14 Which team won the Scottish FA Cup ten times then managed to go 100 years without winning it?

15 Who was the player-manager of the beaten 1994 London finalists?

16 Hednsford Town took the lead against which Premiership side in a 1997 4th Round tie?

17 Before the 1990s, who were the last team not in the top division to win the FA Cup?

18 Mark Bright has played in Finals for which two clubs?

19 Darren Anderton first played in a semi-final for which club?

20 Who was Wimbledon manager when they won in the 1980s?

Quiz 51 Pot Luck 26

Answers – see page 157

LEVEL 2

1 Martin Hicks set a League appearance record at which club?

2 How much to the nearest million did Kevin Keegan spend in transfer fees at Newcastle Utd?

3 For which club did Graeme Le Saux leave Chelsea?

4 Gary Megson followed Martin O'Neill as manager of which club?

5 Which player did manager Bruce Rioch buy in 1995 to set a new English club record?

6 In which decade did Aberdeen first win the Scottish FA Cup?

7 Who moved from Crystal Palace for £4.5 million in June 1995 to set a club record for a transfer fee received?

8 Which is the most southerly English League club?

9 Andy Cole was at which club when he made his international debut?

10 Which World Cup winner was born in Plaistow in 1943?

11 Who plays at home at Brunton Park?

12 Which Mel became boss of Bournemouth in August 1994

13 Which club did Mark Robins leave to join Norwich City?

14 In which decade was Brian Kidd born?

15 Which club has a fanzine called *Tripe'N'Trotters*?

16 What is Vinnie Jones' middle name?

17 Chris Price and Nigel Callaghan were in the same side at which club?

18 Which team were beaten 1–0 by Leeds Utd in the 1972 FA Cup Final?

19 What is the main colour of Rochdale's home shirts?

20 Which country did Billy Hamilton play for?

Pot Luck 25 (see Quiz 49)
1 Burnley. 2 Megson. 3 Reading. 4 Grimsby Town.
5 Newcastle Utd. 6 Millwall. 7 Manchester Utd. 8 Aston Villa. 9 Northern Ireland. 10 Vinnie Jones. 11 Mansfield.
12 Rangers. 13 Notts County. 14 1940s. 15 Hereford Utd.
16 Alexander. 17 Derby County. 18 Earle Barrett.
19 Black. 20 Windsor Park.

1 In what year was Paul Gascoigne born?

2 How much did he cost when he moved from Newcastle Utd to Tottenham Hotspur?

3 In 1991 Gazza hit a screaming FA Cup semi-final goal against which team?

4 Which Glenn was Newcastle Utd skipper when Gazza started out?

5 What is his star sign?

6 Gazza made his international debut against which country?

7 What was his last competitive match of 1991?

8 Which Scottish player's challenge did Gazza ride before scoring for England in Euro 96?

9 Who was the boss at Tottenham Hotspur when Gazza arrived?

10 To one each way, how many league goals did Gazza score in his 28 games for Rangers in 1995–96?

11 What shirt number did Gazza wear at Tottenham Hotspur?

12 What did Gazza manage to break in a training match at Lazio?

13 Who was on the receiving end of the wild FA Cup Final tackle in which Gazza hurt himself?

14 At which club was he rejected after a trial in 1982?

15 Which magazine bought exclusive photos of his 1996 wedding?

16 Who was Newcastle Utd manager when Gazza made his debut?

17 What was the highest position Tottenham Hotspur finished in the League in Gazza's time?

18 What colour are Lazio's home shirts?

19 Who made the original recording of "Fog On The Tyne"?

20 Which Newcastle Utd centre forward came off as Gazza came on as sub for his debut?

Answers

FA and SFA Cup (see Quiz 50)
1 Sheffield Wednesday. 2 Never. 3 Bradford City.
4 Tottenham Hotspur. 5 Peter Osgood. 6 Gary Mabbutt.
7 Manchester Utd. 8 Arbroath. 9 Bon Accord. 10 Liverpool.
11 Woking. 12 Ian Rush. 13 Four. 14 Queen's Park.
15 Glenn Hoddle. 16 Middlesbrough. 17 West Ham Utd –
1980. 18 Crystal Palace and Sheffield Weds. 19 Portsmouth.
20 Bobby Gould.

Quiz 53 Pot Luck 27

Answers – see page 163

1 Which Ian became boss of Bristol Rovers in May 1996?

2 The minimum size of a pitch is 50 yards by how many yards?

3 Which was Steve Bruce's first League club?

4 Glenn Roeder left as boss of which club in February 1996?

5 How many Premiership games did Bolton win in the first half of the 1995–96 season?

6 Albert Ironmonger set a League appearance record for which club?

7 Brian Little followed David Pleat as manager of which club?

8 Which club did Peter Withe join on leaving Nottingham Forest?

9 Which country did George Wood play for?

10 Which England boss was born in Dagenham in 1920?

11 Who plays at home at the Belle Vue Ground?

12 Which team were beaten 2–1 by Rangers in the 1993 Scottish FA Cup Final?

13 Which club did Clive Wilson leave to join Tottenham Hotspur?

14 In which decade was Gerson born?

15 Which club has a fanzine called *Sing When We're Fishing*?

16 Which top manager has a son called Jason who has been part of the Sky Sports' production teams?

17 David Speedie and Cyrille Regis were in the same side at which club?

18 Who moved from Leeds United for £3.5 million in June 1996 to set a club record for a transfer fee received?

19 What colour are Bradford City's home shorts?

20 Stuart McCall made his international debut while at which club?

Quiz 54 World Cup

Answers – see page 164

LEVEL 2

1 In which city was the 1990 England v West Germany semi-final?

2 Who was the Italian skipper in the 1994 World Cup Final?

3 Which country knocked Germany out of the 1994 tournament?

4 Who was the goalkeeper in the controversial "Hand Of God" goal?

5 Who were England's first choice fullbacks for Italia 90?

6 Which three teams were in the Republic of Ireland's group in USA in 1994?

7 Which country hosted the World Cup in the wake of a tragic earthquake?

8 Which 1994 World Cup winner later played for Middlesbrough?

9 England and the Republic of Ireland were in which Group in Italia 90?

10 Who became the first person to captain and manage World Cup winning sides?

11 Which country did Scotland beat in the 1990 finals?

12 Which Trevor came on as an English sub in the 1990 semi-final?

13 What was the score after 90 minutes in the 1994 Final?

14 Who was English boss in Spain in 1982?

15 Before the 90s when did Brazil last win the trophy?

16 Illgner was in goal for which World Cup winning country?

17 McGrath, McCarthy, Morris – who was the fourth defender with an initial M in the Republic of Ireland's great 1990 campaign?

18 Who did England beat in the 1990 quarter-final?

19 Bertoni scored a Final goal for which country?

20 In which year was the Final held at the Rose Bowl?

All Round Sportsmen (see Quiz 56)
1 Andy Goram. 2 Viv Richards. 3 Gary Lineker. 4 Geoff Hurst. 5 Denis Compton. 6 Scunthorpe. 7 Hampshire\ 8 Morris. 9 Bradford. 10 Gaelic football. 11 Neale. 12 Manchester Utd. 13 Charlton Athletic. 14 Balderstone. 15 Mick Channon. 16 West Ham Utd. 17 Goalkeeper. 18 Aston Villa. 19 Bayern Munich. 20 Bairstow.

Quiz 55 Pot Luck 28

Answers – see page 161

LEVEL 2

1 Who was the only Premiership player in 1996 to share his name with a calendar month?

2 In which year did George Best last play for Manchester Utd?

3 What was Clive Allen's first League club?

4 Which David was boss of Chelsea in 1993?

5 Which keeper set a League appearance record for Preston North End?

6 In which decade did Airdrieonians first win the Scottish FA Cup?

7 Who moved from Derby County to Liverpool in July 1991 to set a club record for a transfer fee received?

8 What was the half-time score in the Chelsea v Liverpool 1997 4th Round FA Cup game, which the home side won 4-2?

9 Tim Flowers was at which club when he made his international debut?

10 In which year was Eric Cantona born?

11 Who plays at home at the Underhill Stadium?

12 Howard Wilkinson followed Billy Bremner as manager of which club?

13 Which club did John Spencer leave to join Chelsea?

14 In which decade was Ken Bates born?

15 Which club has a fanzine called *The Red Card*?

16 What is Martin Keown's middle name?

17 Simon Garner and Mark Atkins were in the same side at which club?

18 Which team were beaten 2–0 by Newcastle Utd in the 1951 FA Cup Final?

19 What is the main colour of Rotherham's home shirts?

20 Which country did Joe Kinnear play for?

Answers

Pot Luck 27 (see Quiz 53)
1 Holloway. 2 100 yards. 3 Gillingham. 4 Watford. 5 Two. 6 Notts County. 7 Leicester City. 8 Newcastle Utd. 9 Scotland. 10 Alf Ramsey. 11 Doncaster Rovers. 12 Aberdeen. 13 QPR. 14 1940s. 15 Grimsby. 16 Alex Ferguson. 17 Coventry City. 18 Gary Speed. 19 Black. 20 Everton.

163

1 Which 1990s goalkeeper has played soccer and cricket for Scotland?

2 Which West Indian batsman played for Antigua in the 1978 World Cup qualifying games?

3 Which soccer striker played for the MCC against the Germans, scored a run and said, "It's always nice to score one against the Germans"?

4 Which member of England's 1966 World Cup winning side played first class cricket with Essex?

5 Which England batsman played in the 1950 FA Cup Final for Arsenal?

6 Which Football League club did Ian Botham play for?

7 Which county did England centre forward Ted Drake play cricket for?

8 Which Republic of Ireland defender Chris won cricket honours for Cornish schools?

9 England's cricket captain Brian Close played soccer in the 1950s for which team?

10 Apart from soccer, Kevin Moran was a star in which sport?

11 Which Phil skippered both Lincoln and Worcester CCC in the 1980s?

12 Which club did cricketer Arnold Sidebottom play for in the mid 1970s?

13 England's Mickey Stewart played for which Football League club?

14 Which Chris played for Leicestershire at cricket in the day and for Doncaster Rovers in an evening match on the same date?

15 Which Southampton and England striker turned to breeding and training racehorses?

16 In the 1960s, cricketer Jim Standen played for which London club?

17 Worcestershire CCC's Jimmy Cumbes played which position in soccer?

18 Which 1970s League Cup-winning side was Jimmy Cumbes in?

19 Boris Becker had soccer trials for which club?

20 Which David was a Yorkshire wicket keeper and Bradford City player?

1 What was Matt Busby's occupation before he became a footballer?

2 Which Brian became boss of Manchester City in 1993?

3 Which was Jamie Redknapp's first League club?

4 George Burley was player-manager of which Scottish side?

5 Ian Wood set a League appearance record for which club?

6 Steve Coppell followed Alan Ball as manager of which club?

7 Up to the 1990s how many times have Norwich won the FA Cup?

8 Which team does Angus Deayton support?

9 Which country did Eric Gates play for?

10 In which city was Andy Cole born?

11 Who plays at home at Sixfields Stadium?

12 Which team were beaten 2–1 by Rangers in the 1992 Scottish FA Cup Final?

13 Which club did Russell Hoult leave to join Derby County?

14 In which decade was Roy Keane born?

15 Which club has a fanzine called *Speke From The Harbour*?

16 Mark Robins was leading scorer for which Premiership side when they finished third?

17 Steve Clarke and Clive Wilson were in the same side at which club?

18 Who moved from Ipswich Town to Tottenham Hotspur in 1993 to set a club record for a transfer fee received?

19 What colour are Barnsley's home shorts?

20 Steve Hodge was at which club when he made his international debut?

1 Alex Ferguson managed which two Cup Winners' Cup winners?

2 Which Borussia Dortmund player scored a record 14 goals in 1965-66?

3 Who were the first English team to win the trophy in the 1990s?

4 Kevin Sheedy played in a trophy-winning team with which club?

5 Who were the first Soviet side to win the competition?

6 Which team beat Liverpool in a 1960s Final?

7 Rangers' victory in 1972 was marred by hooligan trouble. What was the Scottish team's penalty for this trouble?

8 Which Italian side were the first winners of the competition?

9 In what year was the first Final played?

10 Who was coach of the Spanish team that won the 1989 Final?

11 Who was in goal for that Final ?

12 What was strange about the West Ham Utd v Castilla 1980 game?

13 Who lost a Final to Valencia in 1980 in a penalty shoot out?

14 Paul Furlong scored three times in the 1994–95 competition for which club?

15 But for UEFA's ban, which two sides would have represented England in 1985-86?

16 And why would it have been two clubs in the 1985-86 season?

17 Which Welsh player, rejected by Barcelona, scored the winning goal against the Spanish side in the 1991 Final?

18 1860 Munich and Anderlecht have both played which English team in Finals?

19 West Ham Utd played their first Final in which stadium?

20 Which Russian side did Rangers beat in the 1972 Final?

LEVEL 2

1 How did keeper Alex Stepney dislocate his jaw in August 1975?

2 Kenny Dalglish's first home game as Newcastle Utd boss was against which team in the FA Cup?

3 What was Leighton James' first league club?

4 Which Graeme became boss of Oldham Athletic in November 1994?

5 Roy Sproson set a League appearance record for which club?

6 In which decade did Celtic first win the Scottish FA Cup?

7 Who moved from Grimsby Town to Blackburn Rovers for £1 million to set a club record for a transfer fee received?

8 ME I'D BLOWN conceals which team?

9 Mark Hateley was at which club when he made his international debut?

10 Which international manager was born in Middlesbrough in 1927?

11 Who plays at home at Springfield Park?

12 Brian Laws followed Alan Buckley as manager of which club?

13 Which club did Ian Bishop leave to join West Ham Utd?

14 In which decade was Brian Clough born?

15 Which club has a fanzine called *Eastern Eagle*?

16 What is Ian Wright's middle name?

17 Carl Leaburn and John Humphries were in the same side at which club?

18 Which team were beaten 2–1 by Aston Villa in the 1957 FA Cup Final?

19 What colour goes with white on Scarborough's home shirts?

20 Which country did Alan Hunter play for?

1 Whose two goals against Hungary clinched England's place in the 1982 World Cup?

2 Which club lost out in both the Scottish League and FA Cup in 1986?

3 Who was sacked to be replaced by Alex Ferguson at Manchester Utd?

4 How many games did England lose in the 1982 World Cup finals?

5 Who scored Tottenham Hotspur's penalty to beat QPR in an FA Cup Final replay?

6 Which Frenchman won the European Footballer of the Year award three consecutive times?

7 Which manager brought Ian Rush back to Liverpool from Juventus?

8 Which Southampton player became the youngest to score a First Division hat-trick v Arsenal on April 9, 1988?

9 How many teams competed in the 1982 World Cup in Spain?

10 Which famous former Liverpool manager died in 1981?

11 Which Portuguese side won the World Club Championship in 1987?

12 Which club paid £2 million to sign Paul Gascoigne?

13 Which club did Bryan Robson play for before joining Manchester Utd?

14 Which manager clashed with fans invading the pitch during a League Cup-tie?

15 Give the first names of the three Wallace brothers who played in the same Southampton team?

16 Which German club did Karl-Heinz Rummenigge play for?

17 Who scored the goal when Wimbledon won the FA Cup in 1988?

18 Which newspaper sponsored the Football League in the 1980s?

19 Which two players were sent off in the "spitting incident" in the 1988 European Championship?

20 Anderson and Sansom were in the same team at which club?

---

1   Which Russell became boss of Bristol City in 1993?

2   How old was Steve Coppell when he retired from playing?

3   Which was Julian Dicks' first League club?

4   The book *Macca Can* was about which player?

5   Who wanted a "loyalty" payment from Tottenham Hotspur after spending season 1992–93 with them before moving to Liverpool?

6   How is Jimmy Gardner better known?

7   Steve Coppell followed Alan Mullery as manager at which club?

8   Terry Phelan first played in an FA Cup Final for which team?

9   Which country did Dave Clements play for?

10   Which future England player was born in Rotherham in 1963?

11   Who plays at home at Love Street?

12   Which team were beaten 4–3 by Motherwell in the 1991 Scottish FA Cup Final?

13   Which club did Paul Rideout leave to join Everton?

14   In which decade was Darren Anderton born?

15   Which club has a fanzine called *Bert Trautmann's Helmet*?

16   What is Dean Holdsworth's middle name?

17   Steve Vickers and Neil Cox were in the same side at which club?

18   Who moved from Southend for £2 million in June 1993 to set a club record for a transfer fee received?

19   What colour are Southampton's home shorts?

20   Terry Fenwick was at which club when he made his international debut?

Answers

Pot Luck 32   (see Quiz 63)
1 Manchester Utd. 2 Terry Venables. 3 West Ham Utd.
4 Leeds Utd. 5 Everton. 6 1890s. 7 Kevin Francis. 8 Sam Bartram. 9 Ipswich Town. 10 Paul Rideout. 11 PSV Eindhoven. 12 Kamara. 13 Crewe Alexandra. 14 1930s.
15 Nottingham Forest. 16 Ron Greenwood. 17 Manchester Utd. 18 Luton Town. 19 Blue and white. 20 Scotland.

1 Miller and Roberts formed a partnership at which London club?

2 Which fullback captained England in the World Cup in Spain?

3 Shaun Teale went to which club after leaving Villa?

4 Which 17-year-old made his debut at left-back for AC Milan in 1985 and was holding the position ten years later?

5 Which club did England's Bob Crompton play for?

6 In a 1994 England game the goalkeeper and two centre halves all came from which club?

7 Whose clubs read: Leeds Utd, Wimbledon, Manchester City, Chelsea, Everton?

8 Which club did Phil Neal play for before he joined Liverpool?

9 To a year each way, when did Stuart Pearce first play for England?

10 Did iron man Tommy Smith ever play for England?

11 Butterworth and Culverhouse were in the same team at which club?

12 Which Scottish side did Neil Pointon move to?

13 Gary Pallister went on loan to which north-east club in his Middlesbrough days?

14 Which left-back was displaced by Graeme Le Saux at Blackburn Rovers?

15 George Cohen was with which club when he played for England?

16 Which club did Booth and Caton play for?

17 Which England full-back Roger died in the Munich air disaster?

18 Which ex-Blackburn Rovers defender faced his old team in the 1994 Charity Shield?

19 Which country did Paul Breitner play for?

20 Which Kevin played for Norwich, Manchester City and Southampton?

Quiz 63 Pot Luck 32

Answers – see page 169

1 Ray Wilkins first played in an FA Cup Final for which team?

2 Which Barcelona manager bought Mark Hughes?

3 What was Mervyn Day's first League club?

4 Eddie Gray followed Allan Clarke as manager at which club?

5 What is the middle name of ex-Liverpool ace Mark Walters?

6 In which decade did Notts County first win the FA Cup?

7 Who moved from Stockport County to Birmingham City for £800,000 in January 1995 to set a club record for a transfer fee received?

8 With 583 games, which goalkeeper established Charlton's League appearance record?

9 In the 1970s, David Johnson was at which club when he made his international debut?

10 In the 1994–95 FA Cup winning season, who was Everton's top League scorer?

11 Which former European Cup-winners play at home at the Philips Stadium?

12 Which Chris became boss of Bradford City in November 1995?

13 Which club did Ashley Ward leave to join Norwich City?

14 In which decade was Gordon Banks born?

15 Which club has a fanzine called *The Tricky Tree*?

16 Which England manager gave Bryan Robson his first cap?

17 Paul Parker and Lee Sharpe were in the same side at which club?

18 Which team was beaten 2–1 by Nottingham Forest in the 1959 FA Cup Final?

19 What are the two colours of Reading's home shirts?

20 In the 1930s, which country did HM Wales play for?

Pot Luck 31 (see Quiz 61)
1 Osman. 2 28. 3 Birmingham City. 4 Steve McMahon.
5 Neil Ruddock. 6 "Five Bellies". 7 Crystal Palace.
8 Wimbledon. 9 Northern Ireland. 10 David Seaman.
11 St Mirren. 12 Dundee Utd. 13 Rangers. 14 1970s.
15 Manchester City. 16 Christopher. 17 Middlesbrough.
18 Stan Collymore. 19 Black. 20 QPR.

Quiz 64 International Scene

LEVEL 2

1 Which country finished fourth in the 1994 World Cup?

2 Which country did Nico Claesen play for?

3 Who scored England's only goal in Euro 92?

4 In which country was Richard Gough born?

5 In which stadium was the 1986 World Cup Final played?

6 Which Dutchman hit a Euro 88 hat-trick against England?

7 Who set a record by playing 96 times for Belgium?

8 How old was Dino Zoff when he was in Italy's World Cup-winning side?

9 Whose World Cup corner flag dance started the craze for dance routine celebrations?

10 Which country did Oscar Ruggeri play for?

11 Which Scot scored in five successive World Cup qualifiers between 1988 and 1989?

12 Which player, who died in 1990, was awarded the Order of Lenin?

13 Which Dutch outfield player was 37 when Holland won Euro 88?

14 Who, with 54 goals, was second only to Pele as a Brazilan scorer?

15 Which Australian manager got off to a winning start in January 1997?

16 Which French player went head to head with Stuart Pearce in Euro 92?

17 How old was Diego Maradona when he first played for Argentina?

18 Who was the first Croatian international to play in the English League?

19 Which Gordon scored Scotland's only World Cup goal in Mexico?

20 Which goalkeeper is Sweden's most capped player?

Defenders (see Quiz 62)

Answers

Defenders (see Quiz 62) 1 Tottenham Hotspur. 2 Mick Mills. 3 Tranmere Rovers. 4 Paolo Maldini. 5 Blackburn Rovers. 6 Arsenal (Seamen, Adams, Bould) 7 Terry Phelan. 8 Northampton. 9 1987. 10 Yes (Once in 1971). 11 Norwich City. 12 Hearts. 13 Darlington. 14 Alan Wright. 15 Fulham. 16 Manchester City. 17 Byrne. 18 David May. 19 West Germany. 20 Bond.

Quiz 65 Pot Luck 33

Answers – see page 175

1 Gary Gillespie first played in an FA Cup Final for which team?

2 Which forename links Hibbitt and Swain, both sacked as managers on the same day in 1994 ?

3 Which was Paul Bracewell's first League club?

4 Which Dave became boss of Brentford in May 1993?

5 Which team were once known as Eastville Rovers?

6 Which player's book *A Double Life* appeared in 1990?

7 George Curtis followed Don Mackay as manager at which club?

8 Which club did Steve Sedgley join on leaving Tottenham Hotspur?

9 Which country did Mark Chamberlain play for?

10 Which England skipper was born in Chester-le-Street in 1957?

11 Which Scottish side plays at home at the Almondvale Stadium?

12 Which team were beaten 1–0 by Celtic in the 1989 Scottish FA Cup Final?

13 Which club did Kevin Richardson leave to join Arsenal?

14 In which decade was Emlyn Hughes born?

15 Which club has a fanzine called *Beyond The Boundary*?

16 A 1994 League Cup defeat by Notts County was the sign for which Tottenham Hotspur boss that his days were numbered?

17 Which club had Venison and Fox on the same team?

18 Who moved from Sheffield Wednesday to Blackburn Rovers in 1993 to set a club record for a transfer fee received?

19 What colour are Sheffield Utd's home shorts?

20 Trevor Francis was at which club when he made his international debut?

Pot Luck 34 (see Quiz 67)
Answers

1 Wolves. 2 Nigeria. 3 Wolves. 4 Fourth. 5 Graeme Le Saux. 6 1930s. 7 Marco Gabbiadini. 8 Carlisle United. 9 Everton. 10 Lou Macari. 11 Everton. 12 Rioch. 13 Derby County. 14 1930s. 15 Plymouth Argyle. 16 York City. 17 Manchester City. 18 Liverpool. 19 Blue. 20 The Republic of Ireland.

1 Which team did Kenny support as a boy?

2 How many Scottish caps did Dalglish win?

3 What is the first name of Mrs Dalglish?

4 In which year did Kenny win his first Scottish Championship medal?

5 Which Liverpool manager signed Kenny?

6 How many times did Kenny win the championship for Liverpool when he was the boss?

7 Which manager gave Kenny his first Scottish cap?

8 What is Kenny's starsign?

9 Who were the opponents on the day that Dalglish's Blackburn Rovers won the Premiership?

10 Kenny replaced Kevin Keegan at Liverpool. Which transfer cost most?

11 Who did Kenny replace as skipper of Celtic?

12 Kenny scored the only goal in the 1978 European Cup Final against which side?

13 Which managers picked Kenny's teams in his 1986 testimonial?

14 Who was Kenny's Liverpool skipper for the 1986 double-winning side?

15 How many World Cup final tournaments did Kenny play in?

16 Who advised Kenny, "If you are going to get kicked, get kicked in the box, it's worth it in there"?

17 How old was Kenny when he first played for Celtic?

18 Who was acting manager at Blackburn Rovers when Kenny arrived?

19 What decoration was Kenny awarded in February 1985?

20 Which former Liverpool teammate was assistant manager at Newcastle Utd when Kenny arrived?

Answers

Merseysiders (see Quiz 68)
1 Howard Kendall (during his second spell). 2 60. 3 Real Sociedad. 4 Phil Neal. 5 Brian Labone. 6 Andrei Kanchelskis. 7 Gary Lineker. 8 Bell. 9 Kenny Dalglish. 10 Bournemouth. 11 Bobby Mimms. 12 1991. 13 Everton in 1890-91, before Liverpool were formed. 14 Blackburn Rovers. 15 Harry Catterick. 16 Joe Fagan. 17 Kenny Dalglish. 18 Oldham Athletic. 19 European Cup. 20 John Wark.

1 Graham Turner followed Brian Little as manager at which club in October 1986?

2 Which country did John Chiedozie play for?

3 Which was Tim Flowers' first League club?

4 From 1965 to 1974 what was the lowest position that Leeds Utd finished in the First Division?

5 Which future England international was born in October 1968 in Jersey?

6 In which decade did Portsmouth first win the FA Cup?

7 Who moved from Sunderland to Crystal Palace for £1.5 million in 1991 to set a club record for a transfer fee received?

8 Alan Ross set a league record for appearances at which club?

9 Paul Bracewell was at which club when he made his international debut?

10 Which manager, still living in England, was dismissed by Celtic in June 1994?

11 Pat Van Den Hauwe first played in an FA Cup Final for which team?

12 Which Bruce became boss of Millwall in 1992?

13 Which club did Paul Kitson leave to join Newcastle Utd?

14 In which decade was Johnny Haynes born?

15 Which club has a fanzine called *Rub of the Greens*?

16 Alphabetically, which is the last English League team?

17 Paul Walsh and Keith Curle were in the same side at which club?

18 Which team were beaten 2–1 by Arsenal in the 1971 FA Cup Final?

19 What is the main colour of Shrewsbury's home shirts?

20 Which country did Mark Lawrenson play for?

1 Who was manager of Everton before Mike Walker?

2 How many League goals did Dixie Dean score in his record-breaking 1927–28 season?

3 From which club did John Aldridge join Tranmere Rovers?

4 Who was Bob Paisley's first buy for Liverpool?

5 Which Everton centre-back played in the 1970 World Cup in Mexico?

6 Which player created Everton's record transfer fee paid in 1995?

7 Which Everton player won the Footballer of the Year award in 1986?

8 Which 'Bunny' scored most goals in a season for Tranmere Rovers?

9 Which ex-Liverpool player holds Scotland's most capped record?

10 From which club did Liverpool sign Jamie Redknapp?

11 Who was in goal for Everton in the 1986 FA Cup Final?

12 Which year did Tranmere Rovers win the play-off final to gain promotion to Division Two?

13 Who won the League championship first – Liverpool or Everton?

14 Before joining Everton, where was Howard Kendall player/manager?

15 Which Everton manager captured the League championship in 1963?

16 Who took over at Liverpool when Bob Paisley retired in 1983?

17 Who hit Liverpool's last League goal in the 1985–86 double season?

18 Which club was Mike Milligan bought from and sold back to?

19 Kevin Keegan's last game for Liverpool was in which competition?

20 Which Scottish midfielder was Liverpool's top league scorer in 1984–85?

Quiz 69 Pot Luck 35

1 Whose book was called *Man On The Run*?

2 Hales, Flanagan and Peacock have all scored goals for which club?

3 Which was David Kelly's first League club?

4 Which Howard became boss of Notts County in 1995?

5 How many goals did Peter Osgood score for England?

6 Which player describing his upbringing said, "There's only one word to describe Raploch, and that's hard"?

7 Ian Porterfield followed Bobby Campbell as manager at which club?

8 Steve Spriggs set an appearance record at which club?

9 Which country did Colin Viljoen play for?

10 Veteran Graham Rix appeared as a substitute in the Premiership for which club in 1995?

11 Scotsman Andy Gray first played in an FA Cup Final for which team?

12 Which team were beaten 3–0 by Aberdeen in the 1986 Scottish FA Cup Final?

13 Which club did David Rocastle leave to join Manchester City?

14 In which decade was Gary Mabbutt born?

15 Which club has a fanzine called *Beat About The Bush*?

16 In what position does Swindon Town's Fraser Digby play?

17 Which club had Lyttle and Chettle in the same side?

18 Who moved from Sheffield Utd to Leeds Utd for £2,700,000 in 1993 to set a club record for a transfer fee received?

19 What colour goes with navy on Torquay's home shirts?

20 Alan Hudson was at which club when he made his international debut?

Quiz 70 League Cup

Answers – see page 180

LEVEL 2

1 Which England international scored in both the FA and Coca-Cola Cup Finals of 1993?

2 To two years each way, when did the first Final go to extra time?

3 Which TV expert scored a Final winner for Wolves?

4 Which manager dealt with four fans who invaded the pitch in a League Cup match at the City Ground in 1989?

5 Which Charlie scored the winner against Liverpool in the 1987 Final?

6 Which team finally landed the trophy in 1985 in their third Wembley Final?

7 What was the added bonus for Stoke City in the 1972 success?

8 In 1983, who became the youngest ever player to score a League Cup Final goal at Wembley?

9 Which player scored his 100th Manchester Utd goal in the 1992 Final?

10 Which London side became the first club to win the trophy twice?

11 Who scored two of Swindon Town's goals to defeat Arsenal in 1969?

12 Which relegated London team reached the semi-finals in 1993?

13 Steve Bruce first played in a Final for which club?

14 Which year was the first-ever all Merseyside Final?

15 Name the grounds of the first two winners of the League Cup?

16 Which club won the trophy four times during the 1980s?

17 Who was injured by his own skipper after the Final in 1993?

18 Which manager was the first to win the trophy as the Coca-Cola Cup?

19 In which year was the Final first played at Wembley?

20 Who beat West Ham Utd 6–1 on their plastic pitch in a League Cup semi-final match in 1990?

Answers

Managers (see Quiz 72)
1 Osman. 2 Arsenal. 3 Coventry City. 4 Crystal Palace.
5 Chelsea. 6 Wilf McGuinness. 7 David Pleat. 8 62.
9 Huddersfield & Arsenal. 10 Peter Withe. 11 Kenny Dalglish.
12 Port Vale. 13 Crystal Palace. 14 Haslam. 15 Bill
Nicholson. 16 Malcolm Crosby. 17 Derby County. 18 Bob
Paisley. 19 Colchester United. 20 Billy McNeill.

178

LEVEL 2

1 Andy Thorn first played in an FA Cup Final for which team?

2 Which player born in Oldham in 1966 set a world record in transfer fees?

3 What was Simon Barker's first League club?

4 Which John became boss of Norwich City in 1994?

5 In 1994 which player was transferred to Blackburn for £5.5 million?

6 In which decade did Dunfermline first win the Scottish FA Cup?

7 Who moved from Swindon Town for £1,300,000 in March 1995 to set a club record for a transfer fee received?

8 Phil Dwyer set a League appearance record at which club?

9 Paul Goddard was at which club when he made his international debut?

10 Dario Gradi became manager for which club in 1983?

11 Which Scottish team plays at home at Central Park?

12 Keith Burkinshaw followed Ossie Ardiles as manager at which club?

13 Which club did Nigel Spackman leave to join Chelsea for the second time?

14 In which decade was Eusebio born?

15 Which club has a fanzine called *The Flashing Blade*?

16 Which country do the club Penarol come from?

17 Alan Smith and Kevin Campbell were in the same side at which club?

18 Which team were beaten 3–2 by WBA in the 1954 FA Cup Final?

19 What colour are Wolves' home shorts?

20 Which country did Roy Vernon play for?

1 Which Russell has been boss of Bristol City and Cardiff City?

2 Don Howe was manager of which team in 1984?

3 Bobby Gould has twice been manager of which club?

4 At which club could fans shout in 1980, "There's only one Ernie Walley"?

5 Which London club did Geoff Hurst manage?

6 Who followed Matt Busby at Manchester Utd?

7 Who was Luton's boss when they went out of the top flight in 1992?

8 How old was Joe Fagan when he became Liverpool manager?

9 With which two sides did Herbert Chapman win the Championship?

10 Who was Wimbledon boss before Joe Kinnear?

11 Who was the first player/manager to win the championship?

12 John Rudge has spent more than ten years as boss of which club?

13 In 1984 Dave Bassett left Wimbledon, but returned after only a few days spent at which club?

14 Which Harry was Luton manager from 1972–78?

15 Who won the Championship as a player and a manager with Tottenham Hotspur?

16 Who was caretaker manager of Sunderland when he took them to the 1992 FA Cup Final?

17 Brian Clough won his first championship as a manager at which club?

18 Who was manager of the year in 1976, 1977, 1979, 1980, 1982 and 1983?

19 Which was Mike Walker's first club as a manager?

20 Who followed David Hay as Celtic manager?

Quiz 73 Pot Luck 37

Answers – see page 183

LEVEL 2 ⚽ ⚽

1 Tony Barton followed Ron Saunders as boss of which club?

2 In which Northumberland village was Bobby Charlton born?

3 Which was Ray Clemence's first League club?

4 Which 1980's and 1990's striker hit 111 Everton League goals?

5 Ian Pearce first played in an FA Charity Shield for which club?

6 Which George became boss of Ipswich Town in December 1994?

7 Jesper Olsen won an FA Cup winners' medal with which club?

8 Which club did Mark Kennedy join on leaving Millwall?

9 Which country did Gerry Peyton play for?

10 Which team play at home in front of the Cobbold Stand?

11 Which ex-England skipper died in September 1994?

12 Which team were beaten 2–0 by Tottenham Hotspur in the 1961 FA Cup Final?

13 In 1996, Kevin Keegan was incensed by Alex Ferguson's comments concerning which opposing team?

14 In which decade was Kenny Dalglish born?

15 Which club has a fanzine called *Red Stripe*?

16 What is the first name of Bolton's De Freitas?

17 Cowan and Bullock were in the same side at which club?

18 Who moved from Leicester City to Aston Villa in July 1995 to set a club record for a transfer fee received?

19 What colour are Watford's home shorts?

20 Andy Townsend was at which club when he made his international debut?

Answers

Pot Luck 38 (see Quiz 75)
1 1–1. 2 Oldham Athletic. 3 Swindon Town. 4 1930.
5 Julian. 6 1890s. 7 Alan Shearer. 8 Bradford City.
9 Rangers. 10 Terry Venables. 11 Hull City. 12 Harford.
13 Poland. 14 1950s. 15 Stoke City. 16 Nigel Clough.
17 Sheffield Wednesday. 18 Everton. 19 White. 20 Northern Ireland.

181

LEVEL 2

1 Which Dutch team were the first to win a major European trophy?

2 As a player which club did Johan Cruyff move to when he left Ajax?

3 With 83 games who set an appearance record for Holland?

4 In which city was Ruud Gullit born?

5 Who was the top scorer in Euro 88?

6 Who were Dutch champions in 1994, 1995 and 1996?

7 Who was the Dutch coach for Euro 88?

8 Which English club did Dennis Bergkamp support as a child?

9 Which Dutch player scored against England in Euro 96?

10 Ruud Gullit became the world's most expensive player when he moved from which club to AC Milan in 1987?

11 Which English manager won two consecutive titles with PSV Eindhoven in the 1990s?

12 Who was top scorer for the Dutch in both 1974 and 1978 World Cups?

13 What are the colours of Ajax?

14 At which club did Ronald Koeman start his League career?

15 Who was the first Dutch skipper to lift a major international trophy for his country?

16 Which team knocked Holland out of the 1994 World Cup?

17 Which Dutch club did the Brazilian Romario play for?

18 In which city is the club Feyenoord?

19 Which was the first World Cup tournament that Holland qualified for after the Second World War?

20 Gullit, Van Basten and Rijkaard lined up at which Italian club?

Answers

Red Card (see Quiz 76)
1 Gianfranco Zola. 2 Chelsea. 3 Johnston. 4 Peter Reid.
5 Trevor Hockey. 6 Andrei Kanchelskis. 7 Stefan Schwartz.
8 Rangers. 9 Dion Dublin. 10 Stimac. 11 Peter Schmeichel.
12 Blackburn Rovers. 13 Sweden. 14 Kidd. 15 Paul
Gascoigne. 16 Hristo Stoichkov. 17 Vinnie Jones. 18 Lee
Chapman. 19 Frank McAvennie. 20 Eric Cantona.

Quiz 75 Pot Luck 38

LEVEL 2

1 What was the 90-minute score in the 1993 Manchester Utd v Liverpool Charity Shield game?

2 Joe Royle followed Jimmy Frizzell as boss of which club?

3 Which was Jimmy Quinn's first League club?

4 When did the USA first take part in the World Cup?

5 What is the first name of Joachim of Leicester City and Aston Villa?

6 In which decade did Hearts first win the Scottish FA Cup?

7 Who moved from Southampton for £3,300,000 to set a club record for a transfer fee received?

8 Cec Podd set an appearance record at which club?

9 Jim Baxter was at which club when he made his international debut?

10 Which England manager was born in London on 6th January, 1943?

11 Which club has a ground situated in Boothferry Road?

12 Which Ray became boss of Wimbledon in 1990?

13 Which country does Dariusz Kubicki come from?

14 In which decade was Liam Brady born?

15 Which club has a fanzine called *The Victoria Voice*?

16 Who was signed by Manchester City from Liverpool in January 1996?

17 Petrescu and Pembridge were in the same side at which club?

18 Which team was beaten 3–1 by Liverpool in the 1986 FA Cup Final?

19 What is the main colour of Tranmere Rovers' home shirts?

20 Which country did Lawrie Sanchez play for?

1 Which Italian got an early bath against Nigeria in the 1994 World Cup?

2 Darren Peacock was sent off as which London club knocked Newcastle Utd out of the 1995–96 FA Cup?

3 Which Scottish winger Willie of the 1960s to the 1980s was sent off 15 times?

4 Which Everton player was fouled when Kevin Moran got his 1985 FA Cup Final marching orders?

5 Who was the first Welsh player to be sent off in an international?

6 Which Manchester Utd player was sent off in the 1994 League Cup Final?

7 Who, ex-Arsenal, saw red in a Sweden v Romania World Cup quarter-final?

8 Woods and Butcher were at which club when they were off in the same game?

9 In 1996–97 which Coventry City player was dismissed in successive League games?

10 Which Igor was the only Croatian to see red in Euro 96?

11 Which keeper was sent off in the quarter finals of the 1994 FA Cup?

12 At which club was Paul Warhurst sent off in a European Cup game?

13 Jonas Thern was playing for which country when he got sent off in a 1994 World Cup semi-final?

14 Which Brian of Everton got an early bath in a 1980 FA Cup semi-final?

15 Which Rangers player saw red in the 1996 European Cup game against Borussia Dortmund in Germany?

16 Which Bulgarian striker was banned for life after a brawl in 1985 to be reinstated six months later?

17 Which Wimbledon player walked in 1995 after tangling with Ruud Gullit?

18 Which striker was sent off on his on-loan return to Leeds Utd in 1996?

19 Which ex-West Ham player at Celtic was sent off with Butcher and Woods?

20 Which Manchester Utd player got a red card after the final whistle in 1993?

1 Which team does Alison Moyet support?

2 Which Brian became boss of Wrexham in November 1989?

3 Which was Gary Mabbutt's first League club?

4 Which club play at the Steaua Stadium?

5 What job did Neville Southall do before becoming a footballer?

6 John Bond followed Malcolm Allison as boss of which club?

7 In which decade did Wolves first win the FA Cup?

8 Earl Barrett first played in an FA Charity Shield for which club?

9 Which country did Tony Grealish play for?

10 Which great Scottish manager was born in Burnbank in October, 1923?

11 Which club have a ground with the Bob Lord stand?

12 Which team was beaten 4–1 after extra time by Aberdeen in the 1982 Scottish FA Cup Final?

13 Which club did Gary Croft leave to join Blackburn Rovers?

14 In which decade was Ivor Allchurch born?

15 Which club has a fanzine called *A Love Supreme*?

16 What is the first name name of striker De Souza, a Wycombe goal grabber in 1996?

17 Wallace and Whelan were in the same attack at which club?

18 Who moved from WBA for £1,500,000 in 1981 to set an English record for a transfer fee received?

19 What colour are West Ham Utd's home shorts?

20 Phil Babb was at which club when he made his international debut?

Answers

Pot Luck 40 (see Quiz 79)
1 Walter Smith. 2 Arsenal. 3 Portsmouth. 4 0–0 (after extra time). 5 Leeds Utd. 6 1880s. 7 Mark Stein. 8 Plymouth Argyle. 9 Birmingham City. 10 Socrates. 11 Carlisle United. 12 Nicholl. 13 South Africa. 14 1940s. 15 Tottenham Hotspur. 16 Edinburgh. 17 Stoke City. 18 Arsenal. 19 White. 20 Wales.

1 Where was Kevin born?

2 Which manager took Keegan to Liverpool?

3 Which was Keegan's first club?

4 What is Kevin Keegan's actual first name?

5 As Newcastle United manager, which former team-mate did Keegan sign as a player?

6 Which Welshman was Kevin's main Liverpool strike partner?

7 Kevin's first three internationals were all against which country?

8 Which manager brought him to England after playing in Germany?

9 To one each way, in which year did Kevin first skipper England?

10 Against which team did Kevin hit two goals in an FA Cup Final?

11 In which country did Keegan briefly take part in a World Cup tournament?

12 At which club did Kevin have Manfred Kaltz as a team-mate?

13 To three each way, how many times did Kevin play for England?

14 Which German player had the task of trying to mark Kevin in Liverpool's epic triumph in the 1977 European Cup Final?

15 Which ex-Liverpool defender did Kevin get to advise Newcastle United about their defence?

16 What was the name of his chart single of the 1970s?

17 To three each way, how many goals did Kevin get for England?

18 At which club did Kevin have Imre Varadi as a strike partner?

19 Which English club did Kevin play against in a European Cup Final?

20 Keegan's last game as Newcastle United manager was an FA Cup tie against which London club?

1 Which manager won his first Scottish Championship after being in charge of the team for only four games?

2 JVC have been long running sponsors of which English club?

3 What was Darren Anderton's first League club?

4 What was the score in the 1991 Arsenal v Tottenham Hotspur FA Charity Shield?

5 Howard Wilkinson followed Billy Bremner as boss of which club?

6 In which decade did Preston North End first win the FA Cup?

7 Who moved from Stoke City for £1,500,00 to Chelsea to set a club record for a transfer fee received?

8 Which club did Peter Shilton join as player/manager in 1992?

9 Trevor Francis was at which club when he made his international debut?

10 Who was captain of Brazil for the 1982 and 1986 World Cups?

11 Which club's ground has the Warwick Road End?

12 Which Chris became boss of Walsall in September 1994?

13 Which country does Phil Masinga come from?

14 In which decade was George Best born?

15 Which club has a fanzine called *Cock A Doodle Do*?

16 In which city was Graeme Souness born?

17 Sheron and Cranson were in the same side at which club?

18 Which team was beaten 1–0 by West Ham United in the 1980 FA Cup Final?

19 What colour goes with blue on Wigan's shirts?

20 Which country did Mark Aizlewood play for?

Pot Luck 39 (see Quiz 77)
1 Southend Utd. 2 Flynn. 3 Bristol Rovers. 4 Steaua Bucharest. 5 Dustman. 6 Manchester City. 7 1890s.
8 Everton. 9 The Republic of Ireland. 10 Jock Stein.
11 Burnley. 12 Rangers. 13 Grimsby Town. 14 1920s.
15 Sunderland. 16 Manuel. 17 Leeds Utd. 18 Bryan Robson. 19 White. 20 Coventry City.

1 Which team won the FA Cup and then found their single at No. 1?

2 How many years of hurt were there in "Three Lions"?

3 Which footballer was "sitting in a sleazy snack bar, sucking sickly sausage rolls"?

4 Which football song was No. 1 for three weeks in May 1970?

5 Who sang with the Scotland squad on "Ole, Ola (Mulher Brasileira)"?

6 In which year did the originally titled "Leeds United" by Leeds United hit the charts?

7 Which Rodgers and Hammerstein song became the Anfield anthem?

8 Which squad charted in 1982 with "We Have A Dream"?

9 What was the England squad's song for Spain in 1982 called?

10 "Ferry Across The Mersey" was a charity song following which soccer disaster?

11 The Bradford City fire disaster led to a June 1985 No. 1 for various performers under which name?

12 Who had the original 1960s hit with the song?

13 Who was Cyril, the subject of "Nice One Cyril"?

14 Which Liverpool record reached No. 3 in the charts in 1988?

15 What was the England squad's song for the 1986 World Cup?

16 Which production team handled the charity version of "Ferry Across The Mersey"?

17 Which team recorded with Paper Lace?

18 "Pure" was the first hit for which soccer connected group?

19 Who recorded the song that topped the charts for 3 weeks in May 1970?

20 Which group helped Manchester Utd for their 1994 chart success?

---

1 In which decade did Wimbledon first win the FA Cup?

2 Which Jan became boss of Swansea in February 1996?

3 With which club did Neil Ruddock make his League debut?

4 Which club's ground is by the River Darwen?

5 What was the Gazza rap record called?

6 Eddie McGoldrick first played in an FA Charity Shield for which club?

7 Arthur Cox followed Roy McFarland as boss of which club in 1984?

8 Which club did Tony Mowbray join on leaving Celtic?

9 Which country did Peter Nicholas play for?

10 Which Southampton keeper came back late from international duty in December 1995?

11 Which club's ground includes the Doug Ellis Stand?

12 Which team were beaten 2–1 by Chelsea in the 1970 FA Cup Final replay?

13 Dani came from Sporting Lisbon on loan to which London club?

14 In which decade was Jim Baxter born?

15 Which club has a fanzine called *Blazing Saddlers*?

16 At which club did Colin Griffin set a League appearance record?

17 In 1995–96 Ball and Hall were in the same side at which club?

18 Who moved from Leyton Orient to Notts County for £600,00 in 1981 to set a club record for a transfer fee received?

19 What colour are Charlton's home socks?

20 Ricky Hill was at which club when he made his international debut?

Quiz 82 Germany

Answers – see page 192

LEVEL 2

1 Who is the most capped German player?

2 What colour are the socks of the German team?

3 Who was in charge of the Euro 96 team?

4 Where in Germany was Jürgen Klinsmann born?

5 Which Hamburg player was European Footballer of the Year in 1978 and 1979?

6 Who was West German manager from 1963–78?

7 In which decade did the Germans first win the World Cup?

8 In 1996 how many teams were there in the German Bundesliga?

9 Which club did Uwe Seeler play for?

10 Who was Germany's top scorer in Euro 96 and with how many goals?

11 Who was skipper of the 1990 World Cup-winning team?

12 Which club were German champions in 1995–96?

13 What two colours are in Hamburg's strip?

14 Who was the Tottenham Hotspur boss when Klinsmann left the club?

15 Which group were the Germans in at the start of Euro 96?

16 Which city do the club team with 1860 in their name come from?

17 To three either way, how many goals did Gerd Müller score for Germany?

18 Which striker had played for Magdeburg, Dynamo Dresden and Nuremberg before coming to play in England?

19 Who took the final spot kick in the England v Germany Euro 96 game?

20 Which German club did England striker Tony Woodcock play for?

Answers

UEFA Cup (see Quiz 84)
1 Parma & Juventus. 2 Newcastle Utd. 3 Anderlecht.
4 Ipswich Town. 5 Ajax. 6 Tottenham Hotspur. 7 Watford.
8 Espanol. 9 Bordeaux. 10 Hungary. 11 1970s. 12 Napoli.
13 1980s. 14 Manchester Utd. 15 Newcastle Utd.
16 Luxembourg. 17 IFK Gothenburg. 18 England.
19 AZ (Alkmaar). 20 Dundee Utd.

Quiz 83 Pot Luck 42

Answers – see page 189

LEVEL 2

1 Who plays at the Royal Dublin Society Showground?

2 Who wrote *Everton Winter Mexican Summer: A Football Diary*?

3 What was Robbie Earle's first League club?

4 Terry Venables followed Tommy Docherty's second term as boss of which club?

5 Which team lost 2–0 to Manchester Utd in the 1994 FA Charity Shield?

6 In which decade did Sheffield Utd first win the FA Cup?

7 Ian Nolan's move to Sheffield Wednesday in August 1994 set a club record for a transfer fee received at which club?

8 To a year each way, when did Neville Southall make his Everton League debut?

9 David Batty was at which club when he made his international debut?

10 At which club did George Curtis set a League appearance record that stood until the mid-90s?

11 Which club have a ground that contains The Milburn Stand?

12 Which Kenny became boss of Watford in May 1994

13 Which country does Frank Yallop come from?

14 In which decade was Billy Bingham born?

15 Which club has a fanzine called *Watch The Bluebirds Fly*?

16 What is the first name of Reading's long-serving Gilkes?

17 Marshall and Claridge were in the same side at which club?

18 Which team were beaten 3–2 by Everton in the 1966 FA Cup Final?

19 What colour are Fulham's home shorts?

20 Which country did Clayton Blackmore play for?

Answers

Pot Luck 41 (see Quiz 81)
1 1980s. 2 Molby. 3 Tottenham Hotspur. 4 Blackburn Rovers. 5 'Geordie Boys'. 6 Arsenal. 7 Derby County. 8 Ipswich Town. 9 Wales. 10 Bruce Grobbelaar. 11 Aston Villa. 12 Leeds Utd. 13 West Ham Utd. 14 1930s. 15 Walsall. 16 Shrewsbury Town. 17 Sunderland. 18 John Chiedozie. 19 Red. 20 Luton Town.

Quiz 84 UEFA Cup

Answers – see page 190

LEVEL 2

1 Which two Italian sides contested the Final in 1995?

2 To which English team did Ujpest Dozsu lose to in the Final?

3 Which Belgian side lost to a London club in the 1970 Final?

4 Trevor Whymark scored four goals in a Euro game for which club?

5 Which Dutch team beat Red Boys a record 14 – 0 in 1984?

6 Who won the trophy the first time it was decided on penalties?

7 Wilf Rostron scored in the competition for which club?

8 Which Spanish side lost the 1988 Final after being three up from the first leg?

9 In 1996, which team became the second from France to reach a Final?

10 Which country did Ujpest Dozsa represent?

11 In which decade did Liverpool win the trophy for the first time?

12 Which winners did Diego Maradona play for?

13 In which decade did Real Madrid win the trophy in successive seasons?

14 Alan Brazil has scored UEFA Cup goals for Ipswich Town and who else?

15 Bobby Moncur led which team to win the trophy?

16 Which country did Red Boys represent?

17 Which Swedish side have won the competition twice?

18 Before 1996–97, which country has provided most winners?

19 The side beaten by Ipswich Town in a Final was prefixed by which two letters?

20 Which Scottish side did Paul Hegarty play for in a Final?

Answers

Germany (see Quiz 82)
1 Lothar Matthäus. 2 White. 3 Berti Vogts. 4 Stuttgart.
5 Kevin Keegan. 6 Helmet Schön. 7 1950s. 8 18.
9 Hamburg. 10 Jürgen Klinsmann, three. 11 Lothar Matthäus.
12 Borussia Dortmund. 13 White and red. 14 Gerry Francis.
15 Group C. 16 Munich. 17 68. 18 Uwe Rosler. 19 Andy
Möller. 20 Cologne (Köln).

192

Quiz 85 Pot Luck 43

LEVEL 2

1   Which club's ground is by the River Wensum?

2   What was Ian Wright's job before he became a footballer?

3   Which was Steve Coppell's first League club?

4   Which Malcolm became boss of Sunderland in 1992?

5   Kevin Campbell first played in an FA Charity Shield for which club?

6   In which decade did West Ham Utd first win the FA Cup?

7   David Pleat followed Bryan Hamilton as boss of which club?

8   In 1985, which Cup finalists recorded 'Here We Go'?

9   Which country did Peter Rodrigues play for?

10 Bobby Gould was born in which city where he went on to manage the football team?

11 Which club has its ground next to Gillespie Road?

12 Which team were beaten 1–0 by WBA in the 1968 FA Cup Final?

13 Which country does Andrea Silenzi come from?

14 In which decade was Bryan Hamilton born?

15 Which club has a fanzine called 'Yidaho'?

16 What is the first name of Ipswich's Ulhenbeek?

17 Batty and Barton were in the same side at which club?

18 Who moved from Norwich City for £5.5 million in July 1994 to set a club record for a transfer fee received?

19 What colours are Colchester United's striped shirts?

20 Gary Charles was at which club when he made his international debut?

Answers

Pot Luck 44 (see Quiz 87)
1 Liverpool. 2 WBA. 3 Leeds Utd. 4 Tommy Smith.
5 The Fourth Division. 6 1880s. 7 Paul Furlong. 8 Yes (Once).
9 Sheffield Utd. 10 1990. 11 Norwich City. 12 Whelan.
13 Bulgaria. 14 1920s. 15 Cambridge United. 16 Nigel.
17 QPR. 18 Newcastle Utd. 19 Blue. 20 England.

LEVEL 2

1 Who became the first goalie to save a penalty in a Wembley FA Cup Final?

2 Which Northern Ireland star is QPR's most capped player?

3 What nationality is West Ham United's Slaven Bilic?

4 If you were walking down South Africa Road, which London club's ground would you be nearest?

5 Have Millwall ever won the FA Cup?

6 Which London side did Johnny Haynes play for?

7 Who holds Chelsea's record for the most League appearances?

8 Goalie Pat Jennings played for which three London area sides?

9 Which London side defeated Wales in a friendly in May 1996?

10 Who play in red and white vertical striped shirts?

11 Chelsea's Dennis Wise was transferred from which other London club?

12 Who was Trevor Brooking's 'minder' on the pitch at West Ham?

13 Who scored the final goal to win Arsenal the title in 1989?

14 Who moved from West Ham United to Celtic for £1.5 million in 1992?

15 At which club did John Barnes make his League debut?

16 Who became the chairman of Leyton Orient in 1996?

17 Which Wimbledon player joined them from Brentford in 1992?

18 Name the London team whose address is 748 High Road?

19 Who did Crystal Palace beat in the 1990 FA Cup semi-final?

20 Frank Clark managed which London side?

Quiz 87 Pot Luck 44

Answers – see page 193

LEVEL 2

1 Which team lost 4–3 to Leeds Utd in the 1992 FA Charity Shield?

2 Brian Talbot followed Ron Atkinson's second spell as boss of which club?

3 What was John Sheridan's first League club?

4 Who had a 1980 book titled *I Did It The Hard Way*?

5 What was formed in 1958 to change the English League?

6 In which decade did Hibernian first win the Scottish FA Cup?

7 Who moved from Watford to Chelsea in May 1994 to set a club record for a transfer fee received?

8 Did Nobby Stiles ever score for England?

9 Noel Blake was at which club when he made his international debut?

10 In what year did the Scotland World Cup squad release "Say It With Pride"?

11 Which club have a River End Stand and City Stand at their ground?

12 Which Ronnie became boss of Southend United in July 1995?

13 Which country does Boncho Guentchev come from?

14 In which decade was Nat Lofthouse born?

15 Which club has a fanzine called *The Abbey Rabbit*?

16 What is much-travelled Gleghorn's first name?

17 Impey and Barker were in the same side at which club?

18 Which team were beaten 3–0 by Liverpool in the 1974 FA Cup Final?

19 What is the main colour of Gillingham's home shirts?

20 Which country did Eddie Hopkinson play for?

Answers

Pot Luck 43 (see Quiz 85)
1 Norwich City. 2 Plasterer. 3 Tranmere Rovers. 4 Crosby.
5 Arsenal. 6 1960s. 7 Leicester City. 8 Everton. 9 Wales.
10 Coventry. 11 Arsenal. 12 Everton. 13 Italy.
14 1940s. 15 Wimbledon. 16 Gus. 17 Newcastle Utd.
18 Chris Sutton. 19 Blue and white. 20 Nottingham Forest.

LEVEL 2

1 Which club announced in November 1995 they were thinking of moving to Dublin?

2 Who performed the "scorpion kick" at Wembley?

3 Who were Britain's last Club in Europe in the 1995–96 season?

4 Which lowly side knocked Manchester Utd out of the 1995–96 Coca-Cola Cup?

5 Who was Peter Shilton playing for when he was sent off for the first time in his career?

6 Which side won promotion but were not allowed to take their place in the top flight?

7 Which team knocked Leeds Utd out of the FA Cup in 1996-97?

8 Dario Gradi said that which ex-Crewe Alexandra player "can go on to become a truly great player"?

9 Who did Liverpool sign from Bolton in September 1995?

10 Who did Berti Vogts succeed as Germany's national team chief?

11 Who tested positive for cocaine following a Serie A game?

12 Which African side reached the 1990 World Cup quarter-finals?

13 Which manager sparked the Manchester City revival in 1997?

14 Which Dutch player was the 1992 European Footballer of the Year?

15 Which two England players missed penalties in Italia 90?

16 Who retired, aged 58, after his club was relegated in 1993?

17 Which chairman said in 1991, "Let's kill off once and for all that Ossie's job is on the line"?

18 In their pre-Euro 96 tour, which countries did England visit?

19 Who only lasted less than a week as captain of the Republic of Ireland?

20 In the 1996–97 season, which two Premier clubs had never appeared in any of the major European competitions?

1 Which international Chris once worked as a sausage seasoning maker?

2 Which John became boss of Shrewsbury in 1991?

3 Which was Alan Hansen's first Scottish League club?

4 Which club's ground is by the River Nene?

5 In which decade did WBA first win the FA Cup?

6 Andrei Kanchelskis first played in an FA Charity Shield for which club?

7 Howard Wilkinson followed Jack Charlton as boss of which club?

8 Which TV presenter did Ryan Giggs go out with?

9 Which country did Phil Woosnam play for?

10 Chris Turner kept goal for Sheffield Wednesday in a League Cup Final when they beat which former club of his?

11 Which club has the Revie Stand in their ground?

12 Which team were beaten a record 6–1 by Celtic in the 1972 Scottish FA Cup Final?

13 Which country does Mixu Paatelainen come from?

14 In which decade was Andrei Kanchelskis born?

15 Which club has a fanzine called *A Load Of Bull*?

16 Which Manchester Utd great made a trademark of pulling his cuffs over his hands ?

17 Pollock and Stamp were in the same side at which club?

18 Who moved from QPR for £6 million in June 1995 to set a club record for a transfer fee received?

19 What is the main colour of Crewe Alexandra's shirts?

20 Tony Currie was at which club when he made his international debut?

Answers

Pot Luck 46 (see Quiz 91)
1 Aberdeen. 2 Liverpool. 3 Tottenham Hotspur. 4 Smith.
5 Morris. 6 1950s. 7 Steve Daley. 8 Wimbledon. 9 Arsenal.
10 Bill Shankly. 11 Nottingham Forest. 12 Oxford United.
13 Norway. 14 1950s. 15 Aston Villa. 16 Francis.
17 Sheffield Wednesday. 18 Manchester City.
19 Black and white. 20 Northern Ireland.

Quiz 90 Golden Goals

Answers – see page 200

LEVEL 2 ⚽ ⚽

1 Which Cliff set a career goals record at Arsenal?

2 Dennis Bergkamp's goals led which team to Euro success in 1992?

3 Who is credited – or blamed – for bringing the shirt-over-the-head-after-scoring routine to English soccer?

4 Which player of the 1950s and 60s set up Chelsea's record for most league goals for the club?

5 Whose amazing Euro 96 lob knocked out Portugal?

6 Neil Shipperley's goals kept which side in the Premiership in 1995–96?

7 Which German striker was known as "Der Bomber"?

8 Steve Bloomer notched 292 League goals for which club?

9 Who dived full length on the pitch after his first goal for Tottenham Hotspur in the Premiership?

10 To 20 each way, what was Dixie Dean's Everton League goals total?

11 Which two clubs has Ian Wright scored for in FA Cup Finals?

12 A Brett Angell goal took which team to the Coca-Cola Cup semi-final in 1997?

13 A Charlie George goal won the FA Cup for which team?

14 A fine Davor Suker shot bamboozled which Danish keeper in Euro 96?

15 Who scored a last gasp equaliser for Manchester Utd v Oldham in a 1990s semi-final?

16 Who was the Brazilian top scorer in the 1994 World Cup tournament?

17 Andy Linighan scored a last minute FA Cup Final winner for which team?

18 Craig Brewster scored the only goal to win the Scottish League Cup for which club in 1993–94?

19 Which Scot was Europe's top league scorer in 1991–92?

20 Who scored England's first in the 1966 World Cup Final?

Answers

Hat-tricks (see Quiz 92)
1 Alan Shearer. 2 Matt Le Tissier. 3 Gary McAllister.
4 Mortensen. 5 West Germany. 6 Everton. 7 John Wark.
8 Ian Wright. 9 Coventry City. 10 Rangers. 11 Alan Shearer.
12 Turkey. 13 Mike Newell. 14 Andy Cole. 15 Gary Lineker.
16 Manchester City. 17 Gordon Durie. 18 Les Ferdinand.
19 Jimmy Greaves. 20 Eric Cantona.

198

1 Alphabetically, which is Scotland's first League side?

2 In 1977 which club released 'We Can Do It'?

3 What was Vinny Samways' first League club?

4 Which Jim became boss of Portsmouth in 1991?

5 Which Desmond's 1981 book was *The Soccer Tribe*?

6 In which decade did Motherwell first win the Scottish FA Cup?

7 Who moved from Wolves to Manchester City for over £1 million in 1979 to set a club record for a transfer fee received?

8 Which team lost 2–1 to Liverpool in the 1988 FA Charity Shield?

9 George Eastham was at which club when he made his international debut?

10 Which great Scottish boss was born in Glenbuck in 1913?

11 The Bridgford Stand is part of the ground of which club?

12 Denis Smith followed Brian Horton as boss of which club?

13 Which country does Justein Flo come from?

14 In which decade was Kevin Keegan born?

15 Which club has a fanzine called *Heroes And Villains*?

16 What is the first name of long serving Southampton defender Benali?

17 Walker and Waddle were in the same side at which club?

18 Which team were beaten 3–2 by Tottenham Hotspur in the replayed 1981 FA Cup Final?

19 What colour are Grimsby Town's striped home shirts?

20 Which country did Alex Elder play for?

Pot Luck 45 (see Quiz 89)
1 Waddle. 2 Bond. 3 Partick Thistle. 4 Peterborough Utd.
5 1880s. 6 Everton. 7 Sheffield Wednesday. 8 Dani Behr.
9 Wales. 10 Manchester Utd. 11 Leeds Utd. 12 Hibernian.
13 Finland. 14 1960s. 15 Wolves. 16 Denis Law.
17 Middlesbrough. 18 Les Ferdinand. 19 Red.
20 Sheffield Utd.

Answers

Quiz 92 Hat-tricks

LEVEL 2

1 Who scored five Premiership hat-tricks in 1995–96?

2 Who finished Southampton's joint top scorer in 1995–96 with 7 goals, having hit a hat-trick in the first game?

3 Which Leeds Utd midfielder hit a 1995 hat-trick against Coventry City?

4 Which Stan hit an FA Cup Final hat-trick in the 1950s?

5 Geoff Hurst hit his first England hat-trick against which team?

6 Who was Andy Gray playing for when he hit a mid-1980s European Cup Winners' Cup treble?

7 Which Ipswich player hit two hat-tricks in 1980–81 UEFA Cup games?

8 Which England player got four against San Marino in November 1993?

9 Who was Dion Dublin playing for when he hit three against Sheffield Wednesday in 1995 and still ended up on the losing side?

10 Robert Fleck has hit three in a Euro game for which club?

11 Who hit a 1997 hat-trick for Newcastle Utd, who were losing 3–1, into a 4–3 victory over Leicester City?

12 Bryan Robson got his only England hat-trick in an 8–0 rout of which country in 1984?

13 Who hit Blackburn Rovers's hat-trick in the 1995–96 European Cup?

14 Who hit three-plus as Manchester Utd beat Ipswich Town 9–0 in 1995?

15 Which England player hit hat-tricks against Turkey in 1985 and 1987?

16 Adcock, Stewart and White each hit three for which team in the same game in 1987?

17 Who hit a Scottish FA Cup Final hat-trick in 1996?

18 Which player hit his first Newcastle Utd hat-trick against Wimbledon in October 1995?

19 Which player hit six England hat-tricks from 1960 to 1966?

20 Who hit a Charity Shield hat-trick for Leeds Utd in 1992?

Golden Goals (see Quiz 90)

1 Bastin. 2 Ajax. 3 Fabrizio Ravanelli. 4 Bobby Tambling.
5 Karel Poborsky. 6 Southampton. 7 Gerd Müller. 8 Derby County. 9 Jürgen Klinsmann. 10 349. 11 Crystal Palace and Arsenal. 12 Stockport County. 13 Arsenal. 14 Peter Schmeichel. 15 Mark Hughes. 16 Romario. 17 Arsenal.
18 Dundee Utd. 19 Ally McCoist. 20 Geoff Hurst.

1   John Docherty followed George Graham as boss of which club?

2   Barry Horne first played in an FA Charity Shield for which club?

3   Which was John Aldridge's first League club?

4   To five each way, in what year did Tottenham Hotspur first win the FA Cup?

5   The team of Archie Gemmill and John McGovern took over which club in September 1994?

6   Who was the first Danish goalkeeper to play in the English League?

7   Which club's ground is by the River Severn?

8   David Beckham has spent time on loan at which Lancashire club?

9   Which country does Jim Magilton play for?

10   In January 1996, which manager announced he would be standing down from his post because of impending litigation?

11   The Kemlyn Road goes past the ground of which club?

12   Which team were beaten 3–1 by Man Utd in the 1963 FA Cup Final?

13   Which country does Jan-Aage Fjortoft come from?

14   In which decade was Jimmy Greaves born?

15   Which club has a fanzine called *The Voice of the Valley*?

16   Who plays at The Stadium Of Light?

17   Clough and Harkness were in the same side at which club?

18   Who moved from Reading to Newcastle United in August 1995 to set a club record for a transfer fee received?

19   What colour are Doncaster's home shirts?

20   Tony Dorigo was at which club when he made his international debut?

Answers

Pot Luck 48 (see Quiz 95)
1 Billy Bremner. 2 Watford. 3 Nottingham Forest. 4 Arsenal.
5 "it's more important than that." 6 1890s. 7 Warren Barton.
8 Bayern Munich. 9 Leeds United. 10 Jairzinho. 11 Sheffield
Wednesday. 12 McGhee. 13 Canada. 14 1920s. 15 Notts
County. 16 Dean. 17 Derby County. 18 Manchester Utd.
19 Blue and white. 20 Wales.

1 Who is the oldest player to turn out for Wales?

2 In which decade did Wales first beat England at Wembley?

3 Who became manager of Northern Ireland in 1994?

4 Which ex-Liverpool player has managed Wales?

5 At which ground do the Republic of Ireland play home matches?

6 Which Peter scored twice for Northern Ireland in their magnificent draw with West Germany in the 1958 World Cup?

7 Who was Tony Cascarino playing for when he won his first cap?

8 When did the Republic of Ireland first qualify for the World Cup finals?

9 Which country has Vinnie Jones played for?

10 Which Welsh player was the most capped before Neville Southall?

11 Which Christian names link Northern Ireland's McIlroy and Quinn?

12 Which Northern Ireland skipper said, "Our tactics are to equalize before the other side scores"?

13 Which Republic of Ireland player was nicknamed "Chippy"?

14 In 1992 Michael Hughes made his debut for which country?

15 Which Republic of Ireland player appeared in five FA Cup Finals between 1963 and 1973?

16 In which year did Jack Charlton become manager of the Republic of Ireland?

17 Which home international countries were present in the 1982 World Cup Finals?

18 Which Arsenal and Tottenham Hotspur manager was also team boss of Northern Ireland?

19 Which London-based striker captained Northern Ireland in 1996?

20 When did Wales last qualify for the World Cup?

Answers

Golden Oldies (see Quiz 96)
1 Stanley Matthews. 2 Preston North End. 3 Leicester City.
4 West Ham Utd. 5 Billy Wright. 6 Dixie Dean.
7 Huddersfield Town. 8 Ted Drake. 9 Joe Mercer. 10 Nat Lofthouse. 11 33 years. 12 Alex James. 13 Mackay.
14 Newcastle Utd. 15 Middlesbrough. 16 Manchester Utd.
17 Scotland. 18 Hungary. 19 Pat Jennings. 20 Yes. (He played once for Scotland).

Quiz 95 Pot Luck 48

Answers – see page 201

LEVEL 2

1 *You Get Nowt For Being Second* was the 1969 book of which player?

2 Steve Harrison followed Dave Bassett as boss of which club?

3 What was Hans Segers' first English League club?

4 Which team lost 1–0 to Liverpool in the 1989 FA Charity Shield?

5 How did Bill Shankly end the observation that, "Football isn't a matter of life and death: ..."?

6 In which decade did Sheffield Wednesday first win the FA Cup?

7 Who moved from Wimbledon for £4 million in June 1995 to set a club record for a transfer fee received?

8 Which club did Jürgen Klinsmann join on leaving Tottenham Hotspur?

9 Allan Clarke was at which club when he made his international debut?

10 How is Brazil's Jair Ventura Filho better known?

11 Leppings Lane runs by which club's ground?

12 Which Mark was Reading boss from 1991 to 1994?

13 Which country does Paul Peschisolido come from?

14 In which decade was Alfredo Di Stefano born?

15 Which club has a fanzine called *The Pie*?

16 What is Mr Windass' first name?

17 Willems and Van Der Laan were in the same side at which club?

18 Which team were beaten 1–0 by Southampton in the 1976 FA Cup Final?

19 What two colours are on Hartlepool's home shirts?

20 Which country did Paul Price play for?

Answers

Pot Luck 47 (see Quiz 93)
1 Millwall. 2 Everton. 3 Newport County. 4 1901.
5 Rotherham. 6 Peter Schmeichel. 7 Shrewsbury Town.
8 Preston North End. 9 Northern Ireland. 10 Terry Venables.
11 Liverpool. 12 Leicester City. 13 Norway. 14 1940s.
15 Charlton Athletic. 16 Benfica. 17 Liverpool. 18 Shaka Hislop. 19 Red. 20 Chelsea.

1 Who was born on Feb 1, 1915, in Hanley, Stoke on Trent?

2 Bobby Charlton came out of retirement to play for which League club?

3 Which club had goalkeepers Banks and Shilton on their books in the 1960s?

4 What was the third London side that Jimmy Greaves played for?

5 Who was travelling on a bus when he learnt that he had been made England skipper?

6 Who fractured his skull in a motorbike accident in the 1920s?

7 With which League club did Denis Law make his debut?

8 Who hit 42 goals in a season for Arsenal in the 1930s?

9 Who was aged 60 when he became England's caretaker manager?

10 Who bagged 255 league goals for Bolton in the 1940s and 1950s?

11 To two each way, how many years did Stanley Matthews play League soccer in England?

12 Who became Britain's most expensive player when he moved from Preston North End to Arsenal in 1929?

13 Which Dave of Tottenham Hotspur broke his left leg twice in a year in the 1960s?

14 Hughie Gallacher hit 36 league goals in a season for which club?

15 Where was Wilf Mannion born?

16 At which club did Brian Kidd begin his career?

17 Liverpool's legendary striker Billy Liddell came from which country?

18 Which country developed the deep-lying centre forward role just after World War II?

19 Which great goalkeeper was born in Newry on June 12, 1945?

20 Did Matt Busby ever play international soccer?

1 In which decade did Sunderland first win the FA Cup?

2 Which Scot played for Torino in 1961–62?

3 With which club did Trevor Sinclair make his League debut?

4 Which Ian became boss of Northampton Town in January 1995?

5 Stuart Ripley first played in an FA Charity Shield for which club?

6 Which club's ground is near the River Don?

7 Ken Brown followed John Bond as boss of which club?

8 In 1996–97, Port Vale were 4–0 up at home yet had to settle for a 4–4 draw against which London team?

9 Which country did John McClelland play for?

10 Which lifelong soccer fan was born in May 1929 in Blackburn?

11 Which club is situated in Moss Side?

12 Which team was beaten 3–1 by Tottenham Hotspur in the 1962 FA Cup Final?

13 Which country does Lucas Radebe come from?

14 In which decade was Johan Cruyff born?

15 Which club has a fanzine called *The Cumberland Sausage*?

16 How many full England caps did Steve Bruce win?

17 Lennon and Parker were in the same side at which club?

18 Who moved from Torquay for £600,000 in May 1988 to set a club record for a transfer fee received?

19 What colour are Exeter City's striped shirts?

20 Gordon Cowans was at which club when he made his international debut?

1 What was Paolo Maldini's first club?

2 Which club have won the League most times?

3 Who was Italy's top scorer in the 1994 World Cup in the USA?

4 How old was Paolo Rossi when he retired from playing?

5 Which club did Graeme Souness join in Italy?

6 German imports Klinsmann and Matthäus brought which club the league title in 1989?

7 Which team are known as the Zebras?

8 Dino Zoff became coach and later president of which club?

9 Which team knocked Italy out of Italia 90?

10 The import of what was banned in 1964, only to be lifted in the 1980s?

11 Who were the opponents for Cesare Maldini's first match as coach?

12 Who was Italy's top scorer in the 1982 World Cup tournament?

13 Michel Platini inspired Juventus to European Cup Final victory over which English side?

14 Gianfranco Zola took over the number 10 shirt at Napoli from which superstar?

15 In which decade did the Italians first win the World Cup?

16 Who were champions of Serie A in 1995–96?

17 Thomas Brolin joined Leeds United from which Italian club?

18 Who missed the final penalty for Italy in the 1994 World Cup Final?

19 Lazio play in which Italian city?

20 Who was in charge of Italy for Euro 96?

Pot Luck 49 (see Quiz 97)
Answers
1 1930s. 2 Denis Law. 3 Blackpool. 4 Atkins. 5 Blackburn Rovers. 6 Sheffield Wednesday. 7 Norwich City. 8 QPR. 9 Northern Ireland. 10 Jack Walker. 11 Manchester City. 12 Burnley. 13 South Africa. 14 1940s. 15 Carlisle United. 16 None. 17 Leicester City. 18 Lee Sharpe. 19 Red and white. 20 Aston Villa.

Quiz 99 Pot Luck 50

LEVEL 2

1 Ray Clemence was an FA Cup winner with which two clubs?

2 Which team took part in the Charity Shield from 1984 to 1987?

3 What was Martin Keown's first League club?

4 Which Lennie became boss of Luton Town in December 1995?

5 *Just Like My Dreams:* was part of the title of which manager's book?

6 In which decade did Southampton first win the FA Cup?

7 Who moved from West Ham Utd to Everton in July 1988 to set a club record for a transfer fee received?

8 Bill Fox was chairman of which club?

9 Mark Chamberlain was at which club when he made his international debut?

10 Bardsley and Brevett were in the same side at which club?

11 Paxton Road goes by the ground of which club?

12 Brian Clough followed Allan Brown as boss of which club?

13 Which country does Claus Thomsen come from?

14 To five years each way, when was Tommy Lawton born?

15 Which club has a fanzine called *Brian Moore's Head (Looks Uncannily Like The London Planetarium)*?

16 What is the first name of the footballing Mr Shakespeare?

17 In January 1996, who lost his appeal for a pay-off from his old club Nottingham Forest?

18 Which team were beaten 3–2 by Tottenham Hotspur in the replayed 1982 FA Cup Final?

19 What two colours are on Hereford United's home shirts?

20 Which country did Malcolm Page play for?

The Hard Questions

If you thought that this section of this book would prove to be little or no problem, or that the majority of the questions could be answered and a scant few would test you then you are sorely mistaken. These questions are the *hardest* questions *ever*! So difficult are they that any attempt to answer them all in one sitting will addle your mind and mess with your senses. You'll end up leaving the building dribbling your dog and toe-punting it into the dustbins outside. What you should do instead is set them for others – addle your friends' minds.

Note the dangerous nature of these questions though. These are your secret weapons so use them accordingly unless, of course, someone or some team is getting your back up. In which case you should hit them hard and only let up when you have them cowering under the bench whimpering "offside".

These questions work best against league teams, they are genuinely tough and should be used against those people who take their pub quizzes seriously. NEVER use these questions against your in-laws.

Quiz 1 Pot Luck 1

Answers – see page 211

LEVEL 3

1 Who played for Croydon, Carshalton Athletic and Sutton and became a Premier League manager?

2 Who was in goal when Leeds Utd won the FA Cup in the 1970s?

3 What is Jimmy Greaves' middle name?

4 At which club did Lee Dixon make his League debut?

5 In what decade did Arsenal first win the Championship?

6 Who scored for the Czech Republic in the Final of Euro 96?

7 Alan Mullery followed Steve Kember as manager of which club?

8 Who moved from Bournemouth to Everton in 1994 to set a club record for a transfer fee received?

9 Which club was once known as Dial Square?

10 To one each way, how many international goals did Viv Anderson score?

11 Kevin Gage and Steve Sims were in the same team at which club?

12 Which Colin became boss of Hull City in 1989?

13 John Bailey first played in an FA Cup Final for which team?

14 What is the historic link between Harrow Chequers, Hitchin Town and Reigate Priory?

15 On the day of the 1995 FA Cup Final which Premiership club announced that their manager was leaving?

16 Which European team did World Cup newcomers Saudi Arabia beat in the first round of Euro 96?

17 Which club used to play at Fullfordgate?

18 Kevin Langley set a League appearance record at which club?

19 Which country did Mike O'Grady play for?

20 How many years was Bruce Grobbelaar at Liverpool?

Answers

Pot Luck 2 (see Quiz 3)
1 West Ham Utd. 2 Everton. 3 Wycombe Wanderers.
4 Wallace. 5 Luton Town. 6 Hereford Utd. 7 Chewing Gum (Dentyne). 8 Tow Law Town. 9 Partick Thistle. 10 Ambrose.
11 Manchester Utd. 12 Westley. 13 Manchester City.
14 Leeds Utd. 15 1950s. 16 Everton. 17 Nottingham Forest.
18 Steve Sedgley. 19 Bristol City. 20 10.

209

1 Liam Brady finished his playing career at which club?

2 Steve Williams and Brian Talbot were together at which club?

3 To two each way, how many caps did Alan Ball win?

4 Which Manchester Utd player scored on his English League debut v Watford in August, 1984?

5 Who was born on September 29, 1939 at Hill o'Beath, Fife?

6 Which club did Billy Bremner move to after the Leeds Utd's glory days?

7 Nick Holmes was a long serving player with which club?

8 Which English team did Roy Keane support as a boy?

9 What was Johan Cruyff's first family links with Ajax?

10 Which heavy-smoking midfielder scored Brazil's second goal in the 1970 World Cup Final?

11 Who was skipper of England from 1960 until involved in a serious car accident in 1962?

12 Johnny Metgod came from Real Madrid to which English side?

13 Micky Horswill played for which team in an FA Cup Final?

14 How old was Ray Wilkins when he was made captain at Chelsea?

15 Graeme Souness was at which club for three years without playing in the first team?

16 Bryan Robson's last England game was against which country?

17 Mills, Wigley and Walsh featured for which top-flight 80s team?

18 Cockerill and Case formed a formidable partnership at which club?

19 What number did Johan Cruyff wear for most of his Ajax career?

20 Bobby Robson was with which club when he first played for England?

Answers

The 1950s (see Quiz 4)
1 Hearts. 2 Red Star Belgrade. 3 Joe Harvey. 4 Portsmouth.
5 Jimmy Greaves. 6 Harold "Bunny" Bell. 7 Arsenal. 8 Alec and David Herd. 9 USA. 10 Leslie Compton. 11 Just Fontaine.
12 Sunderland. 13 Hearts. 14 Ian St John. 15 Ronnie Clayton. 16 Charlton Athletic. 17 Ted Fenton. 18 Bolton Wanderers. 19 Manchester Utd. 20 It finished as a four-way tie.

LEVEL 3

1 At which club did Jimmy Greaves finish his League career?

2 In June 1994 Swedish player Martin Dahlin turned down a transfer to which English club?

3 Which club used to play at Loakes Park?

4 Which Danny played his only England game in 1986 against Egypt?

5 Before meeting up at West Ham Utd, where had Tim Breaker and Les Sealey been in the same side?

6 What was the first club that John Sillett managed?

7 What type of product was advertised on Southampton's open top bus as it paraded the FA Cup in the 70s?

8 Which non League side did Chris Waddle use to play for?

9 Alan Rough set a League appearance record at which club?

10 What was Billy Wright's middle name?

11 Mal Donaghy and Mark Robins were in the same team at which club?

12 Which Terry was in charge at Luton Town during 1995?

13 Ray Ranson first played in an FA Cup Final for which team?

14 At which club did Terry Phelan make his League debut?

15 In what decade did Aberdeen first win the championship?

16 Which club had a fanzine called *When Skies Are Grey*?

17 Dave Mackay followed Matt Gillies as manager of which club?

18 Who was bought by Ipswich Town in 1994 at a club record fee?

19 Which club was once known as Bristol South End?

20 To two each way, how many international goals did Billy Bingham score?

Answers

Pot Luck 1 (see Quiz 1)
1 Lennie Lawrence. 2 David Harvey. 3 Peter. 4 Burnley.
5 1930s. 6 Patrick Berger. 7 Crystal Palace. 8 Joe Parkinson.
9 Arsenal. 10 2. 11 Aston Villa. 12 Appleton. 13 Everton.
14 Entered the first FA Cup competition. 15 Sheffield Wednesday.
16 Belgium. 17 York City. 18 Wigan Athletic. 19 England.
20 13.

1 Which Scottish side hit a record 132 Division One goals in 1957–58?

2 Which team had Manchester United played before the Munich crash?

3 After the 1952 FA Cup Final which Newcastle Utd skipper said, "Joe Mercer is the greatest player I have ever met"?

4 On February 22, 1956, Newcastle Utd visited which club for the first English League game to be played under floodlights?

5 Which Chelsea star finished as the League's top scorer in 1959?

6 Which Tranmere Rovers centre-half made a record 401 consecutive League appearances in the 1950s?

7 Which side narrowly failed to win the double in the 1951–52 season?

8 Which father and son duo played in the same Stockport County side?

9 Who beat England in a Group Two 1950 World Cup match in Belo Horizonte?

10 Who was affectionately known as "Big Ead" by the Arsenal fans?

11 Which French player finished as top scorer in the 1958 World Cup?

12 In 1958 which team were relegated for the first time in 68 years?

13 Who won their first trophy in 50 years when they beat Celtic 3–1 to claim the 1950 Scottish FA Cup?

14 Which Motherwell forward hit three goals in three minutes in 1959?

15 Who took over as England skipper from Billy Wright?

16 Which Division Two side were losing 5–1 to Huddersfield, but fought back to win 7–6 in 1957?

17 Who was manager of West Ham Utd's promotion winning side of 1958?

18 Bill Riding was boss of which team from 1951?

19 Which team was the Anderlecht captain referring to when he said,"Why don't they pick the whole side for England"?

20 What was remarkable about the Home International Championship of 1955–56?

1 In 1966, which Leeds Utd defender won his only Scottish cap?

2 What is Tony Adams' middle name?

3 Which Welsh club used to play at Acton Park?

4 Which England keeper was featured in *Hello* magazine in February 1997?

5 In what decade did Liverpool first win the championship?

6 Which club had a fanzine called *Not The 8502*?

7 Dario Gradi followed Malcolm Allison as manager of which club?

8 Who moved from Brentford to Wimbledon in 1992 to set a club record for a transfer fee received?

9 Which London club once had Alston as part of its name?

10 To one each way, how many international goals did Alan Ball score?

11 Perry Groves and Brian Marwood were in the same team at which club?

12 Which Billy became boss of Leeds Utd in 1985?

13 Ray Wilkins played in an FA Cup Final for which team?

14 To three each way, how many goals did Phil Neal score in his 20-year long League career?

15 What was the first club that Alan Ball managed?

16 Which Millwall defender scored over 40 goals during the 1960s and early 70s?

17 What are the main colours of IFK Gothenburg's home shirts?

18 Who was keeper Ray Cashley playing for when he scored against Hull City in 1973?

19 Tony Fitzpatrick set a Scottish League appearance record at which club?

20 Who was in goal when WBA won the FA Cup in the 1960s?

Answers

Pot Luck 4 (see Quiz 7)
1 Hearts. 2 Ron Greenwood. 3 Wolves. 4 Bournemouth.
5 2 (Steve Daley and Andy Gray). 6 Smith. 7 Elland Road.
8 Cambridge Utd. 9 Harvey. 10 William. 11 Middlesbrough.
12 Machin. 13 Brighton. 14 Chesterfield. 15 1890s.
16 Huddersfield Town. 17 Burnley. 18 Gordon Durie.
19 Cambridge Utd. 20 12.

1 Allan Clarke became the first £150,000 man when he moved to Leicester City from which club?

2 Which player was involved the only time that the British transfer ceiling has been doubled in one move?

3 In the first £5,000 transfer Syd Puddefoot moved to which Scottish club?

4 Alberto Tarantini came from Argentina to which British club?

5 Kevin Moran left Manchester Utd in 1988 for which club?

6 Who was the first player to move for £20,000?

7 Who were Nottingham Forest's main rivals for the signature of Birmingham City's Trevor Francis?

8 Trevor Francis was Britain's most expensive player until who moved?

9 How old was Charles Buchan when he went to Arsenal?

10 Who was the £1 million pound player to leave Norwich City?

11 Ayr's record fee received was £300,000 in 1981 when which player moved to Liverpool?

12 Hughie Gallacher joined Newcastle Utd from which club?

13 Who became the first British player to move in a £500,000 transfer?

14 Who played for Leeds Utd in the first leg of a Fairs Cup Final but was transferred before the second?

15 Where did Charlie George go when he left Arsenal?

16 Partick Thistle's record fee received was £200,000 in 1981 when which player moved to Watford?

17 Arriving in 1972 from Nottingham Forest, who was Manchester Utd's first ever £200,000 signing?

18 Who was Norwich City manager when Chris Sutton left for £5 million?

19 What was the last French club that Eric Cantona played for?

20 Where did Danny Wallace go when he left Manchester Utd?

Answers

Three Lions (see Quiz 8)
1 11. 2 Scotland. 3 Alan Mullery. 4 Peter Ward. 5 3.
6 Tom Finney. 7 Brazil. 8 53. 9 90. 10 QPR & Manchester City. 11 Tony Adams. 12 3. 13 Dave Watson. 14 European Championship 1988. 15 Jimmy Greaves. 16 18 minutes.
17 73. 18 Tommy Lawton. 19 1970. 20 Tony Cottee.

LEVEL 3

1 Comedian Ronnie Corbett had a trial at which Scottish club?

2 Which England manager was born in Burnley in 1921?

3 Which side from the Midlands used to play at Goldthorn Hill?

4 Sean O'Driscoll set a League appearance record at which club?

5 The first £1 million British move was in February 1979. How many more players moved for a million in the same year?

6 Which Alan went on from non-League Alvechurch to play for England?

7 The first home England international since 1966 to be played away from Wembley was in 1995 v Sweden. Where was it played?

8 What was the first League club that Ron Atkinson managed?

9 Which Colin played his only England game in 1971 against Malta?

10 What is John Aldridge's middle name?

11 Peter Davenport and Gary Pallister were in the same team at which club?

12 Which Mel became boss of Manchester City in 1987?

13 Mick Robinson first played in an FA Cup Final for which team?

14 At which club did Steve Ogrizovic make his League debut?

15 In what decade did Hearts first win the Championship?

16 Which club had a fanzine called *A Slice of Kilner Pie*?

17 Jimmy Mullen followed Frank Casper as manager of which club?

18 Who moved from Chelsea to Tottenham Hotspur for £2,200,000 in 1991 to set a club record for a transfer fee received?

19 Which club was once known as Abbey United?

20 To one each way, how many international goals has Tony Cascarino scored?

Answers

Pot Luck 3 (see Quiz 5)
1 Willie Bell. 2 Alexander. 3 Wrexham. 4 David Seaman.
5 1900s. 6 Bournemouth. 7 Crystal Palace. 8 Dean
Holdsworth. 9 Barnet. 10 9. 11 Arsenal. 12 Bremner.
13 Manchester United. 14 73. 15 Portsmouth. 16 Harry
Cripps. 17 White and blue. 18 Bristol City. 19 St Mirren.
20 John Osborne.

Quiz 8 Three Lions

LEVEL 3

1 How many goals did Stanley Matthews score for England?

2 Bobby Charlton's first international goal was against which country?

3 Which player was outjumped by Pele before Banks made his save in Mexico 1970?

4 Which Brighton forward came on as a substitute for eight minutes in his only England appearance?

5 How many internationals did Jimmy Greaves play after the 1966 World Cup?

6 Who was the first player to score 30 goals for England?

7 Gary Lineker missed a penalty against which team in 1992?

8 To two each way, how many caps did Glenn Hoddle win?

9 In how many games was Bobby Moore skipper of England?

10 Rodney Marsh was capped while playing for which two clubs?

11 Who scored for both sides in the friendly v Holland in 1988?

12 How many games did Billy Wright miss between his first and last appearance for England?

13 Who was capped for England while playing for Werder Bremen in 1980?

14 Kenny Sansom played his last England game in which tournament?

15 Who, in a 1962 World Cup match, picked up a dog which urinated on him?

16 To five each way, how many minutes was Kevin Hector on the field for his two England appearances?

17 How many caps did Gordon Banks win?

18 Timed at 17 seconds in 1947, who scored England's fastest goal?

19 In what year did Peter Shilton first play for England?

20 Who is the first striker whose career lasted at least six games but never scored for England?

Transfer Trail (see Quiz 6)
1 Fulham. 2 Trevor Francis. 3 Falkirk. 4 Birmingham City.
5 Sporting Gijon. 6 Tommy Lawton. 7 Coventry City. 8 Steve
Daley. 9 33. 10 Kevin Reeves. 11 Steve Nicol. 12 Airdrie.
13 David Mills. 14 Jimmy Greenhoff. 15 Derby County.
16 Mo Johnston. 17 Ian Storey Moore. 18 John Deehan.
19 Nîmes. 20 Birmingham City.

Answers

Quiz 9 Pot Luck 5

Answers – see page 219

LEVEL 3

1 Which England player went to the same school as Gazza?

2 In Scotland, which club has its ground nearest to the sea?

3 Who was in goal when Sheffield Wednesday lost the FA Cup Final in 1993?

4 At which club did Andy Townsend make his League debut?

5 In what decade did Manchester Utd first win the Championship?

6 Which club had a fanzine called *City Gent*?

7 Bobby Gould followed Dave Sexton as manager of which club?

8 Steve Davis' move to Luton in August 1995 set a club record for a transfer fee received at which club?

9 Which club, formed in 1881, were originally known as Stanley?

10 To one each way, how many international goals did John Barnes score?

11 Neil McDonald and Adrian Heath were in the same team at which club?

12 Which Bobby was Ipswich Town boss from 1982 to 1987?

13 Paul Power first played in an FA Cup Final for which team?

14 Who, at Lincoln in 1972, aged 28 became the youngest ever League manager?

15 Who spent a night in a police cell two days before breaking the British transfer record?

16 What is Clive Allen's middle name?

17 Which present day club used to play at the Memorial Recreation Ground, Canning Town?

18 What was the first club that Ian Branfoot managed?

19 Stuart Taylor set a League appearance record at which club?

20 Bill Shankly played for which FA Cup-winning side?

Answers

Pot Luck 6 (see Quiz 11)
1 John Aldridge. 2 Newcastle Utd. 3 Walsall. 4 Nigel.
5 Bournemouth. 6 Bolton Wanderers. 7 16. 8 Greenwich Borough. 9 Colchester Utd. 10 Steve Perryman. 11 Norwich City. 12 King. 13 Crystal Palace. 14 Wolves. 15 1940s. 16 Ipswich Town. 17 Hull City. 18 Ian Rush. 19 Cardiff City. 20 19.

LEVEL 3

1 With which club did Gordon Banks make his League debut?

2 Who was the first Scottish player to be European Footballer of the Year?

3 Who said that he was "supremely grateful" to have played against the great Hungarian side of the 1950s?

4 Who was Footballer of the Year in 1948 and 1963?

5 Against which country did Jimmy Greaves make his scoring debut?

6 How many championships did Bobby Charlton win with Manchester Utd?

7 At which club did Wilf Mannion end his career?

8 In the season he set a new scoring record how many goals did Dixie Dean get in his last three games?

9 At which Italian club did Dino Zoff begin his career?

10 To two each way, how many caps did Alex James get for Scotland?

11 In which country was Alfredo Di Stefano born?

12 Which county did Raich Carter play cricket for?

13 Which NASL team did George Best play for?

14 What was the job of Stanley Matthew's father?

15 Which team name was one of Bobby Moore's names?

16 Who hit a record 59 goals in a season for Middlesbrough?

17 To three each way, how many goals did Ferenc Puskas score for Hungary?

18 Which free-scoring England forward moved to Germany in 1914 to be interned during the War?

19 Danny Blanchflower started out with which Irish club?

20 How many Scottish League clubs did Denis Law play for?

Answers

Liverpool/Everton (see Quiz 12)
1 Kevin Ratcliffe. 2 Ian Callaghan. 3 Kenny Dalglish.
4 Huddersfield Town. 5 Bill Kenwright. 6 1930. 7 Brian Hall.
8 Home Farm. 9 Telford United. 10 Dixie Dean. 11 68 points.
12 Tottenham Hotspur. 13 Dean Saunders & Mark Wright.
14 Kevin Keegan. 15 Brian Labone. 16 Crystal Palace. 17
John Barnes. 18 Crystal Palace. 19 Billy Liddell. 20 1981.

Quiz 11 Pot Luck 6

Answers – see page 217

LEVEL 3 ⚽ ⚽ ⚽

1 Which player was involved in the substitute row in the Mexico v the Republic of Ireland 1994 World Cup game?

2 Which club boasted the fullback pairing of Ranson and Sansom?

3 Until 1990 which team used to play at Fellows Park?

4 What is Mark Atkins' middle name?

5 What was the first club that John Bond managed?

6 Brian Kidd finished his playing career in England with which club?

7 How many goals did Liverpool's mean machine defence concede in the 42 League games of 1978–79?

8 Which non League side did Ian Wright play for?

9 Micky Cook set a League appearance record at which club?

10 Which Tottenham Hotspur star played his only England game in 1982 against Iceland?

11 Andy Linighan and Mike Phelan were in the same team at which club?

12 Which Andy became boss of Mansfield in 1993?

13 Phil Barber played in an FA Cup Final for which team?

14 At which club did Tim Flowers make his League debut?

15 In which decade did Portsmouth first win the First Division Championship?

16 Which club had a fanzine called *A Load of Cobbolds*?

17 Eddie Gray followed Brian Horton as manager of which club?

18 Who moved from Chester for £300,000 in 1980 to set a club record for a transfer fee received?

19 Which club was once known as Riverside Albion?

20 To two each way, how many international goals did Don Givens net?

1 Who was Everton's skipper in the 1985 European Cup Winners' Cup?

2 Who holds Liverpool's record for most League appearances?

3 Which Liverpool player appeared three times at Wembley in 1977–78, his first season in England?

4 Which Yorkshire team did Bill Shankly manage between 1956 and 1959?

5 At the start of 1996–97, which theatre impresario was listed as one of Everton's directors?

6 To two each way, in what year were Everton first relegated?

7 Which Liverpool outfield player was the only one not to score in the 11–0 rout of Stromsgodset in 1974?

8 Which Irish club did Ronnie Whelan come from?

9 Which non-League side did Everton beat in 1985 in the FA Cup?

10 Which famous player died at Goodison at the 1980 Merseyside derby?

11 Under the 2 points for a win system how many points did Liverpool gain to create a record in 1979?

12 Which side inflicted a 10–4 thrashing on Everton in season 1958–59?

13 Which two internationals – one Welsh, one English – did Graeme Souness sign in July 1992?

14 Which ex Liverpool star played only 27 minutes in the final stages of a World Cup to earn the last of his 63 caps?

15 Who was skipper of Everton's 1966 FA Cup winning side?

16 In 1990, Liverpool beat which club 9–0 in the League and lost to them in an FA Cup semi-final?

17 Which Liverpool player scored his first international goal in Rio?

18 At which ground did Everton gain their first FA Cup win in 1906?

19 Who retired in 1961 to become a lay preacher and a JP?

20 Which year in the 1980s did neither club contest the Charity Shield?

Quiz 13 Pot Luck 7

Answers – see page 223

LEVEL 3

1 Who was 18 years and 14 days old when he played in the Brighton v Manchester Utd FA Cup Final?

2 Sir Stanley Matthews was manager of which English club?

3 Who got into bother for calling referee Robbie Hart a "Muppet"?

4 At which club did Tim Sherwood make his League debut?

5 In which decade did Ipswich Town first win the Championship?

6 Which club had a fanzine called *Voice of the Beehive*?

7 John Neal followed Geoff Hurst as manager of which club?

8 Who moved from Bury to Southampton for £375,000, in October 1991 to set a club record for a transfer fee received?

9 Which club was once known as Christ Church FC?

10 To one each way, how many international goals did Kevin Beattie score?

11 Mike Newell and Gary McAllister were in the same team at which club?

12 Which Pat became boss of Leyton Orient in 1995?

13 Jim Beglin first played in an FA Cup Final for which team?

14 What was the first name of ex-WBA and Ipswich Town player Zondervan?

15 Which defender was making his Leeds Utd debut in the same game as Gordon Strachan's first appearance?

16 Who was in goal when Tottenham Hotspur won the FA Cup Final in the 1987?

17 What was the first club that Billy Bremner managed?

18 Who created a record for Derby County by playing 486 League games?

19 What is Phil Babb's middle name?

20 Which club used to play at Steeles Field and Ravenshaws Field?

Answers

Pot Luck 8 (see Quiz 15)
1 Southampton. 2 Peterborough. 3 Graham Taylor. 4 Sterland.
5 Jonathan. 6 Tottenham Hotspur. 7 Grimsby Town.
8 Wealdstone. 9 Blackburn Rovers. 10 Hartlepool Utd.
11 Oldham Athletic. 12 Todd. 13 Tottenham Hotspur.
14 Norwich City. 15 1890s. 16 Hull City. 17 Southend Utd.
18 Phil Babb. 19 Carlisle Utd. 20 10.

1 Who were the first team to beat Tottenham Hotspur in an FA Cup Final?

2 Which 1990s Final had opposing players with the same surname?

3 In which decade was the trophy won by a team not from England?

4 Which team were the first to arrive at Wembley by helicopter?

5 Kevin Reeves hit a Final goal for which club?

6 Bramall Lane, Goodison Park and Villa Park – which of these grounds has not staged an FA Cup Final replay?

7 In the 1980s and 1990s, which player appeared in four Finals and was on the losing team each time?

8 What was the first FA Cup Final to be drawn at Wembley?

9 Which Arsenal defender brought Paul Allen down from behind in 1980 when he was clear on goal?

10 In which decade could the crowd at a Final correctly name the referee by shouting, "The referee's a Bastard!"?

11 What is the biggest victory in a Final, and who were the teams?

12 Who was in goal for Spurs when they won the trophy in 1981?

13 Where were Finals played immediately before the opening of Wembley?

14 Which club captain played in the Brighton v Manchester Utd replay but not in the first game?

15 In 1978, which spectator said, "I thought the No 10 Whymark played exceptionally well", when in fact he hadn't played at all?

16 Who were the first side to lose a Wembley FA Cup Final?

17 Which brothers played together in a 1970s Final?

18 In which decade was extra time first played?

19 Who scored an own goal for Blackburn in 1960?

20 Andy Lochhead played in a Final for which club?

Quiz 15 Pot Luck 8

1 Dennis Wise joined Wimbledon after which club released him?

2 Which club had 19 points deducted in 1968 for making illegal payments to players?

3 Which manager brought Dwight Yorke to Villa Park?

4 Which Mel was with Sheffield Wednesday when he made his only England appearance in 1988 against Saudi Arabia?

5 What is Nick Barmby's middle name?

6 Which London team used to play at Northumberland Park?

7 With 448 League games in the 1950s and 1960s, Keith Jobling set an appearance record at which club?

8 Which non League club did Stuart Pearce leave to go into the League?

9 Which club in the north of England did Ossie Ardiles play for?

10 What was the first club that Brian Clough managed?

11 Paul Warhurst and Earl Barrett were in the same team at which club?

12 Which Colin became boss of Middlesbrough in 1990?

13 Steve Hodge first played in an FA Cup Final for which team?

14 At which club did Robert Fleck make his English League debut?

15 In what decade did Dumbarton first win the championship?

16 Which club had a fanzine called *Tiger Rag*?

17 Peter Taylor followed Barry Fry as manager of which club?

18 Who moved from Coventry City for £3,750,000 in September 1994 to set a club record for a transfer fee received?

19 Which club was once known as Shaddongate United?

20 To two each way, how many international goals did Leighton James score?

1   At which three clubs did the Futcher twins play together?

2   Who were the first brothers to win European Championship medals?

3   At which club did the Laudrup brothers begin their careers?

4   Who were the only brothers to play on the same side in a 60s FA Cup Final?

5   Which brothers Graham and Ron were at Oxford Utd in the 1960s?

6   In the 1980 Luton v QPR game, which brothers Martyn and Viv were opponents after coming on as subs?

7   Liam Brady's elder brothers Ray and Pat were together at which club?

8   What was the surname of 1950s Newcastle Utd brothers Ted and George?

9   Jimmy and John Conway were at which club together in the 1970s?

10   Mike Gatting's brother Steve played in an FA Cup Final for which team?

11   In the 50s which brothers each reached 200 League goals on the same day?

12   Which brother was at Aston Villa with Bruce Rioch?

13   The Linighan boys – Andy and David – started out at which club?

14   Which brothers were together at Villa for 18 years from the late 1930s?

15   Who were the goalkeeping brothers to be exchanged in the 60s?

16   What was the surname of dad Ken and son Peter both of Manchester City?

17   Which cousins played together in an FA Cup losing team in the 1980s?

18   Which member of a footballing family became the first non-British Scottish PFA Footballer of the Year?

19   Which Manchester City boss bought his own son Kevin?

20   What was the first name of George Eastham's father who played for England in 1935?

Quiz 17 Pot Luck 9

Answers – see page 227

1 What colour are FC Porto's shirts?

2 Mel Pejic set a League appearance record at which club?

3 Who was in goal when West Ham Utd won the FA Cup in 1980?

4 At which club did John McGinlay make his League debut?

5 In what decade did Derby County first win the Championship?

6 Which club had a fanzine called *Trumpton Times*?

7 Jim Smith replaced Gordon Lee as manager of which club?

8 Who moved from Cardiff to Sheffield Utd for £300,000 in 1994 to set a club record for a transfer fee received?

9 Which club was once known as Boscombe St Johns?

10 To one each way, how many international goals did Peter Beardsley score?

11 Haddock and Swan were in the same team at which club?

12 Which John became boss of Lincoln City in 1995?

13 Greg Downs played in an FA Cup Final for which team?

14 Who used to play at Abbs Field, Fulwell?

15 What is Warren Barton's middle name?

16 What was the first club that Bobby Gould managed?

17 Where did Portugal finish in the 1994 World Cup?

18 Which manager was dismissed by Manchester City 12 days into the 1993–94 season?

19 Ferenc Puskas played international soccer for which two countries?

20 John Arlott, the voice of cricket, was a fan of which club?

1 Who were the only team not to score in Euro 96?

2 Which country was the first to appear in three consecutive Finals?

3 In what year was the first European Championship Final played?

4 Which country hosted the 1992 competition?

5 In which year did Spain win the trophy?

6 The home countries, except Scotland, entered the second tournament. When was this?

7 Name the first two cities to have hosted Finals twice.

8 When did Italy win the trophy?

9 Which country won the Championship on penalties in 1976?

10 Who were the Dutch scorers in their Final victory over Russia?

11 Who scored the two goals to win Euro 96?

12 How many games were there in Euro 96?

13 When Andy Sinton went off, who was the last player to come on as a substitute for England in Euro 92?

14 Which French player finished as the top scorer in 1984?

15 At which two grounds were the Euro 96 semi-finals held?

16 Which English headmaster was a referee in Euro 96?

17 Who scored England's first ever European Championship goal?

18 Who inspired the starting of the Championship?

19 Who contested the first ever Championship final?

20 Who were the first host country to win the European Championship?

Answers

Early Days (see Quiz 20)
1 Royal Engineers. 2 Aston Villa. 3 Sunderland.
4 Wanderers. 5 Crystal Palace. 6 Leeds City. 7 Shinguards.
8 Blackburn Rovers. 9 George V was the first monarch at a Final.
10 Lord Arthur Kinnaird. 11 Hyde United. 12 Albert
Ironmonger. 13 Liverpool. 14 FIFA. 15 Ibrox. 16 James
Forrest. 17 Bradford. 18 Professional player. (A Scot paid to
play in England). 19 None. 20 Clydesdale.

1 In which decade did Chester add City to their name?

2 Which Nigel went on from non League St Blazey to play for England?

3 How many points did Newcastle Utd take from their first 10 games of the 1995–96 League season?

4 What is Peter Beagrie's middle name?

5 Which club used to play at the Antelope Ground?

6 Which Brian of Burnley made his only England appearance in 1961?

7 What was the first club that Arthur Cox managed?

8 Peter Allen set a League appearance record at which London club?

9 Gerry Ryan took temporary charge of which club in November 1991?

10 Manchester City in 1995 and Blackburn in 1996 both played how many League games before a win?

11 David Seaman and Peter Reid were in the same team at which club?

12 Which John first became boss of Millwall in 1986?

13 Clive Goodyear played in an FA Cup Final for which team?

14 At which club did England's Mark Wright make his League debut?

15 In what decade did Dundee first win the championship?

16 Which club had a fanzine called *Marching Altogether*?

17 Dave Bassett followed Billy McEwan as manager of which club?

18 Rufus Brevett moved for £250,000 to QPR in 1991 to set a record for a transfer fee received at which club?

19 Which club was once known as Singers FC?

20 To two each way, how many international goals did John Toshack score?

1 Who were the first team to lose an FA Cup Final?

2 William McGregor, who pushed for the formation of a League, was a director of which club?

3 Which club did Alf Common move from in the first £1,000 transfer?

4 Who were the first team to win the FA Cup three times in a row?

5 From 1895 to the First World War where were FA Cup Finals played?

6 Leeds United were formed following the demise of which team?

7 Samuel Widdowson of Nottingham Forest is credited with which innovation?

8 Who were the first team to score six goals in an FA Cup Final?

9 Which important spectator created a first at the Burnley v Liverpool 1914 FA Cup Final?

10 Which player turned out in nine of the first 12 FA Cup Finals?

11 Preston North End's 26 goals in an FA Cup game was against which team?

12 In 1904, which giant keeper made the first of 564 Notts County appearances?

13 Which club was the first to win promotion and the First Division in successive seasons?

14 What was formed in Paris on May 21, 1904?

15 At which ground did terracing collapse in 1902 killing 25 people?

16 Who was the first professional to play for England against Scotland?

17 In 1911 a new FA Cup was made in – and then won by the team from – which place?

18 In footballing terms what was a "Scottish professor"?

19 How many games did Preston North End lose in the first League season?

20 Who were the first team to lose a Scottish FA Cup Final?

Answers

Euro Champ'ship (see Quiz 18)
1 Turkey. 2 West Germany. (1972, 1976, 1980). 3 1960.
4 Sweden. 5 1964. 6 1964. 7 Paris and Rome. 8 1968.
9 Czechoslovakia. 10 Gullit and Van Basten. 11 Oliver Bierhoff.
12 31. 13 Paul Merson. 14 Michel Platini. 15 Old Trafford
and Wembley. 16 David Elleray. 17 Ron Flowers. 18 Henri
Delauney. 19 Soviet Union and Yugoslavia. 20 Spain (In 1964).

Quiz 21 Pot Luck 11

Answers – see page 231

LEVEL 3

1   Who were the opponents when Ian Rush hit his record breaking 24th goal for Wales?

2   Which brothers played in the 1976 European Cup Final?

3   Gary Bull established a record for most League goals in a season at which club?

4   At which club did Keith Curle make his League debut?

5   In what decade did Tottenham Hotspur first win the Championship?

6   Which club had a fanzine called *The Fox*?

7   Vic Crowe followed Tommy Docherty as manager of which club?

8   Who moved from Manchester City to Tottenham Hotspur for £1.7 million in 1988 to set a club record for a transfer fee received?

9   Which club was once known as St Domingo FC?

10 To two each way, how many international goals did Mike Channon score?

11 Goddard and Hebberd were in the same team at which club?

12 Which Sammy became boss of Doncaster in July 1994?

13 Tony Grealish first played in an FA Cup Final for which team?

14 What is Dave Beasant's middle name?

15 With 467 League games from 1964 to 1982 Colin Harrison set an appearance record at which club?

16 Stuart Williams won 33 of his Welsh caps while at which club?

17 Owlerton was the original name of which ground?

18 Who had been brought to Liverpool as Keegan's replacement before Kenny Dalglish's arrival?

19 Aged 29 Frank Sibley became the youngest League manager when he was at which club?

20 In which decade did Wales first win at Wembley?

Answers

Pot Luck 12 (see Quiz 23)
1 Scunthorpe Utd. 2 William. 3 Birmingham City. 4 Billy Bremner. 5 Leeds Utd. 6 Norwich City. 7 Hibernian.
8 Wales. 9 Notts County. 10 Torquay Utd. 11 West Ham Utd. 12 Buxton. 13 Fulham. 14 QPR. 15 1980s.
16 Newcastle Utd. 17 Plymouth Argyle. 18 Richard Money.
19 Clapton Orient. 20 4.

1 Which Scottish team are known as "The Loons"?

2 What was the nickname of Brazil's Garrincha?

3 Who was known as "Pele" in his Ipswich Town days?

4 Which great international forward became known as "The Little Canon"?

5 How was Austria's goal machine of the 1930s Franz Binder known?

6 Which Scottish team are known as Wee Jays?

7 United isn't the most original nickname, but how many teams could that apply to in the Premiership and English League sides in 1996–97?

8 What was Alan Kennedy's nickname at Liverpool?

9 Bauld, Conn and Wardhaugh formed "The Terrible Trio" at which club in the 1950s?

10 What is the nickname shared by clubs situated in Crieff Road, Perth, and Milton Road?

11 Which Scottish team are known as The Ton?

12 What was the nickname of early 20th century keeper Bill Foulke?

13 Which Scotland and Arsenal player was "The Wee Wizard"?

14 Which Manchester Utd player was known as "The Black Prince"?

15 Which international keeper of the 1990s rejoices in the nickname "El Loco"?

16 Which Scottish team are known as The Sons?

17 "The Famous Five" helped which Scottish club to the Championship just after the Second World War?

18 Which Liverpool player was "The Flying Pig"?

19 Who is nicknamed "Choccy"?

20 What was the nickname of Manchester Utd's early 20th century player Enoch Walker?

The 1960s (see Quiz 24)

Answers

1 Tony Kay, David Layne, Peter Swan. 2 Accrington Stanley.
3 Billy Wright. 4 Terry Bly. 5 Denis Law. 6 Tommy Docherty.
7 First League substitute. 8 George Best. 9 Rangers & Hibs.
10 Northampton Town. 11 Malcolm Allison. 12 Wolves. 13 Rest of the World XI. 14 Jimmy Dickinson. 15 Eusebio. 16 Don Revie.
17 Bobby Moncur. 18 WBA. 19 Swiss. 20 George Eastham.

Quiz 23 Pot Luck 12

Answers – see page 229

LEVEL 3 ⚽ ⚽ ⚽

1 Up to the late 1980s who used to play at The Old Showground?

2 What is Ian Bishop's middle name?

3 Joe Bradford set a record for most League goals in a season at which club?

4 Which Scottish captain was banned for life from playing for his country?

5 Hankin and Hart scored in the same European game for which club?

6 At which club did Dion Dublin make his League debut?

7 Keeper Andy Goram was at which club when he scored v Morton?

8 Which country did John Mahoney play for?

9 Who were the first English club to play 3,000 matches in the League?

10 Playing from 1947 to 1959, Dennis Lewis set a League appearance record at which seaside club?

11 Dicks and Dickens were in the same team at which club?

12 Which Mick became boss of Scunthorpe in March 1996?

13 Peter Mellor first played in an FA Cup Final for which team?

14 At which club did Chris Woods make his League debut?

15 In what decade did Dundee Utd first win the Championship?

16 Which club had a fanzine called *The Number Nine*?

17 Steve McCall followed Peter Shilton as manager of which club?

18 Who moved from Fulham to Liverpool for £333,333 in 1980 to set a club record for a transfer fee received?

19 What were Leyton Orient known as from entering the League and the end of the World Wars?

20 How many international goals did Steve Archibald score?

Answers

Pot Luck 11 (see Quiz 21)
1 Belgium. 2 Eddie and Frank Gray. 3 Barnet. 4 Bristol Rovers. 5 1950s. 6 Leicester City. 7 Aston Villa. 8 Paul Stewart. 9 Everton. 10 21. 11 Derby County. 12 Chung. 13 Brighton. 14 John. 15 Walsall. 16 WBA. 17 Hillsborough. 18 Craig Johnston. 19 QPR. 20 1970s.

1 Which three Sheffield Wednesday players were involved in the 1962 match-fixing scandal?

2 Which side resigned from the League in 1962?

3 Who followed George Swindin as manager of Arsenal?

4 Which Peterborough forward hit 52 goals in a season?

5 Who scored six for Manchester City in an abandoned FA Cup game?

6 Who managed Rotherham, QPR and Aston Villa in just six weeks?

7 What first went to Keith Peacock on the first day of the 1965–66 season?

8 Which English player was labelled "El Beatle" by the Portuguese press?

9 Which two Scottish clubs were involved in Colin Stein's £100,000 transfer?

10 In the 1960s, which club went from Division 4 to Division 1 and back again?

11 Who was Joe Mercer's assistant when Manchester City won the Championship?

12 In 1960, which club hit 100 goals for a third successive season?

13 Who did England play to celebrate the centenary of the Football Association?

14 Which Portsmouth and England wing-half retired in 1965?

15 Who was leading scorer in the 1966 World Cup tournament?

16 Who took over as manager of Leeds Utd in 1961?

17 Which Newcastle Utd player hit his first goals for seven years in the 1969 Inter-Cities Fairs Cup Final?

18 Alan Ashman was manager of which FA Cup winners?

19 What was the nationality of the referee in the 1966 World Cup Final?

20 Which player took Newcastle Utd to court?

Answers

Nicknames (see Quiz 22)
1 Forfar. 2 "The Little Bird". 3 Alan Brazil. 4 Ferenc Puskas.
5 "Bimbo". 6 Livingston. 7 16. 8 "Barney". 9 Hearts.
10 Saints (St Johnstone, Southampton). 11 Greenock Morton.
12 "Fatty". 13 Alex James. 14 Alex Dawson. 15 Rene
Higuita. 16 Dumbarton. 17 Hibernian. 18 Tommy Lawrence.
19 Brian McClair. 20 "Knocker".

Quiz 25 Pot Luck 13

Answers – see page 235

LEVEL 3

1 In 1984, who at Derby County became the League's youngest club chairman?

2 Where did Thomas Hässler go when he left Juventus in July 1991?

3 Dick Krzywicki played for which country in the 1970s?

4 At which club did Brian McClair make his League debut?

5 In what decade did Chelsea first win the Championship?

6 Which club has a fanzine called *Into The O Zone*?

7 Willie Maddren followed Malcolm Allison as manager of which club?

8 Who moved from Middlesbrough in August 1989 to set a club record for a transfer fee received?

9 Which club was once known as New Brompton?

10 To one each way, how many international goals did Terry Butcher score?

11 Speedie and Regis were in the same team at which club?

12 Which Peter became boss of Exeter in June 1995?

13 Cyrille Regis first played in an FA Cup Final for which team?

14 Ted Harper established a record for most League goals in a season at which club?

15 What is Clayton Blackmore's middle name?

16 Which club played at the White City in the 1930s and in the 1960s?

17 Mary Brown was involved in an affair with which soccer manager?

18 What was the first London club that Chris Armstrong played for?

19 Who was the Derby County chairman when Brian Clough resigned?

20 Which club claimed to have signed Gordon Strachan before he moved to Manchester Utd?

Answers

Pot Luck 14 (see Quiz 27)
1 Stranraer. 2 Gillingham & Ipswich Town. 3 John Toshack. 4 Port Vale. 5 Lloyd George. 6 Liverpool. 7 David May. 8 Juventus. 9 John Motson. 10 Blackpool. 11 WBA. 12 Smith. 13 Ipswich Town. 14 Port Vale. 15 1960s. 16 Norwich City. 17 Notts County. 18 Hartlepool Utd. 19 Manchester City. 20 Three.

1   Who scored all the goals in Aston Villa's 2–2 draw with Leicester City in 1976?

2   Where are you going if you walk down Bescot Crescent?

3   Who did Stoke sell to Chelsea in October 1993 for a club record fee?

4   Who is Burnley's most capped player?

5   Which famous Midlands side was founded by cricketing enthusiasts of the Wesleyan Chapel?

6   Before the 1990s, when did Manchester City last win the FA Cup?

7   Which club in the north west was the first outside London to install floodlights?

8   Which Wolves player moved for a £1 million to Manchester City in 1979?

9   Which side beat Hyde by a massive 26 goals to nil?

10 Who played for Blackpool, Coventry City, Manchester City, Burnley and Swansea, while clocking up 795 League appearances?

11 Which club did Martin Dobson manage between 1984 and 1989?

12 Blackburn's Colin Hendry began his career with which Scottish club?

13 Who is Blackpool's most capped player?

14 Name the trophy won by Birmingham City in 1991?

15 Who beat Stoke in the First Division play-offs in 1996?

16 Which manager took Coventry City into the first division in the 1960s?

17 Which club's score in two FA Cup Finals is 10 for and none against?

18 How many times did Wolves' Billy Wright play for England?

19 Who was Birmingham City boss between 1965 and 1970?

20 Who was Aston Villa's two goal hero in the 1957 FA Cup Final?

Quiz 27 Pot Luck 14

Answers – see page 233

LEVEL 3

1 Alphabetically, which is the last Scottish League club?

2 Which two English clubs have a badge with a horse on it?

3 Who was manager of Wales for 47 days?

4 In the 1920s, 1930s and 1940s which club used to play at the Recreation Ground, Hanley?

5 What are the two middle names of Noel Blake?

6 Wark and Walsh scored in the same European game for which club?

7 Who scored for Manchester Utd in the Cantona Kung-Fu game?

8 Jürgen Kohler moved for £4 million plus from Bayern Munich to which club?

9 Who commentated, "Stuart Pearce has got the taste of Wembley in his nostrils"?

10 Jimmy Hampson established a record for most League goals in a season at which club?

11 Talbot and Ford were in the same team at which club?

12 Which Alan became boss of Wycombe Wanderers in June 1995?

13 Clive Woods first played in an FA Cup Final for which team?

14 At which club did Mark Bright make his League debut?

15 In what decade did Kilmarnock first win the championship?

16 Which club has a fanzine called *Ferry Cross The Wensum*?

17 Neil Warnock followed John Barnwell as manager of which club?

18 Joe Allon moved to Chelsea in 1991 to set a record for a transfer fee received at which club?

19 Which club was once known as Ardwick FC?

20 To one each way, how many international goals did Chris Nichol score?

Answers

Pot Luck 13 (see Quiz 25)
1 Ian Maxwell. 2 Roma. 3 Wales. 4 Motherwell. 5 1950s.
6 Leyton Orient. 7 Middlesbrough. 8 Gary Pallister.
9 Gillingham. 10 Three. 11 Coventry City. 12 Fox.
13 Coventry City. 14 Blackburn Rovers. 15 Graham.
16 QPR. 17 Tommy Docherty. 18 Millwall. 19 Sam
Longston. 20 Cologne.

235

1 Who was the first player to score a hat-trick in a European Cup Final?

2 Which French team became the first to lose two Finals?

3 Who were the first British team to compete in the European Cup?

4 Which team appeared in the Final in 1993, 1994 and 1995?

5 Who scored the only goal to win the trophy for Aston Villa?

6 Which city hosted the Final when Liverpool first won?

7 Who was Liverpool skipper for the 1981 triumph?

8 Which Lancashire town team represented England in 1960–61?

9 Who met in the first all English tie in 1978–79?

10 Which team has represented Northern Ireland most times?

11 Who were the first club to eliminate Real Madrid from the competition?

12 To two years each way, when was the first Final played at Wembley?

13 Who was in goal for the first British European Cup winners?

14 Which was the first club to play a European Cup Final on their own ground?

15 Which Ipswich Town player scored five goals in the European Cup?

16 Who scored an amazing 46 goals in the European Cup for Benfica?

17 Which were the first team from Holland to win the trophy?

18 Which two clubs from the same British city played in the same competition?

19 Which London club pulled out of the first competition?

20 Who scored first for Manchester Utd in the 1960s Final v Benfica?

LEVEL 3

1 At which club did Terry Paine finish his playing career?

2 Who was the first black player to be named in an England under-21 squad?

3 Frank O'Farrell became manager of which country?

4 At which club did Paul Parker make his League debut?

5 In which decade did Leeds Utd first win the Championship?

6 Which club had a fanzine called *Deranged Ferret*?

7 Frank Worthington followed Bryan Hamilton as manager of which club?

8 Who moved from Oxford Utd to Derby County in 1988 to set a club record for a transfer fee received?

9 What was Grimsby Town once known as?

10 To one each way, how many international goals did Steve Coppell score?

11 Peter Nicholas and Clive Wilson were together at which club?

12 Which Steve became boss of Colchester Utd in January 1995?

13 Chris Waddle first played in an FA Cup Final for which team?

14 Who is Bolton Wanderers' all-time leading goalscorer?

15 Who scored 11 goals in QPR's first European season?

16 Who was boss of Millwall between 1982 and 1986?

17 Which club started out playing at Headington Quarry?

18 What is Reggie Blinker's middle name?

19 Who resigned as Tottenham Hotspur manager on June 23rd 1976?

20 Who retired, as a player in 1975 following the Celtic v Airdrie Scottish Cup Final?

Answers

Pot Luck 16 (see Quiz 31)
1 Manchester Utd (They never scored together at Ipswich Town).
2 Bournemouth. 3 Oldham Athletic. 4 Mike Bamber. 5 Marseille. 6 Glasgow. 7 Stamford Bridge. 8 Derby County. 9 Manchester Utd. 10 John. 11 Southampton. 12 York City. 13 Sunderland. 14 Stoke City. 15 1930s. 16 Nottingham Forest. 17 Chelsea. 18 Darren Peacock. 19 Manchester Utd. 20 Three.

LEVEL 3

1 Who scored an 1980s FA Cup Final replay penalty for Manchester Utd?

2 To three each way, it what year was the penalty kick introduced?

3 Who did Danny Blanchflower score against in the 1962 FA Cup Final?

4 In 1991 who became the first club to win an FA Cup penalty shoot out?

5 To one each way, how many penalty goals did Francis Lee get in 1971–72?

6 Which Birmingham City keeper saved a penalty with his first touch in his first match?

7 John Wark hit a penalty hat-trick against which European team?

8 Who was on the spot for Aston Villa v Manchester Utd in the 1994 League Cup Final?

9 Who missed Italy's final penalty in the 1994 World Cup?

10 Which international keeper scored three penalties in 1988 and 1989?

11 Who were the first nation to win a World Cup shoot out, in 1982?

12 Who saved 8 out of 10 penalties faced in 1979–80?

13 Who was beaten by Nigel Clough's 1989 League Cup Final penalty?

14 How many penalties were there in the Palace 2 v Brighton 1 game in 1989?

15 Ronnie Allen hit an FA Cup Final penalty in 1954 for which club?

16 Who were winners in 1992 in the first game where a top flight team went out of the FA Cup competition in a shoot out?

17 Which Nottingham Forest player was fouled in the incident leading to the penalty in the 1970s League Cup Final replay v Liverpool?

18 Which Manchester Utd keeper was club joint top scorer in mid-season 1974–75 because of his spot kick success?

19 Which nation won in the first major tournament decide on penalties?

20 Eddie Shinwell hit an FA Cup Final penalty for Blackpool in 1948 against which club?

Quote, Unquote (see Quiz 32)
Answers
1 Jasper Carrott. 2 John Motson. 3 Alex Ferguson. 4 Ron Atkinson. 5 Tommy Docherty. 6 Elton John. 7 Bill Nicholson. 8 Roy Hodgson. 9 Barry Fry. 10 Charlie Nicholas. 11 Trevor Phillips. 12 Vinnie Jones. 13 Graeme Souness. 14 Graham Kelly. 15 Ken Bates. 16 Kevin Keegan. 17 Paul Gascoigne. 18 The Chancellor. 19 Bob Paisley. 20 An artist.

Quiz 31 Pot Luck 16

Answers – see page 237

LEVEL 3

1 At which club did Brazil and Muhren score in the same European game?

2 In 1970–71 Ted MacDougall set a record for most League goals in a season at which club?

3 Which club used to play at Sheepfoot Lane?

4 Who was chairman of Brighton when Brian Clough was manager?

5 Dragan Stoijkovic moved from Red Star to which club in July 1990?

6 Which university did Brian McClair attend?

7 Which ground shares its names with a battle in England against the Norman invaders?

8 What was the first English club that Ted McMinn played for?

9 Colin McKee's only Manchester Utd appearance, in the last game of 1993–94, came when which club were champions?

10 What is Mark Bosnich's middle name?

11 Osman and Ruddock were in the same team at which club?

12 John Ward was boss of which club from 1991 to 1993?

13 Vic Halom first played in an FA Cup Final for which team?

14 At which club did Lee Chapman make his League debut?

15 In what decade did Motherwell first win the Championship?

16 Which club has a fanzine called *Garibaldi*?

17 Danny Blanchflower followed Ken Shellito as manager of which club?

18 Who moved from Hereford Utd to QPR in 1990 to set a club record for a transfer fee received?

19 Which club was once known as Newton Heath?

20 To two each way, how many international goals did Jim Baxter score?

Answers

Pot Luck 15 (see Quiz 29)
1 Hereford Utd. 2 Laurie Cunningham. 3 Iran. 4 Fulham. 5 1960s. 6 Lincoln City. 7 Tranmere Rovers. 8 Dean Saunders. 9 Grimsby Pelham. 10 7. 11 Chelsea. 12 Wignall. 13 Tottenham Hotspur. 14 Nat Lofthouse. 15 Stan Bowles. 16 George Graham. 17 Oxford Utd. 18 Waldie. 19 Terry Neill. 20 Billy McNeill.

Quiz 32 Quote, Unquote

Answers – see page 238

LEVEL 3

1 Who said, of Birmingham City, "You lose some, you draw some"?

2 Who said"For those watching in black and white, 'Spurs are in yellow shirts"?

3 Which manager declared, "Goalkeepers are a more protected species than the Golden Eagle"?

4 Who in 1991 would be "bananas" to leave Sheffield Wednesday?

5 Who said in 1977, "I have been punished for falling in love"?

6 Which new chairman said, "I hope people will not treat it as a gimmick"?

7 Who resigned from 'Spurs saying, "Players have become impossible"?

8 "Even the Pope would have second thoughts about the England job," was the response of which international manager?

9 Who was David Sullivan talking about when he said, "...after three years and 61 players, we think it is time someone else is entitled to a go"?

10 Which player's leaving caused Jimmy Greaves to say, "Stringfellows will miss him"?

11 Which FA commercial director had "Not necessarily" resigned in 1996?

12 Who said his pigs did not squeal as much as Ruud Gullit?

13 In 1990 which Scot said, "You cannot guarantee a thing in this game"?

14 Which football executive said, "People ... think I'm a short, fat bloke, whereas I'm really a tall fat bloke"?

15 Who said, "John Hollins ... has a very strong wife, maybe I should have made her manager"?

16 Which manager said, "I don't want to talk about Andy Cole"?

17 Who said, "They say injuries come in threes. In my case it seems to be 33s"?

18 Ossie Ardiles thought the England manager to be the most hated person in the country apart from who?

19 Which boss said, "Nobody has the right to win anything they haven't earned"?

20 According to Eric Cantona, who is "someone who can lighten up a dark room"?

Answers

On the Spot (see Quiz 30)
1 Arnold Muhren. 2 1891. 3 Adam Blacklaw. 4 Rotherham Utd.
5 13. 6 Tony Coton. 7 Aris Salonika. 8 Dean Saunders.
9 Roberto Baggio. 10 Rene Higuita. 11 West Germany. 12 Paul
Cooper. 13 Les Sealey. 14 Five (Palace had four and scored just
one). 15 WBA. 16 Southampton. 17 John O'Hare. 18 Alec
Stepney. 19 Czechoslovakia (1976 European Championship).
20 Manchester Utd.

LEVEL 3

1 What was the most notable feature of David Platt's debut for Bari?

2 What did Leeds Utd's shirts have written on them when they won the 1992 Championship?

3 Howard Kendall moved to Birmingham City as part of the deal that took which player to Everton in the 1970s?

4 At which extinct club did Darren Peacock make his League debut?

5 In which decade did Wolves first win the Championship?

6 Which club had a fanzine called *When Sunday Comes*?

7 Steve Perryman followed Frank McLintock as boss of which club?

8 Who moved from Port Vale to Sheffield Wednesday for £1 million in 1994 to set a club record for a transfer fee received?

9 What was dropped by Hartlepool United in 1968?

10 To two each way, how many England goals did Geoff Hurst score?

11 Eric Gates and Colin Pascoe were in the same team at which club?

12 Which Brian became boss of Huddersfield Town in June 1995?

13 Nigel Worthington first played in an FA Cup Final for which team?

14 In 1976–77 Peter Ward established a record for most League goals in a season at which club?

15 Gary Pierce was in goal as which club won the League Cup?

16 Part of whose CV would read – manager of Grimsby in 1951, moved to Workington in 1953?

17 Which club used to play at the Beeston Cricket Ground?

18 Which country did John Devine play for?

19 Samesh Kumar was first chairman at which club?

20 What is Steve Bould's middle name?

1 Who played on the left when Manchester Utd beat Benfica in the European Cup Final of 1968?

2 Who was Aston Villa's flying winger when they won the 1981 title?

3 Who hit the winning goal in the 1953 Matthews Final?

4 How was Manoel Francisco dos Santos better known?

5 Who was the first player to be Footballer of the Year twice?

6 Keith Gillespie made his League debut while on loan at which club?

7 At which club did Cliff Jones finish his playing career?

8 "This is the best amateur footballer I've seen," was Bob Paisley's assessment of which winger?

9 Which future England left winger was born in Bolton in July, 1971?

10 In which town was Ruel Fox born?

11 Left-winger Alan Hinton won the Championship with which team?

12 Which England winger has the middle names Charles Bryan?

13 A injury to which knee ended Steve Coppell's career?

14 Ryan Giggs scored in his first international against which country?

15 According to Bobby Charlton who "still had his magic" when nearing 50?

16 Which winger John was in England's 1966 World Cup squad?

17 Peter Barnes won England caps while at which three clubs?

18 George Best played for which Scottish club?

19 Which Scottish winger was nicknamed "The Flea"?

20 Which English club did Willie Henderson play for?

1 Which Welshman signed a three-year contract as coach to Sporting Lisbon in July 1984?

2 What is Mark Bright's middle name?

3 Joe Mercer was nearly 38 when he played in an FA Cup Final for which club?

4 In 1995–96, Arsenal, Colchester Utd and Preston North End shared what in common?

5 Which club used to play at the Town Ground?

6 George Beel established a record for most League goals in a season at which club?

7 Which club did Gary Sprake join when he left Leeds Utd?

8 Thomas Doll went from Hamburg to which club in June 1991?

9 At which club did Miller and Hazard score in the same Euro game?

10 Who was stripped of the Carlisle captaincy for playing cricket until the end of the county season?

11 Nigel Pearson and Alan Harper were in the same team at which club?

12 Which John became boss of Wigan in November 1995?

13 Terry Venables first played in an FA Cup Final for which team?

14 At which club did Steve McMahon make his League debut?

15 In what decade did Rangers first win the Championship?

16 Which club had a fanzine called *No More Pie In The Sky*?

17 Gordon Milne followed Joe Mercer as manager of which club?

18 Who moved from Hull to Middlesbrough for £750,000 in 1991 to set a club record for a transfer fee received?

19 What was Mansfield's last name before Town was added?

20 To one each way, how many international goals did Danny Blanchflower score?

Answers

Pot Luck 17 (see Quiz 33)
1 Missed a penalty. 2 Top Man. 3 Bob Latchford. 4 Newport County. 5 1950s. 6 Liverpool. 7 Brentford. 8 Ian Taylor.
9 The letter s from the name Hartlepools. 10 24.
11 Sunderland. 12 Horton. 13 Sheffield Wednesday.
14 Brighton. 15 Wolves. 16 Bill Shankly. 17 Notts County.
18 Republic of Ireland. 19 Birmingham City. 20 Andrew.

1 Who was the first Scottish player to be sent off in an international?

2 Which Scottish player became Charlton Athletic's most capped player?

3 Who is Scotland's youngest player to win a full international cap?

4 In what decade was the first official Scotland v England game?

5 Which club did George Young play for?

6 When Scotland hammered England 5–1 at Wembley in 1928, what nickname were they given?

7 Which Celtic star was diagnosed diabetic after playing in the 1974 World Cup squad?

8 From 1974, how many consecutive World Cup tournaments did Scotland reach?

9 What was the first English club that Alex James played for?

10 Who scored twice for Scotland at Wembley in 1963 in the 2–1 victory?

11 At which Scottish club did Dave Mackay start his career?

12 How many caps did Bill Shankly win?

13 Which Liverpool and Scottish international star played twice for Great Britain against the Rest of Europe?

14 Which Scottish international took Newcastle Utd to the title in 1927?

15 What was the result of Scotland's Group 4 game against Iran in the 1978 World Cup?

16 What nickname was given to striker Charlie Fleming?

17 Who captained the great 1920s, 5–1-winning Scottish side?

18 Whose last game for Scotland was the 1978 World Cup defeat by Peru, in which he missed a penalty?

19 In which year did Scotland pull out of the Rous Cup?

20 Which Scottish manager suffered only three defeats in his 12 games?

1 Signed in the 1990s, who was the first Bolivian to play English football?

2 Which Liverpool manager sold Peter Beardsley?

3 What is Tim Breaker's middle name?

4 At which club did Warren Barton make his League debut?

5 In which decade did Aston Villa first win the Championship?

6 Which club had a fanzine called *No One Likes Us*?

7 Terry Cooper followed Roy Hodgson as manager of which club?

8 Who moved from Dundee Utd to Rangers for £4 million in 1993 to set a club record for a transfer fee received?

9 Which club once had Fosse at the end of its name?

10 To one each way, how many international goals did Bob Latchford score?

11 Curle and Scales were in the same team at which club?

12 Which Dave became boss of Stockport County in March 1995?

13 Terry McDermott first played in an FA Cup Final for which team?

14 In 1981–82 Craig Madden established a record for most League goals in a season at which club?

15 Which club used to play at the The Nest?

16 On Good Friday, 1936, Swansea travelled to Plymouth. In what may be the worst-ever holiday travelling, where did they play the following day?

17 Who went from Real Madrid to Torino in June 1990?

18 Who was top scorer when Manchester Utd were Champions in 1993–94?

19 Which Italian team did Luther Blissett play for?

20 Which former Boston player/manager became England Technical Director?

LEVEL 3 ⚽ ⚽ ⚽

1 Who took Swindon Town to successive promotions in 1986 and 1987?

2 Keith Edwards hit 35 goals in a season to take which club out of the old Fourth Division?

3 Who were the last Fourth Division Champions?

4 Micky Stockwell was ever present as which club made the top flight?

5 Which veteran striker was at Blackburn, WBA and Wycombe in successive promotion seasons?

6 Who was boss when Manchester Utd were last promoted?

7 Which London club were twice Second Division champions in the 1980s?

8 Houston and Holton played in which team on the up?

9 How many points did Newcastle Utd get from the first 10 games of the 1992–93 promotion season?

10 Who was boss when Oxford Utd reached the top flight for the first time ever?

11 Howard Kendall took which team out of the Third Division?

12 Who was top scorer when Swansea hit the First Division in 1981?

13 Peter Hucker was in goal as which club reached the First Division?

14 Who was boss when Norwich City were 1986 Second Division Champions?

15 Noel Blake and Kenny Swain played in which 1980s promoted team?

16 Who was Manchester City's keeper in the 1989 promotion to the top flight?

17 Who was Newcastle Utd's tcp scorer in the 1992–93 promotion season?

18 Who were the first club to gain promotion and win the First Division in consecutive seasons?

19 Who was boss when Chelsea were Division 2 champions in 1988–89?

20 Price and Sellars played in which team on the up?

Going Down (see Quiz 40)
1 Frank Worthington. 2 Tommy Docherty. 3 31. 4 Luton Town. 5 Wolves. 6 West Ham Utd & Ipswich Town. 7 Three.
8 Hammond. 9 18. 10 Notts County. 11 Billy McNeill.
12 Sunderland. 13 Workington. 14 Ipswich Town.
15 Gateshead. 16 Bottom (22nd). 17 Sunderland. 18 Four.
19 Manchester Utd. 20 Bristol City.

LEVEL 3 ⚽ ⚽ ⚽

1 Which defender was the only ever present for England after eight games with Don Revie in charge?

2 Which manager has spent the shortest time as boss of West Ham Utd?

3 Who signed Stuart Pearce at Coventry City?

4 Quantrill was the first English international whose surname began with a Q. Who is the only other one?

5 Which ex Manchester Utd player set up the Bobby Stokes FA Cup winner?

6 Which ground used to be home to Northampton?

7 What is Steve Bruce's middle name?

8 In 1985–86 David Crown set a record for most League goals in a season at which club?

9 What did Kettering do in the mid-1970s that made the FA tell them not to do it again, but everybody does now?

10 Pike and Goddard scored in the same European game for which club?

11 Dave Thomas and John Hollins were in the same team at which club?

12 Which Eddie became boss of Torquay Utd in 1995?

13 Jimmy Gabriel first played in an FA Cup Final for which team?

14 At which club did Mark Hateley make his League debut?

15 In what decade did Newcastle Utd first win the Championship?

16 Which club has a fanzine called *January 3rd 88*?

17 Terry Venables followed Malcolm Allison as manager of which club?

18 Who moved from Lincoln City to Newcastle Utd in 1995 to set a club record for a transfer fee received?

19 Which London club were Rovers, then Athletic, then went to a single name?

20 To two each way, how many international goals did Colin Stein grab?

Answers

Pot Luck 19 (see Quiz 37)
1 Jaime Moreno (Middlesbrough). 2 Graeme Souness. 3 Sean.
4 Maidstone Utd. 5 1890s. 6 Millwall. 7 Bristol City.
8 Duncan Ferguson. 9 Leicester City. 10 5. 11 Wimbledon.
12 Jones. 13 Newcastle Utd. 14 Bury. 15 Norwich City.
16 Newcastle. 17 Martin Vasquez. 18 Eric Cantona. 19 AC Milan. 20 Howard Wilkinson.

1 Who was joint top scorer with Arthur Graham as Leeds Utd went down in 1982?

2 Who was boss when Manchester Utd were last relegated?

3 Cambridge Utd in 1983–84 set a record for the longest sequence without a win. How many games did this last?

4 Kamara and Dreyer played in which team leaving the top flight?

5 Paul Bradshaw was ever present in goal as which team went down in 1982?

6 In the 1990s John Lyall was at which two clubs in relegation seasons?

7 To two each way, how many Division 1 games did Stoke City win in 1984–85?

8 Digby, Sheffield and which other keeper shared the 100 goals Swindon Town let in on leaving the Premier League in 1994?

9 On their way out of the League for ever, Darwen chalked up how many consecutive defeats in 1898–99?

10 Craig and Chris Short played in which team leaving the top flight?

11 Who was Aston Villa boss in their 1986–87 relegation season?

12 Clive Walker was top scorer in which side's relegation season?

13 Which team left the League after being bottom of the Fourth Division in 1976 and 1977?

14 Guentchev and Paz played in which team leaving the top flight?

15 Which team, third from the bottom of the League in 1960, applied for re-election for the first time in over twenty years, yet still got voted out?

16 What was the highest position that WBA reached in 1985–86?

17 Who were in the First Division from 1890 until relegation in 1958?

18 How many keepers did Oldham Athletic use in 1993–94?

19 McCalliog and Macari played in which team leaving the top flight?

20 Which team was relegated in 1980, 1981 and 1982?

Quiz 41 Pot Luck 21

Answers – see page 251

LEVEL 3 ⚽ ⚽ ⚽

1 Who in the 1970s was sacked six weeks after winning the FA Cup?

2 What is Robbie Fowler's middle name?

3 Gary O'Reilly scored in an FA Cup Final for which club?

4 At which club did Andy Sinton make his League debut?

5 In which decade did Nottingham Forest first win the Championship?

6 Which club has a fanzine called *The Holy Trinity*?

7 Dixie McNeil followed Bobby Roberts as manager of which club?

8 Who set the most League goals in a season record at Manchester Utd with 32 in 1959–60?

9 Which club was once known as Thames Ironworks FC?

10 To two each way, how many England goals did Steve Bloomer score?

11 Ossie Ardiles and Trevor Francis were in the same team at which club?

12 Kevin Cullis was briefly boss of which League club in 1996?

13 Alec Lindsay first played in an FA Cup Final for which team?

14 Which club beat Arsenal to win the European Super Cup in 1995?

15 Who was George Chisholm playing for when he scored a League Cup Final own goal?

16 Kindon and Munro hit Euro goals in the same game for which club?

17 Who beat England in the quarter-finals of the 1962 World Cup?

18 Who in 1979 became the first person to play 100 League games for four different clubs?

19 Who was the boss when Bolton Wanderers went down to the Fourth Division for the first time ever?

20 Who lost to Parma in the 1995 UEFA Cup Final?

Answers

Pot Luck 22 (see Quiz 43)
1 Brian Kidd. 2 Bradford Park Avenue. 3 Adrian. 4 Southampton. 5 Malmo. 6 Glenn Cockerill. 7 Eamon Dunphy. 8 Nottingham Forest. 9 Mo Johnston. 10 Manchester City. 11 Leicester City. 12 Eustace. 13 Sunderland. 14 Bournemouth. 15 Notts County. 16 Carlisle Utd. 17 Middlesbrough. 18 Italy. 19 Strollers. 20 10.

1 Who played in both Manchester Utd's 1985 and 1995 FA Cup Final sides?

2 Which two Munich crash survivors played in the 1968 European Cup Final?

3 Who was United's first-ever League substitute?

4 What was the name of Martin Buchan's Manchester Utd playing brother?

5 What was the offence for which Kanchelskis was sent off in the 1994 League Cup Final?

6 In which country was Jimmy Nicholl born?

7 Against which side did Ryan Giggs score his first League goal?

8 In the club's founding days what did the letters LYR stand for?

9 Which other player joined United as part of the Bryan Robson deal?

10 Who took over as an emergency keeper in the 1957 FA Cup Final?

11 To two either way, how many international caps did George Best win?

12 Who was the only ever present in the title winnning team of 1993–94?

13 In what year did Sir Matt become United manager?

14 Against which team did Bryan Robson score his last goal in a competitive match?

15 David Beckham hit his first Euro goal against which team?

16 Who was sent off in the 1990s European Champions League 3–1 defeat in Gothenburg?

17 What shirt number did Mark Hughes usually wear in his first three years at Manchester Utd?

18 Which team did Lee Sharpe support as a boy?

19 Tommy Docherty's first signing was which Scottish fullback?

20 Bobby Charlton's last United League appearance was at which ground?

Answers

The 1970s (see Quiz 44)
1 Peter Bonetti. 2 Czechoslovakia. 3 Sammy Nelson. 4 Allan Simonsen. 5 44. 6 Total football. 7 Denis Law. 8 Jack Charlton. 9 Jan Tomaszewski. 10 Ted MacDougall. 11 Terry Paine. 12 George Best. 13 Pele. 14 Ron Saunders. 15 David Nish. 16 Greaves and Armfield. 17 Colchester Utd. 18 Nottingham Forest. 19 Tottenham Hotspur. 20 Jack Taylor.

1   Which British player played in a European Cup Final on his 19th birthday?

2   Which former league club had a pavilion called the Dolls House?

3   What is Ruel Fox's middle name?

4   Blyth, Gilchrist and Steele played for which 1970s FA Cup Finalists?

5   Who lost 1–0 to Nottingham Forest in the Final of the 1979 European Cup?

6   In 1988, TV film evidence showed that Paul Davis of Arsenal had broken which Southampton player's jaw?

7   Which Republic of Ireland international of the 1960s wrote the book *Only A Game* in the 1970s?

8   Lee Chapman first played in a League Cup Final for which club?

9   Which Catholic international was signed by Graeme Souness at Rangers?

10   Kidd and Power scored Euro goals in the same game for which club?

11   Mike Newell and Gary McAllister were in the same team at which club?

12   Which Peter was Leyton Orient boss from 1991 to 1994?

13   Anton Rogan first played in an FA Cup Final for which team?

14   At which club did Efan Ekoku make his League debut?

15   With 124 goals Les Bradd is all-time top League scorer at which club?

16   Which club had a fanzine called *So, Jack Ashurst, Where's My Shirt*?

17   Malcolm Allison followed Bobby Murdoch as manager of which club?

18   Which team first beat England at Wembley in a World Cup game?

19   What followed West Bromwich before the name Albion was introduced?

20   To one each way, how many international goals did Northern Ireland's Johnny Crossan score in the 1960s?

Pot Luck 21 (see Quiz 41)
1 Tommy Docherty. 2 Bernard. 3 Crystal Palace.
4 Cambridge Utd. 5 1970s. 6 Aston Villa. 7 Wrexham.
8 Dennis Violett. 9 West Ham Utd. 10 28. 11 QPR.
12 Swansea City. 13 Liverpool. 14 AC Milan.
15 Sunderland. 16 Wolves. 17 Brazil. 18 Alan Ball.
19 Phil Neal. 20 Juventus.

Answers

Quiz 44 The 1970s

Answers – see page 250

LEVEL 3 ⚽ ⚽ ⚽

1 Who kept goal as England lost to West Germany in the 1970 World Cup?

2 Who were the opponents when Viv Anderson became England's first black international footballer?

3 Which Arsenal player dropped his shorts to the crowd in a 1979 game against Coventry City?

4 Which Dane was named as European Footballer in the Year in 1977?

5 How many days did Brian Clough reign as boss of Leeds Utd in 1974?

6 What was the term used to describe Holland's fluid soccer?

7 Which ex-Manchester Utd star scored the goal that condemned his old club to relegation?

8 Which manager took Middlesbrough into the top flight?

9 Who kept goal for Poland at Wembley in the 1974 World Cup qualifier?

10 Which Bournemouth striker hit nine goals in an FA Cup tie?

11 Which ex-England player made 824 League appearances?

12 Who scored within 71 seconds of his Fulham debut in 1977?

13 Which international made his final appearance for his current team New York Cosmos against former team from the same continent in front of 77,000 at Giants Stadium?

14 Which manager was in four out of five consecutive League Cup Finals?

15 Which fullback moved for a record fee from Leicester City to Derby County in 1972?

16 Which two ex-England players – both Jimmy – retired in 1971?

17 Which giant-killers knocked Leeds Utd out of the 1970–71 FA Cup?

18 Which team went 42 consecutive League games without defeat?

19 Who did Arsenal beat in the final league game of the double season?

20 Which English referee controlled the 1974 World Cup Final?

Answers

Manchester Utd (see Quiz 42)
1 Mark Hughes. 2 Bobby Charlton & Bill Foulkes. 3 John Fitzpatrick. 4 George. 5 Deliberate handball. 6 Canada. 7 Manchester City. 8 Lancashire and Yorkshire Railway. 9 Remi Moses. 10 Jackie Blanchflower. 11 37 12 Denis Irwin. 13 1945. 14 Oldham Athletic. 15 Galatasaray. 16 Paul Ince. 17 No 9. 18 Aston Villa. 19 Alex Forsyth. 20 Stamford Bridge.

1 Nigel Jemson scored in a League Cup Final for which club?

2 How many days was Jock Stein in charge of Leeds Utd?

3 Who lost to Arsenal in the 1970 UEFA Cup Final?

4 At which club did Pat Nevin make his Scottish League debut?

5 In what decade did Sunderland first win the Championship?

6 Which club had a fanzine called *Beesotted*?

7 Danny Bergara followed Asa Hartford as manager of which club?

8 Which Celtic player fractured his skull against Falkirk in 1972?

9 Which club was once known as West Herts?

10 To two each way, how many international goals did Martin Chivers score?

11 The Harris brothers were in the same team at which London club in the 1960s?

12 Which Alan became boss of York City in 1983?

13 Barry Venison first played in an FA Cup Final for which team?

14 What is Marcus Gayle's middle name?

15 Holland and Jennings scored Euro goals in the same game for which club?

16 With 39 scored, Derek Reeves set the most League goals in a season record at which club?

17 Which European country was the first to stage the World Cup?

18 Stuart McCall scored in an FA Cup Final for which club?

19 Which club beat Rangers to win the European Super Cup in 1972?

20 Colin Irwin played in a League Cup Final for which club?

1 Who was in goal for Nottingham Forest in the 1992 League Cup Final?

2 Who was in goal for England in the 1997 World Cup qualifier v Italy at Wembley?

3 Who was in goal for Leeds Utd in the 1972 and 1973 FA Cup Finals?

4 John Burridge made his League debut for which club who are now no longer in the League?

5 Who, in the 1990s, saved five penalties in three days – three against Tranmere in a League Cup semi-final and two v Tottenham Hotspur?

6 At which League club did Chris Turner make his debut?

7 Which club did Coventry sign Steve Ogrizovic from?

8 Harry Dowd was in an FA Cup winning 1960s team at which club?

9 Phil Parkes made his League debut at which club?

10 Which club did Jim Leighton join when he finally left Manchester Utd?

11 Who was in goal for Oldham Athletic in the 1990 League Cup Final?

12 Who went down from the top flight with Millwall in 1990 and Bolton in '96?

13 Which veteran keeper became player/manager of Exeter in 1995?

14 Which League Cup Final winning side did Alan Judge play for?

15 Which keeper spent 20 years with Portsmouth?

16 Which keeper was injured in the 1957 FA Cup Final?

17 Northern Ireland's Harry Gregg was first capped while at which League club?

18 Who was in goal for Brighton in the 1980s FA Cup Final?

19 At which club did Bobby Mimms make his League debut?

20 Dave Gaskell was in an FA Cup winning 1960s team at which club?

1 What is Bruce Grobbelaar's middle name?

2 Gillard, Hazell and Waddock played for which 1980s FA Cup Finalists?

3 With 171 goals Clarrie Bourton became all-time top League scorer at which club?

4 Hodgson and Neal scored Euro goals in the same game for which club?

5 Which club did Raich Carter and Don Revie play for in the 1950s?

6 What are the first names of the soccer playing Brightwell brothers?

7 Barlow, Barrett and Bunn played for which League Cup finalists?

8 Which two ex-West Ham Utd players have managed Norwich City in the post-war period?

9 With which team did John Lukic make his League debut?

10 Who lost 5–3 to Benfica in the Final of the 1962 European Cup?

11 Mike Hooper and John Barnes were in the same team at which club?

12 Which Tommy became boss of Wolves in 1984?

13 John Harkes first played in an FA Cup Final for which team?

14 At which Scottish club did John Spencer make his League debut?

15 Which German team is the most successful in domestic competitions?

16 Which club has a fanzine called *Hello Albert*?

17 Jim Smith followed Willie McFaul as manager of which club?

18 Liverpool sold Larry Lloyd to which club?

19 Which club once had Town Swifts added to its name?

20 To one each way, how many international goals did Gerry Armstrong score?

Quiz 48 Extra Time

Answers – see page 254

LEVEL 3 ⚽ ⚽ ⚽

1 Who came on in extra time for the Republic of Ireland in the Italia 90 World Cup game against Romania?

2 Preud'homme was in goal for which team sent out of Italia 90 in extra time?

3 An extra time goal by which country sent Nigeria out of the 1994 World Cup?

4 A 1940s extra time FA Cup goal by Duffy won the cup for which club?

5 To three years each way, when did the first FA Cup Final go to extra time?

6 In Italia 90 which country played extra time in both the quarter-finals and semi-finals?

7 English-based Guentchev came on in extra time in USA 1994 against which side?

8 What was the 90-minute score in the Arsenal v Liverpool 1971 FA Cup Final?

9 What was the a.e.t. score in the France v West Germany 1982 World Cup semi-final?

10 Which team won three Scottish FA Cup Finals in a row – all after extra time?

11 An extra-time goal by Ian St John beat which team in an FA Cup Final?

12 Andersson and Raducioiu hit 1994 World Cup ET goals in which game?

13 How many quarter-finals went to extra time in the 1986 World Cup?

14 Which keeper was beaten by Jeff Astle's 1968 FA Cup-winner?

15 What was the 90-minute score in England v Cameroon in Italia 90?

16 Which club beat Tottenham Hotspur after extra time in a League Cup Final?

17 After World War II, which team first won an FA Cup Final a.e.t.?

18 In Mexico 1986 who beat the USSR 4–3 after an extra-time gripper?

19 Which German had a 'goal' disallowed v England in extra time of Euro 96?

20 How many minutes of extra-time were needed in the Euro 96 Final?

Answers

Keepers (see Quiz 46)
1 Andy Marriott. 2 Ian Walker. 3 David Harvey. 4 Workington. 5 Mark Bosnich. 6 Sheffield Wednesday. 7 Shrewsbury Town. 8 Manchester City. 9 Walsall. 10 Dundee. 11 Andy Rhodes. 12 Keith Branagan. 13 Peter Fox. 14 Oxford Utd. 15 Alan Knight. 16 Ray Wood. 17 Doncaster Rovers. 18 Graham Moseley. 19 Rotherham Utd. 20 Manchester Utd.

1 Which American has played in England for Derby County, Sheffield Wednesday and West Ham Utd?

2 Which player of the 1990s with Forest has the middle name Rasdal?

3 Rostron and Gilligan scored Euro goals in the same game for which club?

4 At which club did Les Sealey make his League debut?

5 In what decade did WBA first win the Championship?

6 Which club has a fanzine called *On the 2nd May*?

7 Dave Sexton followed Gordon Jago's first spell as manager of which club?

8 Which ground is in Floyd Road?

9 Which club was once known as Belmont AFC?

10 To one each way, how many international goals did Colin Bell score?

11 The severe weather in 1963 caused which event to be put back three weeks?

12 Which Terry became boss of Birmingham City in 1991?

13 Danny Wallace first played in an FA Cup Final for which team?

14 Which club beat AC Milan to win the European Super Cup in 1994?

15 Williams, Walker and Wassall played in a League Cup Final for which club?

16 What was the name of the ITV theme for the 1986 World Cup Finals?

17 Freddie Steele is all-time top League scorer at which club?

18 Alan Taylor scored twice in an FA Cup Final for which club?

19 Who lost to Leeds Utd on the away goals rule in the 1971 UEFA Cup Final?

20 33 spectators died in 1946 after crash barriers gave way at which ground?

Pot Luck 26 (see Quiz 51)
1 Sheffield Wednesday. 2 Newcastle Utd. 3 Nottingham Forest.
4 Helmut Haller. 5 Southampton. 6 Aston Villa. 7 Leeds Utd.
8 John Barnes. 9 Hamburg. 10 Wayne. 11 Alan Ashman.
12 Everton. 13 Sunderland. 14 Bolton Wanderers.
15 Howard Kendall. 16 Arsenal. 17 Luton Town.
18 Barnsley. 19 Torquay Town. 20 Three.

Answers

Quiz 50 FA Cup

Answers – see page 260

LEVEL 3 ⚽ ⚽ ⚽

1 Brooke and Henry were subs for which two Final opponents?

2 Which player in recent times took the actual FA Cup out of England?

3 Who were the first team outside the First Division to win the FA Cup in the 20th century?

4 What was the cost of the original FA Cup trophy?

5 Barrie Williams was boss of which 1989 giant-killers?

6 Who were the first club from the top flight to go out of the trophy on penalties?

7 Who scored an FA Cup Final winner against Everton in the 1980s and later moved to Goodison Park?

8 David Nish became youngest FA Cup Final skipper with which team?

9 What links the teams of Leicester City in 1961, Sunderland in 1973 and Crystal Palace in 1990?

10 Who was 17 years 256 days old when he played for a London side in a Final?

11 Who were the first team outside the First Division to win the FA Cup after the Second World War?

12 In 1958, 83-year-old Harry Burge claimed what link with the FA Cup?

13 Ian Callaghan played in 88 FA Cup games, mostly with Liverpool, but with which other two clubs?

14 How many teams entered the first FA Cup tournament?

15 Up to the end of the 20th century, which side has appeared in most semi-finals?

16 Where was the Chelsea v Leeds Utd replayed FA Cup Final held?

17 Who was the first post-war player to score in every round of the FA Cup?

18 In the pre shoot-out days, how many hours of play did the 1979 tie between Arsenal and Sheffield Wednesday last for?

19 Who scored within 120 seconds of the 1987 Tottenham Hotspur v Coventry City Final?

20 Who did Billy Hampson, aged 41 years, 257 days, play for in a 1920s Final?

Full Time (see Quiz 52)
1 Germany. 2 Real Zaragoza. 3 Luton Town. 4 Leicester City.
5 Barrow. 6 W Germany. 7 Hewitt. 8 Alan Sunderland.
9 McQueen & McIlroy. 10 Sweden. 11 Michael Thomas.
12 Wigan Athletic. 13 Bobby Moore. 14 Roberto Baggio.
15 Crystal Palace (v Leicester City). 16 Making illegal payments.
17 Bradford Park Avenue. 18 Paul Gascoigne. 19 Sammy McIlroy, Gordon McQueen. 20 Maidstone.

Answers

1 Which club did Alan Harper join when he left Everton for the first time?

2 Richard Dinnis was manager of which club in 1977?

3 Charles, Chettle and Glover played for which 1980s FA Cup Finalists?

4 Who scored first for West Germany in the 1966 World Cup Final?

5 Fullback David Peach scored for which club in a League Cup Final?

6 With 215 goals Harry Hampton is all-time top League scorer at which club?

7 Strachan and Shutt scored Euro goals in the same game for which club?

8 Which England player once played for Sudbury Court?

9 Who lost 1–0 to Nottingham Forest in the Final of the 1980 European Cup?

10 What is Mark Hateley's middle name?

11 Who was Carlisle Utd's manager when they won promotion to the First Division in 1974?

12 Ted Sager played 465 League games for which club from 1929 to 1953?

13 Kevin Ball first played in an FA Cup Final for which team?

14 At which club did Jimmy Phillips make his league debut?

15 In the 1980s, which League-Championship winning manager was labelled "A young pup" by Brian Clough?

16 Which club has a fanzine called *One Nil Down... Two One Up*?

17 Jim Ryan followed Ray Harford as manager of which club?

18 Barry Murphy set an appearance record at which Yorkshire club?

19 What were Torquay once known as before they took on the name United?

20 To one each way, how many international goals did Ronnie Whelan score?

1 Philippe Albert's 90th minute goal did not save Belgium being knocked out of the 1994 World Cup by which team?

2 Nayim scored a last-minute Cup Winners' Cup Final goal for which club?

3 Brian Stein hit a late League Cup Final winner for which club?

4 In 1997 which team led 3–1 at Newcastle Utd in the Premiership but lost 4–3 to a Shearer hat-trick completed in the last minute?

5 Who did Hereford Utd replaced in the League in 1972?

6 Who was Weber playing for when he hit a late World Cup Final equalizer?

7 Who scored Aberdeen's winner in the 1983 Cup Winners' Cup Final?

8 Who scored Arsenal's last-minute winner v Man Utd in the '79 FA Cup Final?

9 Who pegged two late goals back for Manchester Utd in the same game?

10 In the 1994 World Cup quarter-finals, Romania equalised at the death against which country?

11 Who beat Liverpool with the last kick of the 1988–89 season?

12 Which club replaced Southport in the league in 1978?

13 Who sent the ball forward for Geoff Hurst's final goal in the 1966 World Cup Final?

14 In 1994, who equalised for Italy three minutes from time v Nigeria and in the next round hit the winner v Spain two minutes from time?

15 A last-gasp Steve Claridge goal beat which team in a Wembley play-off?

16 It was all over for Leeds City when they were expelled from the League in 1919 – but for what?

17 Cambridge Utd joined the league in 1970 at whose expense?

18 Who provided the free-kick from which David Platt hit the late goal v Belgium in Italia 90?

19 George Mutch won an FA Cup Final with a penalty in the 1930s for which club?

20 It was all over at Watling Street when which league club left the league in the 1900s?

---

1 Viv Anderson played for which three clubs in League Cup Finals?

2 Which club beat Hamburg to win the European Super Cup in 1977?

3 Which Adrian moved to Espanol from Everton in the 1980s?

4 At which club did Mick Harford make his League debut?

5 In what decade did Sheffield Utd first win the Championship?

6 Which club has a fanzine called *Forever and a Day*?

7 Brian Horton followed Mark Lawrenson as manager of which club?

8 Who moved to Sunderland from Millwall in 1996 to set a club record for a transfer fee paid?

9 To five years each way, when did Swansea Town become Swansea City?

10 To two each way, how many international goals did Trevor Brooking score?

11 Chris Whyte and George Wood were in the same team at which club?

12 Which Peter became boss of Southend Utd in 1993?

13 Neil Webb first played in an FA Cup Final for which team?

14 Which Leicester-born striker of the 1990s has the middle names William Ivanhoe?

15 Tuttle and Durie scored Euro goals in the same game for which club?

16 Who said "The years of patching up grounds... must be over"?

17 Who lost to Leeds Utd in the 1968 Fairs Cup Final?

18 Neil Young scored in an FA Cup Final for which club?

19 Who was Graham Taylor's assistant when Watford made the FA Cup Final in 1984?

20 Alan Irvine played in the 1984 League Cup Final for which club?

LEVEL 3

1 Oman Biyik played in the World Cup for which country?

2 In 1994, Leonardo of Brazil was sent off against which country?

3 Which French player was victim of Schumacher's appalling challenge in 1984?

4 Which country took the first penalty in the 1994 Final shoot out?

5 20 of the Republic of Ireland's 22-man USA 94 squad played in the English league – which two didn't?

6 Which country, other than the Republic of Ireland, included a high proportion of English League players in USA in 1994?

7 Which Czechoslovakian player was second-top scorer in Italia 90?

8 In USA 94 which country scored most goals in the group games yet still went out?

9 How many games did England lose in Spain in 1982?

10 Who were the first host country to win the World Cup?

11 What was the half-time score in the 1994 third place match?

12 Olguin, Gallego and Ortiz played for which World Cup-winning team?

13 In 1982, what was the nickname of England's mascot?

14 Felix was in goal for which World Cup winners?

15 Who were Scotland's joint top scorers in Italia 90?

16 Whose last international goal was a World Cup Final winner?

17 Which country were top of the Republic of Ireland's Group in USA 1994?

18 Who were the only team to beat West Germany in the 1974 finals?

19 In Italia 90 who scored England's winner against Egypt?

20 Which country failed to score in the USA in 1994?

---

1 Rod Belfitt scored in a Euro game for which club?

2 What is Andy Hinchcliffe's middle name?

3 Which Jimmy played in 1970s and 1980s FA Cup Finals for different teams and lost both times?

4 McIlmoyle, Keyworth and Cheesebrough played for which 1960s FA Cup Finalists?

5 Who lost 4–3 to Real Madrid in the Final of the 1956 European Cup?

6 Michael Robinson played in 1980s League Cup Finals for Liverpool and which other club?

7 121-goal Bobby Campbell is all-time top League scorer at which club?

8 Which organization is based at Hitzigweg 11, CH–8032 Zurich?

9 Which former Scunthorpe footballer sang solo on "Top Of The Pops" in 1979?

10 Alf Ramsey was the only player bought by which Tottenham Hotspur boss?

11 Who dropped out of the Scottish League in 1967?

12 Which are the three league teams in England with an x in them?

13 David Cross first played in an FA Cup Final for which team?

14 At which club did Gavin Peacock make his League debut?

15 Who was referee at the 1934 FA Cup Final and later became a world figure in soccer administration?

16 Which club has a fanzine called *Hey Big Spender*?

17 Matt Gillies followed Johnny Carey as manager of which club?

18 Which city is home to Fiorentina?

19 Which club once had "and District Teachers' AFC" added to their name?

20 To two each way, how many international goals did Lou Macari score?

Answers

Pot Luck 27 (see Quiz 53)
1 Nottingham Forest, Arsenal and Sheffield Wednesday.
2 Liverpool. 3 Heath. 4 Lincoln City. 5 1890s. 6 Burnley.
7 Oxford Utd. 8 Alex Rae. 9 1970. 10 Five. 11 Arsenal.
12 Taylor. 13 Manchester Utd. 14 Emile Heskey.
15 Tottenham Hotspur. 16 Lord Justice Taylor.
17 Ferencvaros. 18 Manchester City. 19 Bertie Mee.
20 Everton.

Quiz 56 Famous Firsts

Answers – see page 262

LEVEL 3

1 In what decade was the corner-kick first taken?

2 When did the English League adopt three points for a win?

3 Who, during the 1974 World Cup Finals, was the first player to make 55 appearances for Scotland?

4 Which teams were in the first all-British European Final?

5 When – to a year each way – did Stanley Matthews become the first man to be knighted for services to Football?

6 Who was the first Third Division player in the 1980s to be capped by England?

7 Which was the first country to lose two World Cup Finals?

8 Which European Cup-winner was the first player over 35 to make his Scottish debut?

9 Who were the first team to win a replayed Scottish FA Cup Final?

10 What was introduced in 1878 to help control a game?

11 The first FA Cup Final hat-trick was scored by William Townley in 1890 for which northern club?

12 Who was the first substitute to come on in an FA Cup Final?

13 Who was the first Division 3 player in the 1970s to be capped by England?

14 Which club did the first English double of the 20th century?

15 In 1895, what famous first happened in a Birmingham shop?

16 Who was the first person in England to win the Championship as a player and also as a manager?

17 In what decade was the first treble won in Scotland?

18 Which club in the 20th century were the first to retain the FA Cup?

19 What (in)famous first went to Lord Kinnaird in the 1877 FA Cup Final?

20 Who was the first player to make 700 English League appearances?

Answers

World Cup (see Quiz 54)
1 Cameroon. 2 USA. 3 Patrick Battiston. 4 Italy. 5 Bonner and Coyne. 6 Norway. 7 Tomas Skuhravy. 8 Russia. 9 None. 10 Italy (1934). 11 Sweden 4 v Bulgaria 0. 12 Argentina. 13 Bulldog Bobby. 14 Brazil (1970). 15 McCall and Johnston (1 each). 16 Gerd Müller. 17 Mexico. 18 East Germany. 19 Mark Wright. 20 Greece.

264

LEVEL 3 ⚽ ⚽ ⚽

1 Which British team lost to Feyenoord in the 1974 UEFA Cup Final?

2 Which father and son strikers played a total of 16 games for England without managing to score a goal?

3 Which country lost just once in 48 matches between 1950 and 1956?

4 At which club did Phil Neal make his League debut?

5 In which decade did Huddersfield Town first win the Championship?

6 Which club has a fanzine called *The Thin Blue Line*?

7 Dave Stringer followed Ken Brown as manager of which club?

8 Blackburn Rovers established a record of going how many FA Cup games without defeat?

9 Which club was once known as Heaton Norris Rovers?

10 To two each way, how many international goals did Trevor Francis score?

11 Andy Ritchie and Michael Robinson were in the same team at which club?

12 Jimmy Frizzell was boss of which club from 1970 to 1982?

13 Steve Sedgley first played in an FA Cup Final for which team?

14 What is David Hirst's middle name?

15 Which club beat Werder Bremen to win the European Super Cup in 1992?

16 Melville and James scored Euro goals in the same game for which club in their only UEFA Cup run?

17 Haylock and Van Wyck played for which 1980s League Cup winners?

18 Mick Jones scored in an FA Cup Final for which club?

19 With 209 goals Charlie Buchan is all-time top League scorer at which club?

20 Which defender won 77 caps for Scotland between 1980 and 1991?

Pot Luck 30 (see Quiz 59)
Answers
1 Brian. 2 Liverpool. 3 Argentina. 4 Ron Yeats. 5 Oldham Athletic. 6 Ipswich Town. 7 Luton Town. 8 1987–88. 9 Hull City. 10 Real Madrid. 11 Oxford Utd. 12 Manchester Utd. 13 Everton. 14 Mansfield Town. 15 Hearts. 16 Exeter City. 17 Leeds Utd. 18 Nottingham Forest. 19 Southampton. 20 15.

1 Who were the first English club to play in the competition?

2 Who were the first team to appear in three consecutive Finals?

3 When did AC Milan first win the trophy?

4 What was the scoreline in the 1963 Final, the first English success?

5 Who managed the 1963 winners?

6 In which city did Arsenal first win the tournament?

7 Who were the first English clubs to meet in the competition?

8 What is the furthest stage Cardiff City have reached?

9 When did Sunderland appear in the competition?

10 Who won the first Final played at Wembley?

11 Which side was ordered to transfer a home game 250 miles and went to Plymouth?

12 Which British side won the Cup Winners' Cup and their national cup in the same season?

13 Who were the first Eastern European side to win the trophy?

14 In the 1960s Sporting Lisbon set a record by scoring how many in a game?

15 Which English side knocked out Manchester City in 1971?

16 What happened to the referee after Leeds Utd's defeat in the 1973 Final?

17 Who beat Leeds Utd in that Final?

18 Heslop and Towers played for which trophy-winning team?

19 Who was Manchester Utd's victorious skipper in 1991?

20 Keith Weller played for which trophy-winning team?

The 1980s (see Quiz 60)

Answers

The 1980s (see Quiz 60)
1 Ipswich Town. 2 Northern Ireland. 3 Luton Town.
4 Lawrie McMenemy. 5 Scarborough. 6 Eight. 7 Michael Knighton. 8 Spain. 9 Lincoln City. 10 Mark Lawrenson.
11 The Rous Cup. 12 AC Milan. 13 Alan Brazil. 14 Brazil.
15 Fulham & QPR. 16 Trevor Francis. 17 Diego Maradona.
18 Huddersfield Town. 19 Oxford Utd. 20 Six.

1 What is Steve Hodge's middle name that links him to his first boss?

2 Byrne, Lawler and Strong played for which 1960s FA Cup Finalists?

3 Who did Cameroon beat in the 1990 World Cup opener?

4 Which Liverpool skipper said of compatriot Bill Shankly, "His motivation could move mountains"?

5 Which Second Division side reached the Final of the League Cup and the semis of the FA Cup in the same season?

6 Gates and McCall scored Euro goals in the same game for which club?

7 Ashley Grimes played in 1980s League Cup Finals for which team?

8 When was the Football League's Centenary Season?

9 With 195 goals scored in the 1960s and 1970s Chris Chilton became all-time top League scorer at which east coast club?

10 Who lost 1–0 to Liverpool in the Final of the 1981 European Cup?

11 Trevor Hebberd and Kevin Brock were in the same team at which club?

12 Francis Burns was at which club when he won his only Scottish cap?

13 Gary Lineker first played in an FA Cup Final for which team?

14 At which club did Kevin Hitchcock make his League debut?

15 With 44 goals, Barney Battles set a League season scoring record at which Scottish club?

16 Which club had a fanzine called *In Exile*?

17 Allan Clarke followed Jimmy Adamson as manager of which club?

18 Grenville Morris is all-time top League scorer at which midlands club?

19 Which coastal club once had St Mary's added to its current name?

20 To one each way, John Charles got how many international goals?

1 Which team's players gained a 1-2-3 in the PFA Player of the Year awards in 1981?

2 Who won the 1986 – and final – Home International Championship?

3 Which club banned away fans in April 1986?

4 Who resigned as Sunderland manager in 1987 as they dropped into Division Three?

5 Which GM Vauxhall Conference club were first to gain automatic promotion to the League?

6 How many goals did England rattle in v Turkey in 1984?

7 Which property dealer abandoned his hopes of owning Manchester Utd?

8 Which country beat Malta 12–1 to pip Holland to a place in the 1984 European Championship?

9 Who were Bradford City's opponents in the fire disaster game?

10 Who was Liverpool's only English-born player in the 1986 FA Cup Final?

11 Which tournament had only Brazil, England and Scotland competing?

12 After a bribery scandal which Italian side were demoted to Division 2?

13 Who hit five goals for Ipswich Town v Southampton in 1981–82?

14 Pat Jennings played his last international against which team?

15 Which two London clubs were denied a merger by the Football League Management Committee?

16 Rangers signed which player from Atalanta in the late 1980s?

17 Who joined Napoli from Barcelona for a record £6.9 million fee?

18 Malcolm Macdonald briefly took over as manager of which club in 1987?

19 John Aldridge was in which side promoted to the top flight?

20 How many goals did Gary Lineker score in the 1986 World Cup?

Answers

Cup Winners' Cup (see Quiz 58)
1 Wolves. 2 Anderlecht. 3 1968. 4 5–1. 5 Bill Nicholson.
6 Paris. 7 Spurs & Man Utd (1963–64). 8 Semi-final.
9 1973–74. 10 West Ham Utd (1965). 11 Manchester Utd.
12 Aberdeen. 13 Slovan Bratislava. 14 16. 15 Chelsea.
16 He was suspended by UEFA. 17 AC Milan. 18 Manchester City. 19 Steve Bruce. 20 Chelsea.

LEVEL 3

1 Mick Lyons scored in a League Cup Final for which club?

2 Former Prime Minister Harold Wilson supported which club?

3 Who lost to Gothenburg in the 1987 UEFA Cup Final?

4 At which club did Garry Parker make his League debut?

5 In which decade did Sheffield Wednesday first win the Championship?

6 Which club has a fanzine called *The Ugly Inside*?

7 Alan Durban followed Alan A'Court as manager of which club?

8 Which defender went from Scunthorpe to Aston Villa in 1991 to set a club record for a transfer fee received?

9 Which club dropped Lindsey from its name in the 1950s?

10 To one each way, how many international goals did Chris Waddle score?

11 Andy King and Steve McMahon were in the same team at which club?

12 Which Maurice became boss of Oxford Utd in 1985?

13 John Barnes first played in an FA Cup Final for which team?

14 Who is Steve Howey's soccer-playing elder brother?

15 Hughes and Tueart scored Euro goals in the same 1970s game for which club?

16 With 297 goals Andy Jardine became all-time top League scorer at which Scottish club?

17 To three years, when did Fulham install floodlights?

18 Frank Saul scored in an FA Cup Final for which club?

19 Who beat Nottingham Forest to win the European Super Cup in 1980?

20 Who in 1987 became the first team to be automatically relegated from the English League?

Pot Luck 32 (see Quiz 63)
Answers
1 Hibernian. **2** Newcastle Utd. **3** Chelsea. **4** Carl. **5** Bert Trautmann. **6** Barcelona. **7** Tommy Lawton. **8** Alan Smith. **9** Barnsley. **10** Aston Villa. **11** West Ham Utd. **12** Holder. **13** Sunderland. **14** Dumbarton. **15** Scottish League founder members now out of the League. **16** Huddersfield Town. **17** Burnley. **18** Hartlepool Utd. **19** Rotherham Utd. **20** He didn't score any.

Quiz 62 Defenders

Answers – see page 272

LEVEL 3

1 To two each way, how many caps did Phil Thompson win?

2 At which German club did Franz Beckenbauer end his playing days?

3 Which English club did Celtic's fullback Tommy Gemmell play for?

4 Which England defender tried to tackle the Italian Zola as he scored in the 1997 World Cup qualifier at Wembley?

5 Which defender was the last skipper to lift the Jules Rimet Trophy after a World Cup Final?

6 Which club did West Ham Utd sign Slaven Bilic from?

7 To two each way, how many League goals did Jack Charlton score?

8 Branagan, Keeley and Rathbone each played over 200 League games in which club's defence in the 1980s?

9 In Steve Bruce's first season with Manchester Utd who played most times as his central defensive partner?

10 Which defender was 18 years and 183 days old when he made his England debut?

11 At which club did Mick Lyons finish his playing career?

12 Which Jeff of Arsenal won his only England cap against Yugoslavia in 1972?

13 To 20 each way, how many Chelsea League games did Ron Harris play?

14 At which club did Julian Dicks make his League debut?

15 Which defender was born in Alloa on 13th June, 1955?

16 Which England defender scored a screamer against Brazil in June 1995?

17 Angus and Elder formed a fullback pairing at which club?

18 Which defender became the first to skipper both English and Scottish FA Cup winning sides?

19 Which club did Russell Osman go to when he left Ipswich Town?

20 Which player wrote *Soccer The Hard Way*?

Answers

Internationals (see Quiz 64)
1 Paolo Maldini. 2 W Germany (1954). 3 Ajax. 4 Trevor Steven. 5 Brazil & England. 6 Mick McCarthy. 7 Zico. 8 Karl-Heinz Schnellinger. 9 Dino Zoff. 10 Four. 11 Bank clerk. 12 Rudi Voller. 13 Jan Jongbloed. 14 Switzerland. 15 Morocco. 16 Rene Van der Kerkhof. 17 John Barnes. 18 Germany & Holland. 19 Fritz Walter. 20 1954.

1   Blackley and Brownlie scored Euro goals in the same 1970s game for which British club?

2   Bob Stokoe won an FA Cup Winner's medal with which club?

3   Hinton and Houseman played for which 1970s FA Cup Finalists?

4   What is Darren Huckerby's middle name?

5   Which ex-Manchester City keeper recommended Eike Immel to his old club?

6   Who lost on penalties to Steaua Bucharest in the Final of the 1986 European Cup?

7   Who holds the record for the fastest-ever England goal?

8   Which Arsenal player was booked for the first time in his career in the 1993 FA Cup Final replay?

9   Viv Anderson was player/manager of which club in 1993–94?

10 Ray Graydon scored a League Cup Final winner for which club?

11 Slater and Small were in the same team at which London club?

12 Which Phil became boss of Brentford in 1990?

13 Irish international John Byrne first played in an FA Cup Final for which team?

14 At which Scottish club did Graham Sharp make his League debut?

15 What links Abercorn, Cowlairs and Cambuslang?

16 Which club has a fanzine called *Hanging on the Telephone*?

17 Jimmy Mullen followed Frank Casper as manager of which club?

18 In 1993 which club set a record by going 13 games without a goal?

19 Which club was once known as Thornhill United?

20 How many international goals did Terry Venables score?

Quiz 64 Internationals

Answers – see page 270

LEVEL 3 ⚽ ⚽ ⚽

1 Who was Italy's captain in the 1997 World Cup qualifier at Wembley?

2 Turek was in goal for which World Cup-winners?

3 At the time of the 1974 World Cup, Dutch players Rep, Haan and Krol were all with which club?

4 Which England substitute came on in the 1990 World Cup semi-final?

5 Which two countries played, in 1958, in the first ever 0–0 draw in a World Cup finals match?

6 Which Republic of Ireland player committed most fouls in Italia 90?

7 How is Artur Antunes Coimbra more widely known?

8 Which defender hit West Germany's last-minute equaliser in the 1970 World Cup semi-final?

9 In the 1970s, which keeper went 1,143 minutes in international soccer without conceding a goal?

10 Gary Lineker was on the spot twice against Cameroon in Italia 90, but before the game how many years had gone by without an English penalty award?

11 What job did Karl-Heinz Rummenigge once do?

12 Who was the German skipper who broke his arm in his first game in the 1992 European Championship in Sweden?

13 Who was in goal for Holland in the 1974 World Cup Final?

14 Heinz Hermann is the highest capped player for which country?

15 Against which country was England's Ray Wilkins sent off?

16 In the 1978 World Cup Final, which Dutchman wore a cast on his arm?

17 Which Englishman had a 'goal' disallowed in the Belgium game in Italia 90?

18 Which two countries in Euro 92 did not contain any English based players?

19 Who was the first German captain to claim the World Cup?

20 When did Scotland first appear in a World Cup?

Answers

Defenders (see Quiz 62)
1 42. 2 Hamburg. 3 Nottingham Forest. 4 Sol Campbell.
5 Daniel Passarella (Trophy was then awarded to Argentina).
6 Karlsruhe. 7 70. 8 Blackburn Rovers. 9 Mal Donaghy.
10 Duncan Edwards. 11 Grimsby Town. 12 Blockley. 13 655.
14 Birmingham City. 15 Alan Hansen. 16 Graeme Le Saux.
17 Burnley. 18 Martin Buchan. 19 Leicester City. 20 Ron Harris.

1 Roger Smee was a former centre-forward then chairman of which club, where he helped repel Robert Maxwell?

2 Terry Conroy scored in a League Cup Final for which club?

3 Who lost on penalties to Bayer Leverkusen in the 1988 UEFA Cup Final?

4 At which club did Geoff Thomas make his League debut?

5 In which decade did Burnley first win the Championship?

6 Which club had a fanzine called *The Greasy Chip Buttie*?

7 Bill Dodgin Jnr followed Alec Stock as manager of which club?

8 Who moved from Celtic to Chelsea in 1991 to set a club record for a transfer fee received?

9 Which club was once known as St Jude's?

10 To one each way, how many international goals did Bobby Moore score?

11 Alan Shearer and Iain Dowie were in the same team at which club?

12 Which Steve became boss of Plymouth Argyle in 1995?

13 Gary Bailey played in an FA Cup Final for which team?

14 Which QPR winger of the 1990s has the middle name of Rodney?

15 Who beat Hamburg to win the European Super Cup in 1983?

16 Which clubs were involved in Justin Fashanu's £1 million move?

17 What was the title of Crystal Palace's 1990 Cup Final song?

18 Jim McCalliog scored in an FA Cup Final for which club?

19 Conroy and Ritchie scored Euro goals in the same 1970s game for which club?

20 What links Maidenhead, Donington School (Spalding) and the Civil Service?

Answers

Pot Luck 34 (see Quiz 67)
1 Joseph. 2 Sheffield Wednesday. 3 Blackburn Rovers & Bolton Wanderers. 4 QPR. 5 Colin Garwood. 6 WBA, Manchester City & Norwich City. 7 Bobby Charlton. 8 United States Soccer Federation. 9 Hearts. 10 Steaua Bucharest. 11 Manchester City. 12 Beck. 13 Everton. 14 Stoke City. 15 *Turandot*. 16 Leeds Utd. 17 Peterborough. 18 Grimsby Town. 19 Burslem. 20 Eight.

Quiz 66 Derby Games

Answers – see page 276

LEVEL 3 ⚽ ⚽ ⚽

1 Which player hit a hat-trick in the November 1994 Manchester derby?

2 Which is the most isolated British club?

3 Who scored the winner in the all Sheffield FA Cup semi-final of 1993?

4 Who is the only Manchester Utd boss never to have lost to Manchester City?

5 Which derby was England's first live match on Friday September 9, 1960?

6 Irving Natrass played for which two rival sides?

7 Which Scottish clubs with grounds half a mile apart are also alphabetically next to each other?

8 Where was the replayed Mersey League Cup Final of the 1980s held?

9 To three years either way, when was the first Manchester derby in the FA Charity Shield?

10 Which player scored the only goal in the Celtic v Rangers 1980 Scottish FA Cup Final?

11 Which player opened the scoring in the 1986 Mersey FA Cup Final?

12 In what decade was the first Hearts v Hibs Scottish FA Cup Final?

13 To five miles, what is the distance between Norwich City and Ipswich Town?

14 Whose 1970 testimonial was a Manchester derby?

15 Which Nigel has played in Mersey, Glasgow and London derby games?

16 The 4–4 Mersey 5th round FA Cup replay was whose last match at Liverpool?

17 What was the 90-minute score in the 1989 Mersey FA Cup Final?

18 Geographically, which is the nearest club to Aberdeen?

19 Who managed the teams in the first all-London FA Cup Final in the 20th century?

20 Who won a Scottish FA Cup medal for Rangers against Celtic and then for Celtic against Rangers?

Answers

Arsenal & Spurs (see Quiz 68)
1 1913. **2** Arthur Rowe. **3** Alan Ball. **4** Liverpool, 7–0.
5 Five. **6** Ted Ditchburn. **7** A broken nose. **8** Jimmy Greaves.
9 Juventus. **10** 31. **11** Tom Parker. **12** MBE. **13** Ted Drake.
14 Dundee. **15** Frank Stapleton. **16** Graeme Souness.
17 Frank McLintock. **18** 70 points. **19** 1930. **20** 1901.

274

1 What is Denis Irwin's first name – and it isn't Denis?

2 Pugh, Fantham and Quinn played for which 1960s FA Cup Finalists?

3 Which two teams beginning with B were relegated to the Third Division for the first time ever in 1971?

4 Which London side won 6–2 at home in the first leg of a UEFA Cup game in the 1980s and were beaten 4–0 away?

5 Who was top scorer for both Portsmouth and Aldershot in 1979–80?

6 Which three teams has Asa Hartford played for in League Cup Finals?

7 Who scored for England in his 100th international?

8 What do the initials USSF stand for?

9 Baird and Levein scored Euro goals in the same 1990s game for which Scottish club?

10 Who lost 4–0 to AC Milan in the Final of the 1989 European Cup?

11 Matt Busby was in an FA Cup-winning team at which club?

12 Which John became boss of Preston in 1992?

13 Kevin Richardson first played in an FA Cup Final for which team?

14 At which club did Garth Crooks make his League debut?

15 The adopted Italia 90 anthem *Nessun Dorma* comes from which opera?

16 Which club has a fanzine called *The Square Ball*?

17 Chris Turner followed Mark Lawrenson as manager of which club?

18 Kevin Drinkell, Matt Tees and Ron Rafferty were all big scorers for which club?

19 Port Vale used to have which word at the front of their name?

20 To one either way, Tony Grealish scored how many international goals?

1 In what year were Arsenal relegated for the first time in their history?

2 Which manager developed the "push and run" style of soccer?

3 Who joined Arsenal for a record British fee in December 1971?

4 Which side inflicted Tottenham Hotspur's record League defeat?

5 How many times did Arsenal win the championship in the 1930s?

6 Which Gillingham-born Tottenham keeper of the 1940s and 1950s, played over 450 times for them and made six England appearances?

7 Which injury was Andy Linighan carrying when he scored in the 1993 FA Cup Final replay?

8 When Martin Peters joined Tottenham Hotspur, who moved to his old club?

9 Which foreign team did Liam Brady join in 1980?

10 How many League games did Tottenham Hotspur win in 1960–61 when the team created a record for most wins in a season?

11 Who was skipper of Arsenal's FA Cup-winning side of 1930?

12 Which honour did Ray Clemence of Tottenham Hotspur receive in the Queen's Birthday Honours' List in 1987?

13 Who scored seven times for Arsenal against Aston Villa in 1935?

14 Which club was keeper Bill Brown with before he came to Spurs?

15 Which ex-Arsenal player played for both Ajax and Le Havre?

16 Who made just one appearance for Tottenham Hotspur as a substitute in a UEFA Cup game before joining Middlesbrough?

17 Which Arsenal player was Footballer of the Year in 1971?

18 In 1919–20 Tottenham Hotspur established a record for points in the Second Division under the two-point system. How many did they get?

19 What year did Arsenal first win the FA Cup?

20 What year did Tottenham Hotspur first win the FA Cup?

LEVEL 3

1 Which great player made a presentation to Kenny Dalglish on his 100th international appearance?

2 Ray Houghton scored in a League Cup Final for which club?

3 Which Arsenal midfielder of the 1990s has the middle name Faxe?

4 At which club did Eric Young make his League debut?

5 In which decade did Manchester City first win the Championship?

6 Which club has a fanzine called *The Seadog Bites Back*?

7 Who followed Alf Ramsey as manager of Ipswich Town?

8 Charnley, Mudie and Perry have all hit 100+ goals for which club?

9 Which club was once known as Argyle Athletic Club?

10 To one each way, how many international goals did Ray Kennedy score?

11 In the 1990s Abel Resino went 1,275 minutes without conceding a goal at which Spanish club?

12 Howard Wilkinson was player/manager of which non-League side?

13 John Scales first played in an FA Cup Final for which team?

14 Who lost to Napoli in the 1989 UEFA Cup Final?

15 Armstrong and Moran scored Euro goals in the same game for which club?

16 Major Frank Buckley and Raich Carter both managed which club in the 1940s and 1950s?

17 Chris Waddle scored in an FA Cup Final for which club?

18 Which club beat Liverpool to win the European Super Cup in 1984?

19 Silvio Berlusconi put his money into which club?

20 Which club play at Bayview Park?

1 Les Sealey has played in League Cup Finals for which two clubs?

2 Who were the first club to retain the League Cup?

3 It was third time lucky for who when he took Aston Villa to success in 1975?

4 Which Final had two teams both to be relegated from the top flight in that same season?

5 Who were the first team to win the Scottish League Cup in the 1990s on a penalty shoot out?

6 Which year did the League Cup become the Milk Cup?

7 Which two teams appeared in it?

8 In which season did it become compulsory for all 92 League clubs to enter the English trophy?

9 Who made his twelfth and last visit to Wembley as a manager for the 1983 Final?

10 Who were the first team to retain the Scottish League Cup?

11 Which Fourth Division side competed in the 1962 Final?

12 Who were the first London side to win the trophy?

13 Which three English clubs has Chris Woods played for in Finals?

14 Which club first won the League Cup three years in a row?

15 When did Manchester Utd first win the League Cup?

16 Mick Channon first played for which club in a Final?

17 After winning the Scottish League Cup five years in a row from 1966 –70, how many times did Celtic win the trophy in the following 25 years?

18 Which WBA forward became the first player to score in every round of the competition?

19 Who were Villa's opponents in the first Final needing a second replay?

20 Who was the first player to appear in three League Cup Finals with different clubs?

Answers

Managers (see Quiz 72)
1 Scunthorpe Utd. 2 Eddie May. 3 QPR. 4 Johnny Giles.
5 Peter Reid. 6 Doug Ellis. 7 46 years. 8 Carlisle Utd.
9 Cardiff City. 10 Graham Taylor. 11 West Ham & Manchester Utd. 12 Charlton Athletic. 13 Lou Macari. 14 John Toshack.
15 Barry Fry. 16 Five days. 17 Ipswich Town. 18 Howard Kendall. 19 Eight. 20 Terry Venables (Spurs).

1 Roy Wegerle played in a League Cup Final for which club?

2 Who were the first club to win promotion on a penalty shoot out?

3 What is Matt Le Tissier's middle name?

4 Lovett, Collard and Hope played for which 1960s FA Cup Finalists?

5 Which England player hit 22 goals in just 23 games?

6 Which League do FC Sion play in?

7 Grant and Rideout scored Euro goals in the same 1990s game for which club?

8 What FA Cup Final tradition was altered in 1992?

9 Which turn-of-the-century Celtic striker was known as "The Iron Man"?

10 Who lost 1–0 to AC Milan in the Final of the 1990 European Cup?

11 Paul Rideout and Dale Gordon were in the same team at which club?

12 Which Eddie became boss of Chelsea in 1975?

13 Gordon Hill first played in an FA Cup Final for which team?

14 At which Scottish club did Steve Archibald make his League debut?

15 Who was Blackburn Rovers' chairman when Kenny Dalglish went to Rovers?

16 Which club had a fanzine called *Where's The Money Gone*?

17 Ray Harford followed Malcolm Macdonald as manager of which club?

18 Joe Baker set a most goals in a season record at which British club?

19 Which club was once known as Headington?

20 To one each way, how many international goals did Joe Jordan score?

Quiz 72 Managers

Answers – see page 278

LEVEL 3 ⚽ ⚽ ⚽

1 In 1959 Neil Lambton managed only three days as boss of which club?

2 Who was sacked in November 1994 by Cardiff City then reappointed in March 1995?

3 Tommy Docherty managed only 29 days at which club in 1968?

4 Which ex-WBA manager said, "the only certainty about management is the sack"?

5 Who was sacked at Manchester City 12 days into the 1993–94 season?

6 Who in 1994 said, "I believe Ron to be one of the top three managers in the country" – and then sacked him three weeks later?

7 Fred Everiss was doing something right at WBA as he holds the record of longest reign as a boss – how long?

8 Which club did Bob Stokoe manage on three separate occasions?

9 Which club did Phil Neal leave to join Steve Coppell at Manchester City?

10 Which manager said, "Napoleon wanted his generals to be lucky. I don't think he would have wanted me"?

11 Which two English League clubs went 50 years after the Second World War with only seven managers?

12 From 1933 to 1956 Jimmy Seed was boss of which club?

13 Who was the first Celtic manager sacked by Fergus McCann?

14 In 1983–84, who resigned as Swansea City boss, returned and even played and was sacked in the same season?

15 Who had an ansaphone message in 1996 that went, "Kristine's out shopping as usual. I'm down the Job Centre looking for employment"?

16 In 1980 Steve Murray was manager of Forfar for how long?

17 Brian Clough's last League game as Forest boss was against who?

18 Who said, "If I made a mistake at Notts County it was probably to mention publicly that I'd never been sacked in my life" just after he was fired?

19 How many times was Stan Flashman supposed to have sacked Barry Fry at Barnet?

20 Which sacked boss said, "I feel like Robin Hood – feared by the bad, loved by the good"?

Answers

League Cup (see Quiz 70)
1 Luton Town and Manchester Utd. 2 Nottingham Forest.
3 Ron Saunders. 4 Norwich City v Sunderland 1985. 5 Raith Rovers. 6 1982. 7 Liverpool v Spurs. 8 1967–68. 9 Bob Paisley.
10 Dundee. 11 Rochdale. 12 Chelsea. 13 Nottingham Forest, Norwich City, Sheffield Wednesday. 14 Liverpool. 15 1992.
16 Norwich City. 17 Twice. 18 Tony Brown. 19 Everton.
20 George Graham.

Quiz 73 Pot Luck 37

Answers - see page 283

LEVEL 3

1 Martin Hayes scored in a League Cup Final for which club?

2 Which film featured Bobby Moore and Pele?

3 Who lost to Tottenham Hotspur in the 1984 UEFA Cup Final?

4 At which club, no longer in the League, did Peter Withe make his League debut?

5 In which decade did Blackburn Rovers first win the Championship?

6 Which club had a fanzine called *Windy and Dusty*?

7 Alex Smith followed Ian Porterfield as manager of which club?

8 What is the name of Glenn Hoddle's brother, once with Barnet?

9 Which club was once known as Pine Villa?

10 To one each way, how many international goals did Francis Lee score?

11 Who said, "As much as I love women and music, my first love will always be football"?

12 Peter Schmeichel scored in a UEFA game against which club?

13 Nigel Spackman first played in an FA Cup Final for which team?

14 What England player of the 1990s has the middle name Pierre?

15 Who beat Red Star Belgrade to win the European Super Cup in 1991?

16 Which is the oldest Scottish team?

17 Paul Stewart scored in an FA Cup Final for which club?

18 Bart-Williams and Warhurst scored Euro goals in the same game for which club?

19 What work did Pat Jennings do before he become a footballer?

20 What is the inscription above the Bill Shankly gates at Anfield?

Pot Luck 38 (see Quiz 75)
1 Dundee Utd. 2 Glenn Hoddle. 3 Oldest player (41 years 257 days). 4 AS Roma. 5 Manchester City. 6 Alan Ball. 7 1951. 8 Athletic Bilbao. 9 Kingsley Black. 10 Francis. 11 Manchester Utd. 12 Buxton. 13 Nottingham Forest. 14 Swansea City. 15 Boca Juniors. 16 Leyton Orient. 17 Portsmouth. 18 Plymouth Argyle. 19 1913. 20 Seven.

Quiz 74 Double Winners

Answers – see page 284

LEVEL 3

1 Cantona scored for Manchester Utd in his 1995 October comeback game against which team?

2 In 1970–71 Arsenal were 2–0 down to which team in an FA Cup semi-final?

3 George Ramsay guided which team to the double?

4 Who in a double season beat Bootle, Grimsby Town and Wolves in the FA Cup?

5 Which midfielder sent a glorious pass to set up Ian Rush for his first goal in the 1986 FA Cup Final?

6 Who beat Manchester Utd 3–1 on the opening day of the 1995–96 season?

7 Who were Tottenham Hotspur's wing duo in their double season?

8 What was the 90-minute score in the 1971 Arsenal v Liverpool FA Cup Final?

9 Which is the only team to go through a League season without losing?

10 Which subsequent double-winners, in the 1950s, won the Championship but missed the double by losing the FA Cup Final?

11 Who was Liverpool's only League ever-present in the 85–86 double season?

12 In 1960–61 Tottenham Hotspur started by winning how many League games in a row?

13 Who was in goal for Manchester Utd in 1995–96 for the League games that Schmeichel missed?

14 Who replaced Alan Kennedy for Liverpool in 1985–86?

15 Who came on as a sub for Arsenal in the 1971 FA Cup Final?

16 Which player opened the scoring for Spurs in the 1961 FA Cup Final?

17 Which player started most League games for Manchester Utd in 1995–96?

18 John and James Cowan played for which double winners?

19 Which Kevin played for Liverpool in the 1985–86 double season?

20 Which team did not concede a goal in winning the FA Cup in their double season?

Answers

Early Bath (see Quiz 76)
1 Leeds Utd. 2 Crewe Alexandra. 3 Paul Gascoigne. 4 Billy Ferguson. 5 Doug Rougvie. 6 First player sent off at Wembley. 7 Ray Wilkins. 8 Sent off on his debut. 9 Luxembourg. 10 Russia. 11 Peter Willis. 12 Alvin Martin. 13 Poland. 14 Five. 15 Peruvian. 16 32. 17 He was a sub on the bench. 18 Uruguay. 19 Stoke City. 20 Four.

282

1 Kirkwood and Milne scored Euro goals in the same 1980s game for which club?

2 Who in 1979 scored on his England debut v Bulgaria?

3 What did Newcastle Utd's Billy Hampson achieve in the 1924 FA Cup Final?

4 Who lost on penalties to Liverpool in the 1984 European Cup Final?

5 Gow, Power and McDonald played for which 1980s FA Cup Finalists?

6 Which England midfielder played in white boots for Everton?

7 To five years each way, when did Arsenal install floodlights?

8 Which Spanish side did Howard Kendall manage?

9 Who has played in League Cup Finals for Luton Town and Nottingham Forest?

10 What is Neil Lennon's middle name?

11 Colin Gibson and Terry Gibson were in the same team at which club?

12 Which Mick became boss of Sunderland in 1993?

13 Gary Crosby first played in an FA Cup Final for which team?

14 At which club did Dean Saunders make his League debut?

15 Diego Maradona made his name playing for which Argentine team?

16 Which club had a fanzine called *Frankly Speaking*?

17 Frank Burrows followed John Gregory as manager of which club?

18 Kevin Hodges set up a League appearance record at which club?

19 In which year did keepers have to wear different coloured shirts from their team mates?

20 To one each way, how many international goals did Andy Gray score for Scotland?

LEVEL 3

1 Duncan McKenzie was sent off in a European game playing for which club?

2 Who was keeper Mark Smith playing for when he was sent off after 19 seconds in a 1993–94 match against Darlington?

3 Who in January 1991 became the first player to be sent off in a live TV League match?

4 In 1966, which Northern Ireland player became the first to be sent off in a British Home International match?

5 Which Aberdeen player saw red in the 1978–79 Scottish League Cup Final?

6 What famous first goes to Boris Stankovic?

7 Which England player was sent off in the Mexico 1986 World Cup?

8 What unwanted first did John Burns of Rochdale achieve in 1923?

9 Gilbert Dresch was sent off at Wembley in 1977 playing for which country?

10 Republic skipper Roy Keane was red carded in 1996 against which country?

11 Which referee sent off Manchester Utd's Kevin Moran in an FA Cup Final?

12 Which West Ham Utd player had his red card reduced to a yellow one after TV evidence showed he was wrongly dismissed v Sheffield Wednesday?

13 England's Alan Ball was sent off in 1973 against which country?

14 How many players were sent off in the 1967 World Club Championship between Celtic and Racing Club?

15 What nationality was De Las Casas, the first player sent off in the final stages of a World Cup tournament?

16 In 1971, Sammy Chapman became the first Nottingham Forest player to be sent off for how many years?

17 What was unusual about the dismissal of Ian Banks in December 1989?

18 Jose Battista was sent off in 55 seconds playing for which country against in the World Cup?

19 In 1972, John Ritchie was sent off within 30 seconds as appearing in a Euro game for which club?

20 How many players did Hereford Town have sent off against Northampton in September 1992?

Answers

Double Winners (see Quiz 74)
1 Liverpool. 2 Stoke City. 3 Aston Villa. 4 Preston North End. 5 Jan Molby. 6 Aston Villa. 7 Cliff Jones & Terry Dyson. 8 0–0. 9 Preston North End. 10 Manchester Utd (1957). 11 Bruce Grobbelaar. 12 11. 13 Keith Pilkington. 14 Jim Beglin. 15 Eddie Kelly. 16 Bobby Smith. 17 Andy Cole. 18 Aston Villa. 19 MacDonald. 20 Preston North End.

LEVEL 3 ⚽ ⚽ ⚽

1 Mick Harford scored in a League Cup Final for which club?

2 Who lost to Liverpool in the 1976 UEFA Cup Final?

3 What is Gary Mabbutt's middle name?

4 At which club did Paul Mariner make his League debut?

5 In what decade did Portsmouth first win the Championship?

6 Which club had a fanzine called *Exceedingly Good Pies*?

7 John Barnwell followed Sammy Chung as manager of which club?

8 In which decade did Ipswich Town enter the League?

9 Who was Keith Edwards playing for when he was the League's leading scorer in 1981–82?

10 To one each way, how many international goals did Frank Worthington score?

11 Jim Lawrence set an appearance record at which club?

12 Bryan Hamilton was boss of which club twice in the 1980s?

13 Vinny Samways first played in an FA Cup Final for which team?

14 McAnespie and Rougier scored Euro goals in the same 1990s game for which club?

15 Bobby Charlton scored in a 1956 Youth Cup Final against which Chesterfield keeper?

16 In the 50 years following the Second World War which clubs had the fewest managers?

17 Which club beat Sampdoria to win the European Super Cup in 1990?

18 Norman Deeley scored twice in an FA Cup Final for which club?

19 At which non-League club did Jimmy Greaves play out his career?

20 In which year did the FA Cup Final become an all-ticket game?

Quiz 78 England Managers

Answers – see page 288

LEVEL 3

1 Which England manager was born in Worksop?

2 How many games did Joe Mercer serve as caretaker manager?

3 Which was Alf Ramsey's first club as a player?

4 Who were the opponents in Terry Venables' first game as boss?

5 How many of his 29 games did Don Revie lose as England boss?

6 Which manager accused his players of "running round like headless chickens"?

7 Walter Winterbottom led England into how many World Cups?

8 How many England caps did Bobby Robson win as a player?

9 For how many games was Alf Ramsey in charge of England?

10 Which manager had his biggest victory in his last game?

11 Who formed a management partnership with Joe Mercer at Coventry in the 1970s?

12 Who was made skipper in Terry Venables' first game in charge?

13 Ron Greenwood's 1982 World Cup campaign was marred by injuries to which two key players?

14 Who scored for England in the Swedes 2 v Turnips 1 game?

15 Which England manager has won most World Cup games?

16 Where was Walter Winterbottom born?

17 Including penalty shoot-outs, who scored the last England goal under Terry Venables?

18 Which club did Ron Greenwood become a director of in 1983?

19 Who scored the last England goal for Graham Taylor?

20 How many England managers did Kevin Keegan play for?

Answers

Champions (see Quiz 80)
1 Dave Mackay (Derby). 2 Bill Nicholson (Spurs). 3 Alan Shearer. 4 Bryan Robson. 5 Jimmy Rimmer. 6 1947. 7 John McClelland. 8 Derby County. 9 Hearts & Kilmarnock. 10 Liverpool. 11 O'Hare & McGovern. 12 Chelsea. 13 David Seaman. 14 John Barnes. 15 14. 16 Blackburn Rovers. 17 Aberdeen & Rangers. 18 Chelsea. 19 Joe Mercer. 20 Eight.

1 Owers, Atkinson and Armstrong played for which 1990s FA Cup Finalists?

2 Who knocked Dundee out of the semis of the 1962–63 European Cup?

3 Which soccer soap was shown on BBC in the mid 1960s?

4 Jimmy Neighbour played for which two clubs in League Cup Finals?

5 Which striker at Leeds Utd was known as "The Shark"?

6 Rioch and George scored Euro goals in the same 70s match for which club?

7 What was Tommy Docherty's first League club as a manager?

8 Which great ex-Newcastle Utd player committed suicide on a railway track?

9 Who lost 5–3 on penalties to Red Star Belgrade in the Final of the 1991 European Cup?

10 Which Republic of Ireland defender of the 1990s has the middle name Barry?

11 Which English keeper was on the bench in a 1960s European Cup Final and started a 1980s Final?

12 Don Welsh and Phil Taylor have managed which club?

13 Carlton Palmer first played in an FA Cup Final for which team?

14 At which club did Frank Worthington make his League debut?

15 Which Middlesbrough manager said – days before resigning – "we are on the crest of a slump"?

16 Which club had a fanzine called *Our Days Are Numbered*?

17 Billy McNeill followed John Benson as manager of which club?

18 Who was Fred Binney playing for when he was the League's leading scorer in 1972–73?

19 Ron Ashman set an appearance record at which club?

20 How many international goals did Kevin Moran score?

Quiz 80 Champions

Answers – see page 286

LEVEL 3

1 Which member of the Tottenham Hotspur double side went on to manage a Championship team ?

2 Who was the first person to play in and manage League Championship sides at the same club?

3 Who was Blackburn Rovers's only League ever present in 1994–95?

4 Who scored his first and Manchester Utd's last goal of the 1992–93 season?

5 Who played every game in goal for Aston Villa in the 1981 side?

6 When did Bob Paisley play in a Championship-winning side at Liverpool?

7 Which Rangers and Watford defender featured in Leeds Utd's 1992 triumph?

8 Which club in the 70s won the Championship while on holiday in Majorca?

9 Which two Scottish teams met in the final game of the 1964–65 season to decide which of them were champions?

10 David Burrows won a Championship medal with which club?

11 Which two Johns were with Clough's champions at Derby County and Nottingham Forest?

12 Who were the first post-war English champions to have won less than half their fixtures?

13 Who played every League game in his first season with the club as Arsenal won the 1990–91 title?

14 Who was top scorer in Liverpool's 1989–90 Championship team?

15 How many players did Villa use in their 1980s Championship success?

16 Tony Gale won a Championship medal at which club?

17 Which two Scottish teams met in the final game of the 1990–91 season to decide which of them were champions?

18 In 1993–94, Manchester Utd only lost four League games but which team beat them home and away?

19 Who was the first person to play for two different English League Champions sides and then become manager of champions?

20 How many Championship medals did Phil Neal win?

Answers

England Managers (see Quiz 78)
1 Graham Taylor. 2 Seven. 3 Southampton. 4 Denmark.
5 7. 6 Graham Taylor. 7 Four. 8 20. 9 113. 10 Graham Taylor v San Marino 7–1. 11 Gordon Milne. 12 David Platt.
13 Keegan and Brooking. 14 David Platt. 15 Bobby Robson.
16 Oldham. 17 Teddy Sheringham. 18 Brighton.
19 Ian Wright. 20 Four.

LEVEL 3

1 Who lost to Juventus in the 1990 UEFA Cup Final?

2 Stuart Pearson scored in an FA Cup Final for which club?

3 Who is the soccer playing son of former Everton winger Johnny Morrissey?

4 At which club did Alex Matthie make his League debut?

5 Which club used to be the 'third' Edinburgh side?

6 Which club had a fanzine called *In The Loft*?

7 Nobby Stiles followed Harry Catterick as manager of which club?

8 To three years each way, when did Gillingham install floodlights?

9 Whose 1985 autobiography was called *No Half Measures*?

10 To one each way, how many international goals did Johnny Haynes score?

11 Scotsman Andy Gray and Simon Stainrod were in the same team at which club?

12 Which Peter became boss of Derby County in 1982?

13 Cyrille Regis first played in an FA Cup Final for which team?

14 Which Scottish winger has the middle names Kevin Francis Michael?

15 Which club beat Barcelona to win the European Super Cup in 1989?

16 Bannister and Stainrod scored Euro goals in the same 1980s game for which club?

17 John Harkes scored in a League Cup Final for which club?

18 Who did Graham Kelly succeed at the Football Association?

19 Which famous Brazilian player died of alcohol poisoning in 1983?

20 Who left Charlton Athletic for Sampdoria in July 1955?

Answers

Pot Luck 42 (see Quiz 83)
1 Celtic. 2 QPR. 3 John. 4 Coventry City. 5 Neville.
6 Bobby Charlton. 7 Portsmouth. 8 Peterborough.
9 Coventry City. 10 Oldham Athletic. 11 Newcastle Utd.
12 Mackay. 13 Arsenal. 14 Barnsley. 15 Manchester City.
16 Luton Town. 17 Chelsea. 18 Steve Archibald. 19 Jim
Baxter. 20 Six.

Quiz 82 Hat-tricks

Answers – see page 292

LEVEL 3 ⚽ ⚽ ⚽

1 Alan Shearer's first Newcastle Utd hat-trick was against which side?

2 Who scored a 1991 UEFA Cup hat-trick for Liverpool v Swarovski Tirol?

3 Who scored England's first ever hat-trick in a World Cup match?

4 Who scored the first European Cup Final hat-trick?

5 Which Colin marked his Southampton debut in 1986 with a hat-trick?

6 Who hit a hat-trick when Chelsea beat Manchester City 5–4 in the Full Members Cup?

7 Robert Bell became the first player to score a League triple hat-trick but for which club?

8 David Platt's first England hat-trick was against which country?

9 Who is the youngest scorer of a hat-trick in top flight English soccer?

10 Before hitting his Final hat-trick how many goals had Geoff Hurst scored in the 1966 World Cup?

11 Who was Joe Harper playing for when he hit a Scottish League Cup hat-trick and still ended up a loser?

12 Who scored England's first hat-trick in the 1990s – against which country?

13 Roger Hunt and Fred Pickering both scored hat-tricks in a 1960s 10–0 thrashing of which country?

14 Who hit the first post-war FA Cup Final hat-trick?

15 Which Celtic player hit three in the 1972 Scottish FA Cup Final?

16 Four of Alan Shearer's five Blackburn Rovers hat-tricks in 1995–96 were scored at home where was the away hat-trick scored?

17 How many times did Jimmy Greaves score three or more for England?

18 Who scored a double hat-trick on his Newcastle Utd debut in the 1950s?

19 Who was the first British player to score a hat-trick of penalties in a Euro game?

20 Which Jimmy of Celtic hit the first hat-trick in a Scottish FA Cup Final?

UEFA Cup (see Quiz 84)
1 Ferencvaros. 2 John Wark. 3 London XI. 4 Valencia.
5 Bayer Leverkusen. 6 Jeremy Goss. 7 Thomas Helmer & Mehmet Scholl. 8 Galatasaray. 9 PSV Eindhoven. 10 Wolves.
11 The toss of a coin. 12 Juventus (lost on away goals rule).
13 Bertie Mee. 14 Lothar Matthäus. 15 All blue. 16 Tony Parks. 17 Newcastle Utd. 18 Stan Bowles. 19 Ipswich Town.
20 Billy Thompson.

Quiz 83 Pot Luck 42

Answers – see page 289

LEVEL 3

1 Who lost 2–1 to Feyenoord in the Final of the 1970 European Cup?
2 John Byrne played in a League Cup Final for which club?
3 What is Niall Quinn's middle name?
4 McGrath, Peake and Gynn played for which 1980s FA Cup Finalists?
5 What was England winger Mark Chamberlain's soccer playing brother called?
6 Who captained the Manchester Utd team to lift the European Cup in 1968?
7 Which was the first team since the Second World War to win the Championship two seasons in a row?
8 With 482 League games Tommy Robson set an appearance record at which club?
9 Martin and O'Rourke scored Euro goals in the same 1970s game for which club?
10 Which ground has the Lookers Stand and the George Hill Stand?
11 Goddard and Gascoigne were in the same team at which club?
12 Which Dave became boss of Birmingham City in 1989?
13 Steve Walford first played in an FA Cup Final for which team?
14 At which club did David Speedie make his League debut?
15 With 158 goals in the 1920s Tommy Johnson set up a scoring record for which club?
16 Which club has a fanzine called *Mad As A Hatter*?
17 Danny Blanchflower followed Ken Shellito as manager of which club?
18 Mark Hughes had his registration at Barcelona cancelled to make way for which player?
19 Which soccer player told his story in the book *The Party's Over*?
20 To one each way, how many international goals did Andy McEvoy score?

Answers

Pot Luck 41 (see Quiz 81)
1 Fiorentina. 2 Manchester Utd. 3 John. 4 Celtic.
5 Meadowbank. 6 QPR. 7 Preston North End. 8 1963.
9 Graeme Souness. 10 18. 11 Aston Villa. 12 Taylor.
13 Coventry City. 14 Pat Nevin. 15 AC Milan. 16 QPR.
17 Sheffield Wednesday. 18 Ted Croker. 19 Garrincha.
20 Eddie Firmani.

LEVEL 3 ⚽ ⚽ ⚽

1 Who were the first Eastern European trophy winners?

2 Which Scot scored 14 goals in the 1980–81 competition?

3 What was the generic title of the first ever team to represent England in the competition?

4 Which Spanish side were first to reach three consecutive Finals?

5 South Korea's Cha Bum-Kun played for which trophy winners in the late 1980s?

6 Who was top scorer in Norwich City's UEFA games in 1993–94?

7 Who were the two scorers in the 1996 Final?

8 Which team did Dean Saunders play for in the 1995–96 competition?

9 Who knocked Leeds Utd out of the 1995–96 tournament?

10 Jim McCalliog scored a Final goal for which team?

11 After three drawn games, the Racing Strasbourg v Barcelona game of 1964–65 was decided which way?

12 In 1970–71 which team played 12 games without defeat yet failed to win the trophy?

13 Who was manager of the English side that won the trophy in 1970?

14 Which German captain won the trophy with Internazionale in 1991?

15 When Juventus were beaten in the 1971 final what unfamiliar colour did they play in?

16 Who was in goal for Tottenham Hotspur for the 1984 triumph, achieved after a shoot out?

17 Which English team knocked Southampton out of the 1970 competition?

18 Which QPR player scored 11 goals in 1976–77?

19 Kevin Steggles was a Euro scorer for which English team?

20 Who was in goal for both legs of Dundee Utd's 1987 Final?

1 Who scored an own goal in the Aston Villa v Everton replayed League Cup Final in the 1970s?

2 Birtles and Bowyer scored Euro goals in the same game for which club?

3 Who is Peter Reid's soccer playing brother?

4 At which club did Brian Talbot make his League debut?

5 Who handed out Fulham's record 10–0 defeat in a League Cup game in 1986?

6 Which club has a fanzine called *Blue and White*?

7 What was the lowest position Manchester Utd finished in the League under Ron Atkinson?

8 John Gavin is the all-time top scorer at which club?

9 Which manager had the backroom staff of Owen, Lindley and Cocker?

10 To one each way, how many international goals did Tony Woodcock score?

11 Paul Ince and Liam Brady were in the same team at which club?

12 Which Martin was boss of Bury from 1984 to 1989?

13 Ian Wilson first played in an FA Cup Final for which team?

14 What is Jamie Redknapp's middle name?

15 Who lost to Internazionale in the 1991 UEFA Cup Final?

16 Under what name did Rod Argent record music used by ITV for the Mexico World Cup finals in 1986?

17 In what year was the World Cup first transmitted in colour in the UK?

18 Which club beat Barcelona to win the European Super Cup in 1982?

19 Alan Sunderland scored in an FA Cup Final for which club?

20 Ace scorer Arthur Rowley was player-manager of which club when he hung up his boots?

1 What did Celtic's Chalmers and Rangers' Wilson achieve when they went out for the 1966–67 Scottish League Cup Final?

2 In what year was the first Old Firm Cup Final played?

3 What year this century was the Scottish FA Cup withheld after two draws between Rangers and Celtic?

4 Who won the first game between the sides back in 1888?

5 Which team with a ground in England knocked Rangers out of the 1967 Scottish FA Cup?

6 Who said, "For a while I did unite Rangers and Celtic fans. There were people in both camps that hated me"?

7 How many players were red carded in the March 1991 League game?

8 Which Celtic keeper let nine goals in in an international match?

9 When Rangers won the Scottish Southern Cup in 1946 it was the forerunner of which tournament?

10 Who is Celtic's all time top goalscorer?

11 What did Rangers achieve in season 1898–99?

12 Who was Rangers manager for 37 years from 1920 to 1957?

13 In 1977 who became the first player to win Scottish FA Cup medals with both clubs?

14 Jim Baxter joined Rangers from which club?

15 What season did Celtic achieve Scotland's first double?

16 Which two players called Woods did Graeme Souness bring in from England to Rangers?

17 Who scored Celtic's 1967 European Cup Final winner?

18 Whohas won most Scottish caps during their time with Rangers?

19 When did Rangers first achieve the treble?

20 What season did Aberdeen beat Rangers and Celtic in major Cup Finals?

1 Which Lewisham-born midfield England player has the first names David Carlyle?

2 McNab, Storey and Simpson played for which 1970s FA Cup Finalists?

3 In the 1995–96 season, which was the first English club to field four overseas players?

4 Which player of the 1930s has scored most goals in a season for Luton Town?

5 Which player wrote *So Far So Good*?

6 Birchenall and Boyle scored Euro goals in the same 1960s game for which club?

7 Which ground had the Cowshed covered terrace?

8 Which Nigerian became Leyton Orient's most capped player?

9 Perry Groves played in a League Cup Final for which club?

10 Who lost 1–0 to Barcelona in the Final of the 1992 European Cup?

11 Alan Brazil and David Seaman were in the same team at which club?

12 Manager George Allison followed which legend in 1934?

13 Tony Currie first played in an FA Cup Final for which team?

14 At which club did Terry McDermott make his League debut?

15 Roger Palmer became all time top scorer at which club?

16 Which club had a fanzine called *Red Issue*?

17 Bobby Gould followed Dave Sexton as manager of which club?

18 Which 40-something keeper turned out for Northampton in 1993–94?

19 Which club originally played at the Red House ground?

20 To one each way, how many international goals did Liam Brady score?

1 Which club did Juninho play for before joining Middlesbrough?

2 Which British manager was sacked by Real Madrid in 1990?

3 When Millwall's Malcolm Allen was red-carded in 1992–93 what unwelcome first did he achieve?

4 Who did Elton John sell Watford to for £6 million in 1991?

5 Who received a £20,000 fine from the FA for voicing a video nasty?

6 How many players were sent off in the 1997 Chesterfield v Plymouth Argyle Division Two League game?

7 Which Dutch side did Bobby Robson manage after leaving England?

8 Which country did Scotland beat in the 1990 World Cup tournament?

9 Which club finished third in 1993 in the Premier League but with a 61–65 goal difference?

10 Which London-based player was stabbed in a domestic row?

11 What season was the new back-pass law seen for the first time?

12 Gary Lineker played his last international against which country?

13 Who became the first man to manage and captain World Cup winning teams?

14 A FIFA ruling stated that all international referees must be able to speak what language?

15 What are the first names of Juventus' 1993 UEFA Cup-winning Baggios?

16 What championship win number was it for Arsenal in 1991?

17 Which keeper did a goalmouth sit-in at half time in 1990?

18 In 1992 Jürgen Klinsmann left Inter Milan to join which club?

19 Simply Red's cover of "Daydream Believer" was for which manager?

20 Who were the beaten semi-finalists in the 1995–96 FA Cup?

Answers

Rangers & Celtic (see Quiz 86)
1 First subs to be used in a Final. 2 1894. 3 1909. 4 Celtic.
5 Berwick Rangers. 6 Mo Johnston. 7 Four. 8 Frank Haffey.
9 Scottish League Cup. 10 Jimmy McGrory. 11 Won all their
League games. 12 Bill Struth. 13 Alfie Conn. 14 Raith
Rovers. 15 1906–07. 16 Chris and Neil. 17 Steve Chalmers.
18 George Young. 19 1948–49. 20 1989–90.

1 Who lost to Ajax on away goals in the 1992 UEFA Cup Final?

2 Bobby Gould scored a League Cup Final goal for which club?

3 In which country was John Salako born?

4 At which club did Emlyn Hughes make his League debut?

5 When did Chelsea hit the charts with "Blue Is The Colour"?

6 Which club has a fanzine called *No More Pie In The Sky*?

7 John Docherty followed Ron Atkinson as manager of which club?

8 Which non-League side does John Motson follow?

9 Where was Welsh international Mark Crossley born?

10 To one each way, how many international goals did Neil Webb score?

11 Wayne Clarke and Alan Harper were in the same team at which club?

12 Which Dennis has been boss at Bristol City, Oxford, Sunderland and York?

13 Mark Bright first played in an FA Cup Final for which team?

14 What is David Seaman's middle name?

15 Which club beat Liverpool to win the European Super Cup in 1978?

16 Which Irishman personality took charge of the Greek national side in 1970?

17 Bowen and Goss scored Euro goals in the same game for which club?

18 Which Scottish player scored for the Italian League in 1961?

19 Roger Osborne scored in an FA Cup Final for which club?

20 Fullback Chris Lawler scored goals for Liverpool, Stockport and which other club?

Quiz 90 Golden Goals

Answers – see page 300

LEVEL 3 ⚽ ⚽ ⚽

1   Who failed to stop a shot from the halfway line on the opening day of the 1997–97 Premier League season?

2   Who scored a great Final Euro 92 goal and then moved to play in London?

3   Which Liverpool player scored from a free-kick to beat Blackburn Rovers in the last game of the 1994–95 season?

4   How many goals did Gary Lineker score for England?

5   Who scored Manchester Utd's goals v Barcelona in the 1991 European Cup Winners' Cup Final?

6   Which German player scored the only goal of the 1990 World Cup Final?

7   Who was the first ever winner of the Golden Boot award?

8   Which Wimbledon player scored the only goal of the 1988 FA Cup Final?

9   Which Italian player scored six goals in Italia 90?

10   Who scored Liverpool's extra time winner v Leeds Utd in 1965?

11   In Manchester Utd's 1968 Euro trail who was the unlikely scorer of the last goal v Real Madrid?

12   Who scored twice for Colchester Utd in the 1970s as they toppled Leeds Utd in the FA Cup?

13   Who scored Forest's European Cup Final goal to beat Hamburg?

14   Who scored Arsenal's first goal in the title decider at Anfield in 1989?

15   Brian Talbot scored in an FA Cup Final for which club?

16   Who scored in the 1970 England v Brazil World Cup game?

17   Which Scottish player scored a goal v Holland in the 1978 World Cup?

18   Which Northern Ireland player scored to defeat W Germany in a European Championship qualifier in 1983?

19   Which defender Roy of Blackpool and Manchester City managed 415 League games without ever scoring?

20   Which Polish international hit 4 goals for Celtic v Partizan Belgrade in 1989?

Answers

Englishmen Abroad (see Quiz 92)
1   42. **2** Barcelona & Grampus Eight. **3** Gerry Hitchens.
4   Glenn Hoddle & Mark Hateley. **5** AC Milan. **6** Jack Taylor.
7   Marseille. **8** Vancouver Whitecaps. **9** AC Milan.
10   Standard Liege. **11** Johan Cruyff. **12** Des Walker.
13   Hamburg. **14** Mark Hateley. **15** Steaua Bucharest.
16   Nick Barmby. **17** France. **18** Bob Houghton. **19** 44.
20   Kevin Richardson.

1 In which country was Mark Stein born?

2 Who lost 1–0 to Marseille in the Final of the 1993 European Cup?

3 Hancock, Pye and Shorthouse played for which 1940s FA Cup Finalists?

4 Paul Power was a Championship winner at which club?

5 Gus Caesar played in a League Cup Final for which club?

6 Donnelly and Walker scored Euro goals in the same 1990s game for which club?

7 "Guantanamera" – the tune of a thousand terrace chants – was a 1960s hit for which group ?

8 Ian Woan joined Nottingham Forest from which non-League team?

9 Gordon McQueen scored in an FA Cup Final for which club?

10 What is Gordon Strachan's middle name?

11 Lee Chapman and Mark Chamberlain were in the same team at which club?

12 Stan Seymour won the FA Cup once as a player and twice as a manager with which club?

13 Laurie Cunningham first played in an FA Cup Final for which team?

14 At which Scottish club did Steve Nicol make his League debut?

15 Which 16-year-old became the First Division's youngest scorer with a goal for Ipswich Town in 1984?

16 Which club had a fanzine called *Follow The Yellow Brick Road*?

17 Neil Warnock followed John Barnwell as manager of which club?

18 Graeme Souness was first capped while at which club?

19 Who is Dundee's all-time top League scorer?

20 To one each way, how many international goals did Alan Gilzean score?

Quiz 92 Englishmen Abroad

Answers – see page 298

LEVEL 3

1 How many League games did Gazza manage in three years at Lazio?

2 Which two foreign teams did Gary Lineker play for?

3 Who was the first player to be capped for England while on the books of a foreign team?

4 In 1988 which Englishmen played for the French Champions?

5 Which foreign club did Ray Wilkins play for?

6 Which English referee officiated in the 1974 World Cup Final?

7 Chris Waddle was at which club when he played in Italia 90?

8 Which foreign team did Peter Beardsley play for?

9 Luther Blissett joined which Italian club in the mid 1980s?

10 Which club in Belgium did Mike Small play for?

11 Which manager sold Gary Lineker to Tottenham Hotspur?

12 Which defender took a detour to Sampdoria on his way from Nottingham to Sheffield?

13 Southampton manager Lawrie McMenemy brought Kevin Keegan back to England from which side?

14 Who in the 1980s went from Portsmouth to AC Milan?

15 Which team did "El Tel" lose to in the 1986 European Cup Final?

16 Which English player scored two goals against China in 1996?

17 Which country did Graham Rix go to play his football in?

18 Who was Malmo's English manager when they met Nottingham Forest in the European Cup Final?

19 How many goals did Gary Lineker score in his 99 League games for Barcelona?

20 Which English midfielder joined John Aldridge at Real Sociedad in 1990?

Golden Goals (see Quiz 90)
1 Neil Sullivan. 2 John Jensen. 3 Jamie Redknapp. 4 48.
5 Mark Hughes. 6 Andy Brehme. 7 Eusebio. 8 Lawrie Sanchez. 9 Schillachi. 10 Ian St John. 11 Billy Foulkes.
12 Ray Crawford. 13 John Robertson. 14 Alan Smith.
15 Arsenal. 16 Jairzinho. 17 Archie Gemmill. 18 Norman Whiteside. 19 Gatrix. 20 Dariusz Dziekanowski.

1 Mike Doyle scored a League Cup Final goal for which club?

2 Who lost to Juventus in the 1993 UEFA Cup Final?

3 Which former Bolton centre-half Alan was born in Liverpool in 1971?

4 At which club did Joe Jordan make his League debut?

5 Martin Allan with 343 league games broke the appearance record at which Scottish club?

6 Which club had a fanzine called *The Almighty Brian*?

7 Who was manager of Brighton for the 1980s FA Cup Final?

8 Who moved from Walsall to West Ham Utd in 1988 to set a club record for a transfer fee received?

9 Which players, with the same surname, scored in consecutive European Championship Finals?

10 To one each way, how many international goals did Mike Summerbee score?

11 Steve Hodge and Chris Waddle were in which same club side?

12 Which Jim was boss of Birmingham from 1978–82?

13 Justin Edinburgh first played in an FA Cup Final for which team?

14 What is Chris Sutton's middle name?

15 Coyne and Kirk scored Euro goals in the same 1990s game for which club?

16 Which Derek scored most goals in a season for Sheffield Wednesday?

17 Which club used to play at Totteridge Lane?

18 Which club beat Barcelona to win the European Super Cup in 1979?

19 Keith Houchen scored in an FA Cup Final for which club?

20 Who – after being made boss of Arsenal – said,"I hadn't planned to be a football manager"?

Answers

Pot Luck 48 (see Quiz 95)
1 Andy Townsend. 2 West Ham Utd. 3 Barcelona. 4 Original Scottish FA Cup entrants. 5 Hereford Utd. 6 Charlie George.
7 Aston Villa. 8 Dundee Utd. 9 Oldham Athletic. 10 Tanner.
11 Leeds Utd. 12 Porterfield. 13 Manchester City.
14 Everton. 15 Kevin Richardson. 16 Middlesbrough.
17 Jimmy Dickinson. 18 WBA. 19 QPR. 20 Three.

1 Who is the Luton Town and Everton forward who went on to manage Northern Ireland?

2 When was the last time Wales qualified for the World Cup tournament?

3 In what year did the Republic of Ireland become the first team outside the UK to defeat England in England?

4 Which was the Republic of Ireland's keeper in the penalty shoot out v Romania in the 1990 World Cup?

5 When was Neville Southall voted Footballer of the Year?

6 Which Manchester Utd and Republic of Ireland player was known as "Gentlemen John"?

7 Which Welsh player capped over 50 times, won the double with Spurs?

8 Who made his debut for Wales aged 18 years 71 days?

9 At which ground did the last Home International match in 1984 between Wales and England take place?

10 Against which of the home countries did Ian Rush make his debut?

11 A late goal by which team meant the Republic of Ireland failed to reach the semi-finals of the 88 Euro Championship?

12 Who kept goal for Northern Ireland in the 1958 World Cup?

13 Who beat Ivor Allchurch's appearance record – 20 years after it was set?

14 World champions West Germany were beaten 2–1 by which home international team in 1991?

15 Who did Wales beat 3–2 to celebrate their FA's centenary in 1951?

16 Don Givens was at which club when he was first capped?

17 Which Welsh player was 45 years and 229 days old when he won a cap for England in 1920?

18 While at Crystal Palace, who was the first Fourth Division player to be picked for Wales?

19 How many international goals did Trevor Ford score?

20 Northern Ireland beat Italy at which English ground to qualify for the 1958 World Cup?

Answers

Int'l Managers (see Quiz 96)
1 Johnny Giles. 2 Six. 3 Matt Busby. 4 Craig Brown.
5 Austria. 6 Argentina. 7 Mike Smith. 8 Eoin Hand. 9 Josef Herberger. 10 Bristol City. 11 Gusztav Sebes. 12 Brazil.
13 Helmut Schön. 14 Wales. 15 Bayer Leverkusen. 16 Vittorio Pozzo. 17 Franz Beckenbauer. 18 Paolo Maldini.
19 Decorate his kitchen. 20 Open University.

Quiz 95 Pot Luck 48

LEVEL 3

1 Which Republic of Ireland international was born in Maidstone in July 1963?

2 Bond, Brown and Bovington played for which 1960s FA Cup Finalists?

3 Who lost 4–0 to AC Milan in the Final of the 1994 European Cup?

4 What links Blytheswood, Renton, Southern and Western?

5 Who was Dixie McNeil playing for when he was the League's leading scorer in 1974–75 and 1975–76?

6 Which English double winner lost a finger in an accident with a lawnmower?

7 Gibson and Ormsby scored Euro goals in the same 1980s game for which club?

8 Eamonn Bannon's goal in April 1983 clinched the Scottish Championship for which team?

9 Rick Holden played in a League Cup Final for which club?

10 Which Ipswich player Adam was banned after a drug test?

11 Mervyn Day and Vince Hilaire were in the same team at which club?

12 Which Ian became boss of Sheffield Utd in 1981?

13 Steve MacKenzie first played in an FA Cup Final for which team?

14 At which club did Ian Bishop make his League debut?

15 Who played in League Cup Finals for Everton, Arsenal and Aston Villa?

16 Which club had a fanzine called *Fly Me To The Moon*?

17 Who followed Ian St John as manager of Portsmouth?

18 Who was Colin Suggett first playing for in a 1970s League Cup Final?

19 Tony Ingham set up a League appearance record at which club?

20 To one each way, how many international goals did Billy Bremner score?

---

1 Who resigned as the Republic of Ireland's manager in April 1980?

2 How many different Scotland managers did Kenny Dalglish play for?

3 Who managed the Great Britain team in the 1948 Olympic Games?

4 Which future national manager was born in Lanarkshire July on 1, 1940?

5 Hugo Meisl was manager and general secretary of which country from 1906 to 1937?

6 In which country was Helenio Herrera born?

7 Who was Welsh boss for the vital 1977 World Cup qualifier v Scotland?

8 Who was manager of the Republic of Ireland directly before Jack Charlton?

9 Who was manager of the West German World Cup winners in 1954?

10 Before Switzerland, Roy Hodgson used to manage which English League club?

11 Which coach created the "Magic Magyars" of the 1950s?

12 Which country did Tele Santana manage?

13 Who managed West Germany in the 1966 World Cup Final?

14 Norwich City coach David Williams took charge of which country for one game?

15 Dutch master Rinus Michels coached which German League side?

16 Who took Italy to World Cup triumphs in the 1930s?

17 Who was the first person to coach and captain World Cup winners?

18 Which international manager captained AC Milan to their first European Cup success as a player?

19 What had Denmark's manager Richard Moller Nielsen reputedly planned to do during Euro 92, before his team's surprise late call up?

20 Where is Craig Brown's university degree from?